D1478924

# TEXTILE DYEING OPERATIONS

# TEXTILE DYEING OPERATIONS

## Chemistry, Equipment, Procedures, and Environmental Aspects

by

**S.V. Kulkarni, C.D. Blackwell, A.L. Blackard**
**C.W. Stackhouse, M.W. Alexander**
Radian Corporation
Research Triangle Park, North Carolina

np

NOYES PUBLICATIONS
Park Ridge, New Jersey, U.S.A.

Library of Congress Catalog Card Number 85-25931
ISBN: 0-8155-1060-8
Printed in the United States

Published in the United States of America by
Noyes Publications
Mill Road, Park Ridge, New Jersey 07656

10 9 8 7 6 5 4 3 2 1

Library of Congress Cataloging-in-Publication Data
Main entry under title:

Textile dyeing operations.

Bibliography: p.
Includes index.
1. Dyes and dyeing--Textile fibers. I. Kulkarni, S.V. (Satish V.)
TP897.T25 1986 667'.3 85-25931
ISBN 0-8155-1060-8

# Foreword

This book describes textile dyeing operations with emphasis on the chemistry and composition of textile dyes currently in use and the equipment and dyeing procedures found in the textile dyeing industry. The information provided will serve as background data for estimating the properties and evaluating the associated risks of new commercial dyestuffs, particularly for those seeking compliance with, or review under, the Toxic Substances Control Act (TSCA).

The book contains data on typical textile dyeing and finishing plant size, associated wastewater volumes, and typical dyeing equipment capacities. Major classes of dyestuffs are categorized with respect to dye chemistry, dyeing properties, physical/chemical properties, type of fabric dyed, and the machine types most used for each dye class. It should be a valuable guide for managers, engineers, and scientists in the textile industry.

The information in the book is from *Textile Dyes and Dyeing Equipment: Classification, Properties, and Environmental Aspects,* prepared by S.V. Kulkarni, C.D. Blackwell, A.L. Blackard, C.W. Stackhouse, and M.W. Alexander of Radian Corporation for U.S. Environmental Protection Agency, February 1985.

The table of contents is organized in such a way as to serve as a subject index and provides easy access to the information contained in the book.

Advanced composition and production methods developed by Noyes Publications are employed to bring this durably bound book to you in a minimum of time. Special techniques are used to close the gap between "manuscript" and "completed book." In order to keep the price of the book to a reasonable level, it has been partially reproduced by photo-offset directly from the original report and the cost saving passed on to the reader. Due to this method of publishing, certain portions of the book may be less legible than desired.

## NOTICE

The materials in this book were prepared as accounts of work sponsored by the U.S. Environmental Protection Agency. They have been reviewed by the U.S. Environmental Protection Agency, and approved for publication. Approval does not signify that the contents necessarily reflect the views and policy of the Agency or the Publisher, nor does mention of trade names or commercial products constitute endorsement or recommendation for use.

# Contents and Subject Index

# 1. Introduction

Section 5 of the Toxic Substances Control Act (TSCA) requires that any person who intends to manufacture (or import) a new chemical substance for commercial use in the United States must submit a notice to the United States Environmental Protection Agency (EPA) at least 90 days before commencing manufacture (or import) of the substance. The notice must contain information specified in Section 5(d) of TSCA, including any information derived from testing for health and environmental effects. The EPA Office of Toxic Substances (OTS) administers a three-phase review process for chemicals submitted in compliance with Section 5(d) of TSCA.

A major portion of these submittals to OTS are for dyestuffs that are to be used in the textile industry. These dyestuffs include many toxic substances whose life cycle utilization, and environmental release and exposure risks have not been adequately assessed.

The objective of this study is to provide OTS with background information about the emission and release of dyestuffs from textile dyeing operations that will aide in their review and evaluation of Premanufacturing Notifications (PMN) under Section 5 of TSCA. Specifically, this study synthesizes available information to characterize the use of dyes in the textile industry, emphasizing factors that affect the release and exposure of dyes to man and the environment. This study focuses on two major areas to accomplish the objective: physicochemical categories of textile dyes, and types of textile dyeing equipment. Available information in these two areas was compiled and is presented in this report, which is an information document designed to acquaint the reader with textile dyes and dyeing equipment. A list of textile dyeing terms used in the text are contained in Appendix A: Glossary.

# 2. Summary

This document presents information about textile dyeing operations with emphasis on the chemistry and composition of textile dyes in use and the equipment and dyeing procedures found in the textile dyeing industry. The document also contains information on typical textile dyeing and finishing plant size, their associated wastewater volumes, and typical dyeing equipment capacities. Based on data collected during two plant visits conducted during the study, mass balance profiles were developed to characterize the quantity of dyestuffs released to the environment from dyeing equipment per 454 kilograms (1,000 pounds) of fabric dyed. Additionally, information on worker exposure was compiled.

All information contained in this report was assembled on an "as available" basis. However, special emphasis was placed upon several dye classes and types of dyeing equipment in accordance with the priorities determined by the U.S. EPA Office of Toxic Substances.

In Section 6, the major classes of textile dyestuffs are categorized with respect to their dye chemistry, dyeing properties, physical/chemical properties, type of fabric dyed, and the machine types most suited for use with each dye class. A total of 18 dye classes are described with six of these classes receiving special investigation. The six classes are:

- Acid Dyes
- Substantive Direct Dyes
- Azoic Dyes
- Disperse Dyes
- Sulfur Dyes
- Fiber Reactive Dyes

Other dye classes investigated include:

- Basic Dyes
- Oxidation Base Dyes
- Acid-Milling Dyes
- Acid-Premetalized Dyes
- Neutral-Premetalized Dyes
- Mordant (chrome) Dyes
- Developed Dyes
- Vat Dyes
- Reactive Dyes
- Pigments
- Optical Brightners
- Solvent Dyes

In Section 7, the principal types of dyeing equipment and their uses are described. Special emphasis is placed on the following machine types:

- Beck
- Semicontinuous (pad, batch)
- Transfer Printing
- Direct Textile Printing

Other machine types investigated include:

- Beam
- Jig
- Jet
- Package
- Vat

Descriptions of the dyeing procedures associated with each machine and fabric/dye combination is included in this chapter (and in Appendix B). These procedures detail the times, temperatures and additional chemicals needed for proper dyeing. Mass balance and dyestuffs release estimates are included in this section.

Section 8 presents the results of a statistical summary designed to characterize the volumes of wastewater discharge from textile dyeing operations in relation to the plants' production volumes.

Section 9 summarizes available information on air emissions from textile dyeing operations.

# 3. Data Limitations

The purpose of this section is to briefly list the limitations of the data contained in this report.

Useful information was collected during two plant visits conducted for this study. Care must be exercised when attempting to extend this data to other specific operations. The process data may not be representative of certain operations. Examples of processes not represented include such textile operations as carpet processing, pigment printing, heavy fabrics finishing, mills that process other than piece goods, and small (less organized) mill operations. Some figures on dyestuff release levels were available, but there was little information on worker exposures. Consequently, while the information presented in this report is valid for estimation purposes, caution should be used in applying the emission/release data to the entire textile dyeing industry.

Section 4 of this report contains recommendations on further data collection activities necessary to fill the existing data gaps. The outstanding data limitations are as follows.

- Data on physical/chemical and toxicological properties of most specific dyestuffs were unavailable in the literature.
- Available information used to characterize the size, capacity, production rates, number of machines in use, etc. of dyeing operations is incomplete and somewhat outdated (Circa 1973).
- Data were generally unavailable on worker exposure and specific worker activities.
- The number of plants visited was small (two), and the length of visits was less than one day.

# 4. Recommendations

During the data collection phase of this project, several textile dyeing operation areas were identified for which information was unavailable. In most instances, the unavailable information was nonexistent; obtaining it would require detailed research efforts. In other instances information was available, but the database was insufficient to establish reliable and representative estimates. The areas of textile dyeing operation recommended for additional study are:

- Develop Information on Properties of Dyestuffs - Most of the information available on physical/chemical dyestuff properties is general and does not describe properties of specific large volume dyestuffs currently in use. The use of chemical property estimation techniques and/or actual testing of specific dye substances would provide EPA with additional information in this area. This effort could also be enhanced by preparation of environmental fate and accumulation estimates for the dyestuffs, using recently compiled estimation methods.

- Characterize the Size, Capacity and Dye Usage of Textile Dyeing Operations - The most recent data available is from the EPA Effluent Guidelines Division and is approximately six to ten years old. Since that time, new dyes and fabric combinations have replaced older dyestuffs and machines. This information also focuses primarily upon textile finishing operations rather than dyeing operations.

- Develop Data on Worker Exposure to Dyestuffs - Little data is available in the literature on worker exposure to dyestuffs, with the exception of benzidene-based dyes which have been largely dropped from use by the industry. Parameters to be considered include: frequency, duration, and exposure concentrations.
- Study Advanced Wastewater Treatment of Dyes - Much information is currently available on wastewater treatment of textile effluents. However, this data does not focus upon the removal of dyestuffs by these technologies.
- Investigate Multi-Media Transfer of Dyestuffs - Both existing and advanced candidate wastewater treatment technologies produce wastewater sludge or other liquid concentrates that must be disposed. Little to no data is available for the quantity of dyestuffs transferred to the residual wastes from textile dyeing wastewater treatment.
- Compile Information on Dyeing of Leather and Non-woven Textile Products - Data on these topics is available, but was not included in great detail in this study.
- Conduct Additional Plant Visits to Textile Dyeing Operations - Additional plant visits to collect information similar to that shown in Appendix C and D of this document are needed to broaden the data base for plant operations and dyestuff release estimates.

# 5. Conclusions

Several significant trends in the types of textile dyes employed, materials colored, and dyeing equipment utilized have been identified. These trends are mutually dependent and have also been influenced by market, economic, and environmental factors.

Based upon the information collected during the course of this study, a continued or increased rate of replacement of the older dyes by new dyestuffs is expected. In the textile industry, the two dye classes that will experience the most growth are fiber-reactive dyes and disperse (sublimable) dyes.

A concurrent increase in the use of dyeing equipment such as the pressure beck (jet) and transfer and direct printers is expected because of their high dyeing efficiency and exhaustion rates. For these reasons and since this type of equipment uses little or no water compared with other equipment such as the beam, pad-batch operation, and atmospheric beck, many dyers will be reducing the quantity of wastewater and dye solids discharged to the environment. However, because the new dry printing method (transfer printing) employs dyes that sublime, use of this method may transfer the dye emissions from a water medium to the atmosphere surrounding the machine. Use of this method could have a greater impact on worker exposure than wet dyeing methods.

Both plant visits revealed that dye operations can, with proper machine operation, achieve a very high degree of dye exhaustion onto the fabrics. Based upon observations at the two plants visited, it is found that such an effort is already made in order to maximize the effective use of dyestuffs and minimize the cost of dye purchases.

# 6. Dye Class Categorization

## 6.1 OVERVIEW

In 1980, approximately two-thirds of the 111 million kilograms (245 million pounds) of synthetic organic dyestuffs (excluding pigments) produced in the U.S. were used by the textile industry. That same year, an additional 12 percent, or 13 million kilograms (29 million pounds), of synthetic organic dyestuffs was imported into the United States (ITC, 1980). The total amount imported was composed of the following dye classes:

| Dye class | Percentage of total 1980 U.S. import quantity |
|---|---|
| Acid | 18 |
| Basic | 9 |
| Direct | 7 |
| Disperse | 10 |
| Vat | 16 |
| Other than above (not specified) | 40 |
| | 100 |

A breakdown of the dye application classes used in textile dyeing, along with their percentage of the total U.S. production in 1980 follows.

| Dye application class | Percent of total U.S. production in 1980 |
|---|---|
| Disperse | 19% |
| Vat | 16% |
| Fluorescent brighteners | 15% |
| Direct | 13% |
| Misc. (azoic, sulfur, oxidation bases, etc.) | 11% |
| Acid | 10% |
| Basic | 6% |
| Fiber-reactive | 2% |
| Mordant | 0.1% |
| | 92.1% |

The total U.S. production of organic dyes in 1980 declined by 7.7% from 1979. Production in all application classes declined except for fluorescent brighteners which rose 12.7% and direct dyes which rose 9.2% from the 1979 production figures (ITC, 1980).

The U.S. production of synthetic organic pigments was 31.5 million kilograms (69.4 million pounds) in 1980. This indicated a 21.4% reduction in production volume from 1979. Approximately one-half of 1980 production volume was used by the printing industry, while the remaining half was divided among textile usage, paper, plastics, and surface coatings. Approximately one-sixth of the production volume of synthetic organic dyes was used as raw materials for pigment production.

Dyes are sold as pastes, powders, lumps, solutions, and presscakes and are "standardized" in color strength by addition of inorganic salts to produce dyestuffs that contain from 6 to 100% of the actual colorant. The advertised standardization percentage is not a direct measure of chemical concentration (e.g., standardizations of 50% to over 300% are available). Organic pigments are mostly sold as concentrated dispersions and pastes and are generally categorized into two groups: 1) toners - full strength coloring materials; and 2) lakes - organic coloring materials mixed with inert materials.

As of 1977, approximately 66% by volume of the dyes produced in the United States were from the chemical categories of azo, anthraquinone, and stilbene (Steadman, 1981). Stilbene dyes are chemically azo compounds but are prepared by a unique process from aminostilbenes and triazinylstilbenes. Some of the dyes prepared from stilbenes are direct yellows, direct oranges, and possibly up to 80% of the fluorescent brighteners. Anthraquinone derived dyestuffs include acid, disperse, metallized, and vat dyes in a full range of colors. In 1978, azo dyes alone accounted for 35% of the total U.S. production volume or 40.8 million kilograms (90 million pounds). Azo dyes, which can be subdivided into monoazo, disazo, and trisazo dyestuffs,* are found in numerous application categories - acid dyes, basic dyes, direct dyes, disperse dyes, azoic dyes, and pigments. Until recently, azo-type acid dyes, direct dyes, and pigments based on benzidine and benzidine congeners were very popular dyestuffs. With recent concern over worker exposure, wastewater treatment, and release of benzidine based dyes and pigments to the environment, there has been a concerted effort to develop new non-benzidine based acid dyes, direct dyes, azoic dyes, and pigments to replace older products shade for shade. Some older products are being replaced by new azo dyestuffs, the composition of the new dyes are proprietary (Stead, 1975).

Since dyes must be soluble in the application medium itself, either permanent or temporary chemical solubilizing groups must be present (AATCC, 1981). These solubilizing groups are important because dyes with similar solubilizing groups show similar dyeing behavior even though their chemical structures may be quite dissimilar (Kirk-Othmer, 1978).

---

*Alternately, these are also referred to in the literature as monazo, diazo, or triazo type dyes.

| Permanent Solubilizing Groups | Application Classes |
|---|---|
| $-SO_3Na$ | Acid, Direct, Mordant, Reactive |
| $-NH_3Cl$, $-NR_3Cl$ | Basic |
| $-OH$, $-NH_2$, $-SO_2NH_2$ | Disperse |

| Temporary Solubilizing Groups | Application Classes |
|---|---|
| $-ONa$ | Vat, Solubilized Vat |
| $-OSO_3Na$ | Solubilized Vat |

6.1.1 Market Trends in the Dye Industry

The U.S. dye industry, which dates back to World War I, is a relatively mature industry but is small compared to the U.S. textile industry. Of the estimated $790 million of dye sales in 1980, approximately two-thirds or $530 million were to the textile industry (Sullivan, 1982). The annual dye production volumes for the ten years between 1970-1980 are presented in Table 1. These production figures were obtained from yearly reports to the International Tariff Commission with categorization by application classes. Table 2 presents the dye production trends as a percent growth rate from the 5-year period 1976-1980 and the 10-year period 1971-1980 with the projected production volumes for the years 1985 and 1990.

6.1.2 Trends in the Textile Dyeing Industry

A variety of dyestuffs are used in the textile industry. Table 3 presents the dye types used in the textile industry and relates them to the fibers they are generally used to color. The relative amounts of each dye used by the textile industry (EPA, 1974) are also shown in this table. Table 4 subdivides dyes into chemical class and application class (Horning, 1978). Most textile fiber types may be grouped into one of the following three chemical "substrate" types: 1) hydrophilic cellulosics; 2) hydrophilic proteins, and 3) hydrophobic synthetics. However, not all synthetic fibers are represented as hydrophobic synthetics (e.g., Nylon 4). Synthetics are further subdivided in three categories. Cellulose acetate, triacetate, and polyester are often nonionic substrates

TABLE 1. ANNUAL PRODUCTION VOLUMES FOR THE DYE INDUSTRY FROM 1971-1980 (ITC, 1980)

| Class of application | Yearly production (1,000 kg) | | | | | | | | | |
|---|---|---|---|---|---|---|---|---|---|---|
| | 1971 | 1972 | 1973 | 1974 | 1975 | 1976 | 1977 | 1978 | 1979 | 1980 |
| Acid | 59078.9 | 65562.6 | 70622.2 | 58047.1 | 41380.3 | 62275.5 | 67692.2 | 86936.2 | 100164.0 | 56457.6 |
| Azoic dyes and components | 22789.0 | 22520.0 | 17630.2 | 8489.9 | 3518.5 | 4193.1 | 4082.9 | 3725.8 | NR | NR |
| Basic | 36552.3 | 39680.6 | 47118.9 | 44255.1 | 25840.1 | 32176.1 | 37705.3 | 33856.0 | 35024.5 | 32173.9 |
| Direct | 76510.7 | 83051.7 | 86764.2 | 71133.6 | 55869.0 | 73913.6 | 67758.4 | 62579.8 | 63025.1 | 68821.0 |
| Disperse | 76889.8 | 88023.1 | 110389.0 | 111978.0 | 75794.2 | 86199.9 | 95375.4 | 97767.4 | 103127.0 | 102999.0 |
| Fiber-reactive | 8183.5 | 8154.8 | 8143.8 | 7530.9 | 5357.2 | 7729.3 | 11360.3 | 12169.4 | 14098.4 | 12634.6 |
| Fluorescent brightening agents | 65723.5 | 60231.9 | 71537.1 | 90589.2 | 84874.9 | 95743.6 | 73311.8 | 65990.3 | 74237.7 | 83640.3 |
| Food, drug, and cosmetic colors | 8703.8 | 10238.2 | 11560.9 | 12621.3 | 8143.8 | 12691.9 | 12663.2 | 13503.2 | 16078.1 | 13392.9 |
| Mordant | 2859.4 | 3229.7 | NR | 1884.9 | 1144.2 | 1455.0 | 1332.2 | 828.9 | 992.1 | 903.9 |
| Solvent | 23448.1 | 27487.0 | 30837.9 | 36285.5 | 21900.5 | 26322.9 | 28657.6 | 30626.3 | 29224.2 | 23421.7 |
| Vat. | 112269.0 | 121562.0 | 124192.0 | 119481.0 | 93620.6 | 117353.0 | 133330.0 | 83228.1 | 102801.0 | 88691.1 |
| All other | 44316.9 | 50738.8 | 47809.0 | 44047.9 | 36889.6 | 114874.6 | 49358.8 | 61658.3 | 69436.1 | 57758.3 |
| TOTAL | 537477.0 | 580480.0 | 626605.0 | 606344.0 | 454223.0 | 564929.0 | 582828.0 | 552870.0 | 586161.0 | 540894.0 |

NR - Not reported in yearly ITC report.

TABLE 2. DYE PRODUCTION TRENDS

| Class of application | 1980 production (1,000 kg) | Estimated[a] 1985 production (1,000 kg) | Estimated[a] 1990 production (1,000 kg) |
|---|---|---|---|
| Acid | 56457.6 | 75877.9 | 81803.9 |
| Basic | 32173.9 | 27707.4 | 23113.0 |
| Direct | 68821.0 | 52381.3 | 42610.5 |
| Disperse | 102999.0 | 108568.0 | 115786.0 |
| Fiber-reactive | 12634.6 | 16195.0 | 19700.3 |
| Fluorescent brightening agents | 83640.3 | 86854.0 | 92257.0 |
| Food, drug, and cosmetic colors | 13392.9 | 17570.7 | 20524.8 |
| Mordant | 903.9 | 0.0 | 0.0 |
| Solvent | 23421.7 | 27413.4 | 27519.0 |
| Vat. | 88691.1 | 81839.2 | 67200.6 |
| All other | 57758.3 | 70553.8 | 81008.0 |
| TOTAL | 540894.0 | 548427.0 | 540608.0 |

[a]Projected with linear regression analysis on past 10 year production volumes shown in Table 1.

TABLE 3. TYPES AND AMOUNTS OF DYES USED IN THE TEXTILE INDUSTRY (EPA, 1974)

| Fibers<br>Dye types | Acrylic | Cotton | Wool | Acetate | Rayon | Polyester | Polyester PE/cotton | Nylon | Nylon/ cotton | Amount[a] used % |
|---|---|---|---|---|---|---|---|---|---|---|
| Acid | X | | X | | | | | X | X | 10 |
| Azoic | | X | | | X | X | X | | | 3 |
| Aniline black | | X | | | | | | | | - |
| Basic (cationic) | X | | | X | | X | X | X | | 6 |
| Developed | | X | | | X | | | | | - |
| Dye blends | | | | | | | X | | | - |
| Direct | | X | | | X | | X | | X | 17 |
| Disperse | X | | | X | | X | X | X | | 15 |
| Fiber-reactive | | X | | | | | X | X | | 1 |
| Fluorescent | X | X | X | X | X | X | X | X | X | 1 |
| Indigo | | X | | | | | | | X | - |
| Sulfur | | X | | | X | | X | | | 10 |
| Vats | | X | | | X | | X | | | 26 |
| Natural | | X | | | | | | | | - |
| Oxidation base | | X | | | | | | | | - |
| Mordant | | | X | | | | | X | | 1 |
| Pigments | | X | | | X | | X | X | X | |

[a]Approximate percent of total textile use. Usage of dyes for which amounts are not shown total approximately 10 percent (not including dye blends).

Note: Some of the above dye types have limited use on the fibers shown, and may apply only to specific fiber variations (e.g., basic dyes on nylon and polyester, and acid dyes on acrylics).

TABLE 4. CHEMICAL AND APPLICATION CLASS OF DYES USED IN THE TEXTILES INDUSTRY

| Chemical class | Cellulosic | | | | | Protein | | Cellulose Esters | Polyamide | | | Polyester | | Polyacrylic | | |
|---|---|---|---|---|---|---|---|---|---|---|---|---|---|---|---|---|
| | Direct | Sulfur | Naphthol | Vat | Reactive | Acid | Mordant | Disperse | Acid | Disperse | Cationic[a] | Disperse | Cationic[a] | Acid | Disperse | Cationic |
| Azo | X | | | | X | X | X | X | X | X | X | X | X | X | X | X |
| Stilbene | X | | | | X | | | | | | | | | | | |
| Quinoline | X | | | | | X | | X | X | X | X | X | X | X | X | X |
| Methine | X | | | | | | | | | | X | | X | | | X |
| Oxazine | X | X | | | | | X | | | | X | | X | | | X |
| Anthraquinone | X | | | X | X | X | X | X | X | X | X | X | X | X | X | X |
| Phthalocyanine | X | X | X | X | X | X | | | X | | X | | X | X | | X |
| Acridine | | X | | | | | | | | | X | | X | | | X |
| Diphenylmethane | | | | | | | | | | | | | | | | |
| Thiazole | | X | | | X | | X | | | | X | | X | | | X |
| Indamine, Indophenol | | | | | | | | | | | | | | | | |
| Azine | | X | | | | X | | | X | | X | | X | X | | X |
| Thiazine | | X | | X | | | | | | | X | | X | | | X |
| Sulfur | | X | | X | | | | | | | | | | | | |
| Azoic | | | X | | | | | | | | | | | | | |
| Indigoid | | | | X | | X | | | X | | | | | X | | |
| Nitroso | | | | | | X | X | X | X | X | | X | | X | X | |
| Nitro | | | | | | X | X | X | X | X | | X | | X | X | |
| Triarylmethane | | | | | | X | X | | X | | X | | X | X | | X |
| Xanthene | | | | | | X | X | | X | | X | | X | X | | X |
| Indamine, Indophenol | X | | | | | X | | X | X | X | X | X | X | X | X | X |

while polyamides (nylons) are often cationic and polyacrylics are often anionic.* The chemical fiber types listed in Table 4 relate to the following common fibers:

- Cellulosic - cotton, linen, regenerated cellulosic rayon.
- Proteins - wool, silk.
- Cellulosic Esters - acetate, triacetate.
- Polyamide - nylon, "Quiana."
- Polyester - "Dacron," "Fortrel."
- Polyacrylic - "Acrilan," "Orlon."

The application of a particular dye to a certain textile or fiber is usually the same. The dye is most often transferred from a bath, usually aqueous, into or onto the fiber. The dyestuff-to-fabric ratio is usually under 3% to be economically feasible, so the dyestuff used must show a particular affinity (substantivity) for the textile (fiber) to be colored. However, this ratio is not always under 3%, and may be as high as 5%. For some shades, it could be in excess of 10%. This concept of substantivity explains the fiber-to-dyestuff relationships seen in Table 4. The different dye classes have various methods for forming the color on or inside the fiber. The mechanism of dye retention can be chemical (covalent bonding) or physical bonding (ionic, Van der Waals, hydrogen bonding) or a combination of the two. Removal of temporary solubilizing groups and resultant "precipitation" into the fiber is a third mechanism. The basic application methods of the dye classes are summarized below in general terms and are described further in the following subsections.

Azoic coloring materials are referred to as Naphthol dyes. The application method for Naphthol dyes is to combine two soluble components (an azoic coupling component and an azoic diazo component) inside the fiber to form an insoluble color molecule.

---

*There are exceptions to these broad generalizations since anionic polyamides and polyesters (dyeable with cationic dyes) do exist and cationic polyacrylonitriles (SP) (dyeable with acid dyes) also exist. Dyeable end groups can be adjusted by manufacturers of syntheic fibers.

Vat and sulfur dyes have basically the same application procedures as azoic dyes. The dye is chemically reduced to the "leuco" or soluble form. The soluble form may exhibit an affinity for the textile fiber or may require physical forcing into the fiber. The dye is then oxidized and reforms the insoluble dyestuff inside the fiber.

Direct dyes are applied from an aqueous bath containing ionic salts or electrolytes. The anionic nature of direct dyes combined with the ionic nature of the electrolyte induces bonding with textile fibers such as cellulose. Aftertreatments are often advisable to finalize chemical reactions, thereby insuring fastness.

Reactive dyes form a covalent bond with textile fibers. Some of these dyes require an alkaline treatment before dyeing to increase the affinity of the fiber for the dye.

Acid dyes are applied on nitrogenous fibers. The chemical interaction of a water-soluble anionic dye with a cationic fiber forms a chemically bonded, insoluble color molecule on the fiber.

Disperse dyes are frequently applied through the process of sublimation. The subliming process employs heat to transform the dye molecules into the vapor state (transfer printing). The dye is condensed back to the solid form once it is inside the fiber. Disperse dyes, however, are more often applied as water dispersions from a dyebath.

The various "wet" dye application processes may involve simply dissolving the dye in water, or more sophisticated operations using chemical additives to control the solubility, substantivity, leveling, fastness, or other qualities of the dyestuff. A list of auxiliary chemicals required for specific dye classes is presented in Table 5 (EPA, 1974).

## 6.2 ACID DYES

### 6.2.1 General Description

Acid dyes are so called because they are normally applied to the fabric being dyed in organic or inorganic acid dyeing solutions. The term applies to a large number of anionic dyes with relatively low molecular weight which carry from one to three sulfonic acid groups

TABLE 5. CHEMICALS USED IN APPLICATION OF DYES (AATCC, 1981; SDC, 1971)

| Dye type | Auxiliary chemicals necessary[a,b] | Purpose |
|---|---|---|
| Vat | sodium hydroxide | reducing agent/pH adjustment |
| | sodium hydrosulfite | solubilizing agent |
| | dispersant | dispersing agent |
| | hydrogen peroxide | oxidizing agent |
| | acetic acid | pH adjustment |
| | sodium perborate and alternatives | oxidizing agent |
| Direct | sodium chloride | exhausting agent |
| | sequesterer | sequestering agent |
| | sodium sulfate | exhausting agent |
| Disperse | orthophenylphenol | dye carrier |
| | butyl benzoate carriers | dye carrier |
| | chlorobenzene | dye carrier |
| | methyl naphthalene | dye carrier |
| | acetic acid | pH adjustment |
| | dispersant and many other carriers | dispersing agent |
| Sulfur | sodium sulfide | reducing agent |
| | sodium carbonate | pH adjustment |
| | sodium dichromate | oxidizing agent |
| | acetic acid and alternatives | pH adjustment |
| | hydrogen peroxide | oxidizing agent |
| | acetic acid | pH adjustment |
| Acid | acetic acid | pH adjustment |
| | ammonium sulfate | pH adjustment/ionic agent |
| | ammonium acetate | pH adjustment/ionic agent |
| | sulfuric acid | pH adjustment |
| | sodium sulfate | ionic agent |
| | monosodium phosphate | pH adjustment |

(continued)

TABLE 5. CHEMICALS USED IN APPLICATION OF DYES (AATCC, 1981; SDC, 1971) (continued)

| Dye type | Auxiliary chemicals necessary[a,b] | Purpose |
|---|---|---|
| Cationic (Basic) | acetic acid | pH adjustment |
| | formic acid | retarder/leveling agent |
| | oxalic acid | retarder/leveling agent |
| | sodium sulfate | leveling agent |
| | sodium acetate | retarder/leveling agent |
| | ethylene carbonate | retarder/leveling agent |
| Reactive | sodium chloride | exhausting agent |
| | urea | printing carrier |
| | sodium carbonate | fixing agent/printing carrier |
| | sodium hydroxide | fixing agent |
| Developed | dye specific developer | development |
| | sodium chloride | exhausting agent |
| | sodium nitrite | diazotization agent |
| | sulfuric acid | diazotization agent |
| | sodium carbonate | fixing agent |
| | hypochloric acid | diazotization agent |

[a]In addition to the chemicals listed, all of the dye types normally use a small amount of surfactant. After the dyeing has been completed, the dyed goods may be washed and/or rinsed. Washing involves use of a detergent as well as soda ash and a phosphate.

[b]The use of these auxiliary chemicals is believed to vary both in terms of the exact combinations and the relative amounts of the substances used. This is a result of the use of empirically determined, company-specific dyeing "recipes."

(i.e., R - $SO_3$ Na). These groups dissociate in water or varying acidic solutions to form colored anions ($R-SO_3^-$) and colorless cations ($Na^+$). The dyes are used commercially for polyamides (80-85%) and wool (10-15%), as well as silk, acrylic, polyproplene, and blends of these materials (5-10%). They are normally distributed as the sodium salts mentioned, which are dissociated in water for use.

The majority of the acid dyes used commercially are azo, anthraquinone, and triarylmethane dyes. Although there are other acid dyes, including pyrazolone, azine, nitro, and quiniline dyes, these are of limited commercial value.

Acid dyes traditionally have been broken into four classes, based on physical/chemical properties and end usage. These are:

1) leveling dyes;
2) milling dyes;
3) super milling dyes; and
4) metal complex dyes.

This classification system was developed for use in wool dyeing (as the term "milling" indicates) and its application to synthetics must be used judiciously. A more recent method of categorizing acid dyes is based on the number of sulfonic acid groups present. This method of classification is more applicable to man-made fibers such as texturized nylons. Although metallized dyes are classified as acid dyes, in the dye trade it is important to distinguish the various types of metallized dyes from one another and from non-metallized dyes.

Acid dyestuffs made up 10% of the total U.S. production of organic dyes in 1980 or 11.6 million kilograms (25.6 million pounds). The following statistics were derived from information found in the 1980 U.S. International Trade Commission report on synthetic organic chemicals.

6.2.1.1 Color Categories of Acid Dyes. The following list gives the percentages of total 1980 acid dye production for individual color categories.

| Color Category | Percentage of Total Acids |
|---|---|
| Acid Yellows | 34.2% |
| Acid Blues | 18.4% |
| Acid Oranges | 17.6% |
| Acid Reds | 15.0% |
| Acid Blacks | 9.6% |
| Acid Browns | 3.7% |
| Acid Greens | 0.9% |
| Acid Violets | 0.6% |
| | 100.0% |

6.2.1.2 Outstanding Volume Products. The three dyestuffs below were the only acid dyes reported with production volume of 0.4536 million kilograms (1 million pounds) or more. However, over 150 products are listed with production volumes of 2,268 kilograms (5,000 pounds) or greater in 1980 (ITC, 1980).

| C.I. Name | Percentage of Total Acids |
|---|---|
| Acid Yellow 151 | 9.5% |
| Acid Blue 40 | 4.4% |
| Acid Red 337 | 3.6% |
| | 17.5% |

6.2.2 Types of Acid Dyes

The following sections describe each of the acid dye classes based on its properties and uses.

6.2.2.1 Leveling Dyes. As the name implies, these acid dyes have excellent leveling properties. As a class, they normally exhibit good light fastness, but are lacking in wet fastness. They distribute evenly.

For wool dyeing, the leveling dyes are normally low molecular weight, monosulfonic, and require a highly acidic dyebath for good dye exhaustion. For dyeing of polyamide, the dyes are normally of higher molecular weight, and can be applied in weakly acidic or even neutral dyebaths. Since their wet fastness is normally marginal, these dyes are used where superior leveling is of primary importance, and wet fastness is not a major concern. Because of this, the leveling dyes are used primarily for apparel, knit goods, carpet, upholstery, etc. Wet fastness can be significantly improved by aftertreatment of dyed goods with tannic acid/tartar emetic or any other synthetic fixer. The fixers must be of excellent quality, however, if the leveling and coloring properties of the dye are to be maintained. Acid Blue 80 and Acid Red 337 are both leveling-type acid dyes.

6.2.2.2 Milling Dyes. Milling dyes are suitable for use on wool that is to be milled into felt. The primary advantage of these dyes is their improved wet fastness over the leveling dyes, This allows for the heavy soaking and mechanical action involved in the milling process. These dyes are limited by decreased leveling action, leading to spots, streaks, or a barre coloring. Additionally, the dyes lack the color brightness characteristic of leveling dyes.

Milling dyes have higher molecular weight than leveling dyes and may be disulfonated or polysulfonated. They are normally applied from weak (pH 5-6.2) acidic dyebaths, usually acetic acid. As was the case with leveling dyes, milling dyes generally have good light fastness.

6.2.2.3 Super Milling Dyes (Neutral). Super milling acid dyes normally have high molecular weights, and are applied from neutral solutions. They exhibit extremely good light and wet fastness, at the expense of poor to very poor leveling. As such, their use requires a great deal of care in application if any degree of leveling is to be obtained.

In practical dyeings, a blocking effect is obtained with mixtures of leveling and milling type dyes. When polyamide fibers are dyed with such mixtures, the uptake rate of the monosulfonated dyes is great enough to significantly block the polysulfonated dye uptake.

6.2.2.4 Metal Complex Dyes ("Premetallized"). Although products of dyestuff and metal ion reactions, metal complex dyes are normally considered acid dyes.

Selected acid dyes are reacted with chromium or cobalt ions in 1:1 or 1:2 metal to dye equivalent ratios. The resulting products are either mono or disulfonated (for the 1:1 reaction product) or unsulfonated (for the 1:2 product). The sulfonated compounds normally are applied from a strongly acidic solution. The unsulfonated compounds have an overall negative charge which is not localized but distributed over the dye molecule. As such, these dyes provide excellent light fastness and wash fastness, again at the expense of poor leveling.

6.2.3 Application Properties of Acid Dyes

This section presents the available data for acid dyes. Where possible, the data are presented for the acid dye category rather than specific dyes. However, in some cases data for individual dyes are given.

Table 6 presents the application data available for the acid dyes. These data are compiled from various sources, as referenced on the table. As indicated in previous sections, the general trend is that increasing molecular weight degrades the leveling performance and brightness while improving fastness. Table 7 compares the specific properties of the acid dye subclasses.

Acid dyes, distributed as liquids may be applied from thickener solutions without being dissolved in water. In either case, the dyes are usually applied from liquid dyestocks, and normally at elevated (>39°C, 102°F) temperatures. Acid dyes may be used for transfer printing onto paper from aqueous, thickened solutions and then heat transferred (195°-215°C) to the fabric. The heat causes the dyes to sublime and then condense immediately on the fabric. The use of acid dyes for printing is of very minor significance since feasible printing methods have not been fully developed.

6.2.4 Chemical and Physical Properties

Acid dyes are normally distributed for application as sodium salts which are soluble in water. The salt forms also are easier to handle and much less hygroscopic than the free acids (Shenai, 1973). As water solubility is complete, acid dyebaths are required with many of the dyes

TABLE 6. ACID DYES: APPLICATION DATA

| | | Reference |
|---|---|---|
| Fabrics dyed | Mostly for nylon (polyamides) 80-85% and wool (10-15%) as well as silk, acrylic, polypropylene, and blends. Most newer dyes have been developed for nylon. See Note 1. | SDC, 1971<br>Stead, 1975 |
| Fabrics printed | Direct printing of silk, wool, nylon, and animal fibers. | SDC, 1971<br>Clarke, 1977 |
| Leather dyeing | Many new non-benzidine acid dyes for both blacks and browns on leather have been developed in recent years. | SDC, 1971<br>SDC, 1973 |
| Fabrics stained | Acetate and cellulose (varies from dye to dye) | SDC, 1971 |
| Disposable fabrics | | |
| Leveling | Poor to very good. Very good for "leveling acid dyes" only. | SDC, 1971<br>Kirk-Othmer, 1978 |
| Exhaustion | Good for "leveling acid dyes" only. | |
| Migration | Poor to very good. | Kirk-Othmer, 1978 |
| Dischargeability | Poor to very good. | SDC, 1971 |
| Water solubility | Highly soluble even in cold water (as sodium salts). | Patterson, 1972 |
| Acid fastness | Fair. Index 2-3. | SDC, 1971 |
| Alkali fastness | Poor to good. Index 1-4. | SDC, 1971 |
| Heat resistance | Dye specific. | — |
| Light fastness | Good to very good. Index 4-7. | SDC, 1971 |
| Chlorine fastness | Fair to good. Index 2-4. | |

(continued)

TABLE 6. ACID DYES: APPLICATION DATA (continued)

| | | Reference |
|---|---|---|
| Washfastness | Poor to very good. Index 1-5. Very good for premetallized acid dyes only. See Note 2. | SDC, 1971<br>Kirk-Othmer, 1978 |
| Peroxide fastness | Poor to very good. Index 1-5. | SDC, 1971 |
| Perspiration fastness | Fair to very good. Index 2-5. | SDC, 1971 |
| Useful colors | Full color range | |
| Bonding mechanism | Acid dyes are anionic and form salt links to the fiber which are stronger than hydrogen-bonds. | Shenai, 1973 |
| Rate of dyeing | Relative rates not available. | — |
| Pretreatment | Simple scouring and bleaching. | AATCC, 1981 |
| Aftertreatment | Treatment with tannic and/or synthetic mordants for leveling acids can be used. | Kirk-Othmer, 1978 |
| Dyeing process | Exhaust. | |
| Typical equipment used | Beck. | |

Note 1: 80-85% of all textile use is for nylon. 10-15% used for wool. Not useful for cellulosics.

Note 2: Generally the better leveling acid dyes yield lower wetfastness.

Index Values:

Gray scale: 1 - very poor, 2 - poor, 3 - fair, 4 - good, 5 - excellent.

Lightfastness scale: 1 - very poor, 2 - poor, 3 - fair, 4 - fairly good, 5 - good, 6 - very good, 7 - excellent, 8 - outstanding, 9 - superlative.

TABLE 7. COMPARISON OF ACID DYE SUBCLASSES

| Property | Leveling acid | Milling acid | Supermilling acid | Premetallized |
|---|---|---|---|---|
| Color brightness | Good | Lower than leveling acid | Fair (deep shades) | Lowest of acid dyes |
| Leveling | Very good | Poor to fair | Very poor to fair | Poor |
| Wetfastness | Poor to fair | Good | Very good | Excellent |
| Lightfastness | Very good | — | Good | Excellent |
| Dyebath pH | Highly acid: 2-4 | Weakly acid: 4-6 | Neutral: 6-7 | Highly acid |
| Dyebath additives | Sulfuric or acetic acid | Acetic acid | Ammonium acetate | — |
| Molecular weight | Low (200 - 400 gm/mole) | High (500 - 900 gm/mole) | High (500 - 900 gm/mole) | High (500 - 900 gm/mole) |
| Water solubility | High (40 - 80 gm/L) | Low (13 - 30 gm/L) | Low (3 - 20 gm/L) | — |
| Solution behavior | Ionizes | Aggregates | Aggregates | — |
| Protein affinity | Low | High | Very high | — |
| Cellulose staining | None | Stains | Stains | — |
| Exhaustion | Driven by formic acid | — | Driven by ammonium acetate or sulfate | Driven by formic acid |

to permit exhaustion of the dyebath. Obviously, the water solubility of the dyes leads to poor wet fastness, which can be improved by fixing the dyed fabric with tannic acid or synthetic fixers.

In addition to classifying acid dyes as leveling acid, milling acid, and super milling acid dyes, acid dyes also may be grouped under two broad classes depending on their behavior in water:

1) Completely ionized; and
2) Molecular aggregate.

The acid dyes that completely ionize in water have exceedingly high water solubility and form clear solutions. They have no affinity for cellulose and only poor affinity for protein fibers. They are applied in acidic dyebaths and produce dyeings possessing poor wet fastness, but very even coloration (i.e. leveling acid dyes). Thes second class, molecular aggregating dyes, still ionize to some degree. The size of the aggregates that form in solution are inversely proportional to the dyebath temperature. These dyes have poor solubility in water and form cloudy solutions. They have high affinity towards protein fibers, and this affinity increases with the acidity of the dyebath. They stain cellulosic fibers. Their wetfastness is good, but they exhibit poor leveling (Shenai, 1973). Milling and supermilling acid dyes fall into this category.

Acid dyes range in molecular weight from 200 to 900 and exist in either solid or liquid form. Many of their applicable chemical and physical properties are outlined in Table 8. Figure 1 gives examples of various acid dyes.

## 6.3 DIRECT (SUBSTANTIVE) DYES

### 6.3.1 General Description

Direct dyes derive their name from the absence of mordants in their application. In the past, mordants were required for fabric treatment before dyeing. Natural dyes showed affinity to the mordant-fiber substrate whereas they were not substantive to the untreated fiber. Direct dyes

TABLE 8. PHYSICAL/CHEMICAL PROPERTIES OF ACID DYES

| | | Reference |
|---|---|---|
| Chemical structure | Mostly mono-, di-, and trisulfonic acids of azo, anthraquinone, and triarylmethane chromophores. See Note 1. | Kirk-Othmer, 1978 |
| Physical state | Actual form is non-critical, but manufacturers tend to use granulated forms with surfactants added to diminish caking. See Note 2. | Patterson, 1972 |
| Particle size | Variable - depending on the method of manufacture and individual dye. | |
| Mole weight | Ranges from 200-900 gm/mole. The best level dyeing is obtained with monosulfonated dyes of 400-500 gm/mole and disulfonated dyes of about 800 gm/mole. Higher molecular weights yield reduced washfastness. See Note 3. | Stead, 1975<br>Horning, 1978 |
| Melting point | The vast majority melt (or decompose) above 300°C. A smaller group decomposes at 275-290°C, while a few decompose at 150-190°C. | Aldrich, 1978 |
| Boiling point | Probably decompose first. | |
| Vapor pressure | Dye specific. | |
| Water solubility | Highly soluble even in cold water for their sodium salts. Comparable to soluble basic dyes but very much more soluble than disperse, vat, or pigments. Solubility ranges 3-80 gm/L, but most are soluble to the extent of 8-40 gm/L. | Patterson, 1972 |
| Other solubility | Dye specific. | |

(continued)

TABLE 8. PHYSICAL/CHEMICAL PROPERTIES OF ACID DYES (continued)

| | | Reference |
|---|---|---|
| Hydrolysis | | |
| Partition coefficient | | |
| Soil adsorption/desorption | | |
| Dissociation constant | | |
| Spectra | | |
| Toxicity | Dye specific, e.g., Acid Red 26 is a proven animal carcinogen. | NIOSH, 1979 |

Note 1: Minor chemical categories include pyrazoline, azine, nitro, and quinoline dyes.

Note 2: Handling of very fine colorants of high staining value is avoided because of difficulty in weighing, health hazards due to dust, and cross-contamination of dyeings from flying flecks.

Note 3: Generally nylon uses low molecular weight dyestuffs while other fibers use high molecular weight dyes. Increasing molecular weights provide better fastness but poorer leveling.

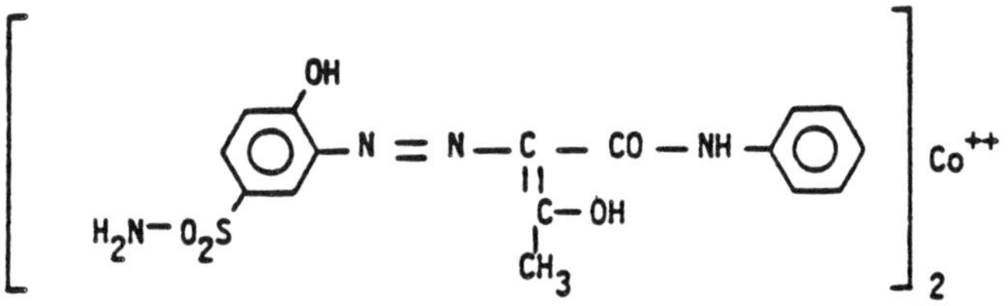

C.I. Acid Yellow 151 - 1:2 Cobalt complexed acetoacetanilide monoazo

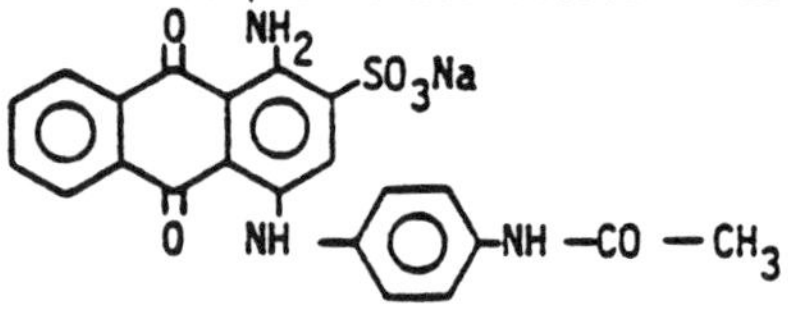

C.I. Acid Blue 40 - Anthraquinone

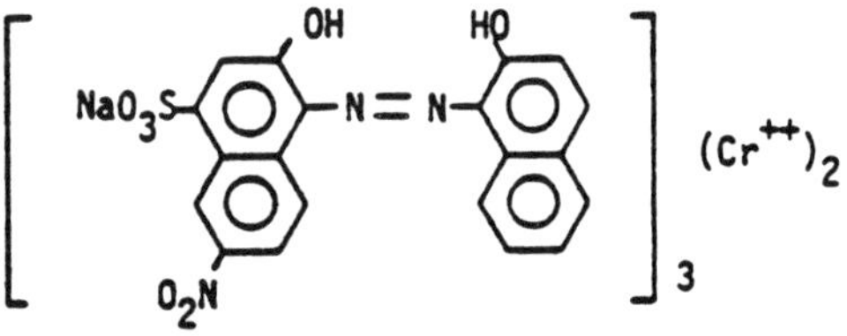

C.I. Acid Black 52 - 2:3 Chromium complexed monoazo

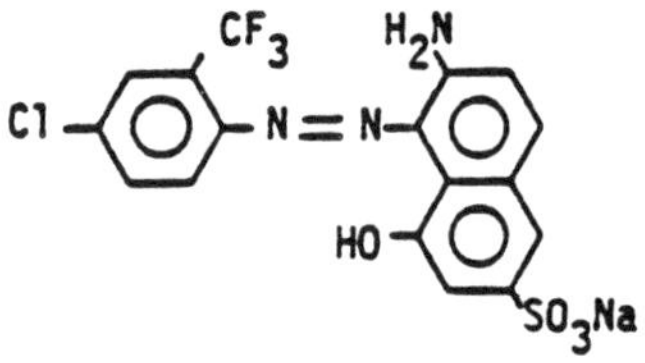

C.I. Acid Red 266 - Monazo

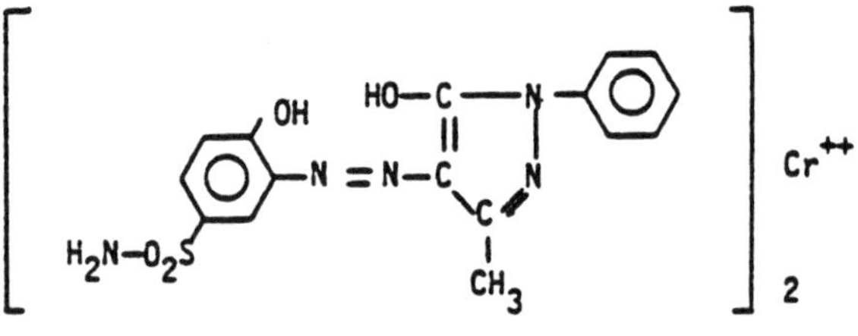

C.I. Acid Orange 60 - 1:2 Chromium complexed pyrazolone monoazo

Figure 1. Chemical structures of various acid dyes.

in contrast, are applied directly to the fiber and bond to the fiber by electrostatic forces. These dyes sometimes are called substantive dyes in reference to their substantivity to cellulose fibers.

From 1979 to 1980, U.S. production of direct dyes increased by 9.2%, while at the same time, production of most other dye application classes declined. Direct dyes have the advantages of excellent penetration and leveling plus ease of application from simple water (including cold) solutions. Almost all cellulosic garment materials today are dyed with direct dyes.

Direct dyestuffs accounted for 13% of the total 1980 U.S. dyestuff production or 14.2 million kilograms (31.2 million pounds). Direct yellow dyes dominated with production totaling 45.7% of all direct dyes produced. The following statistical information was derived from the 1980 U.S. International Trade Commission report.

6.3.1.1 Color Categories of Direct Dyes. The following is a breakdown of the direct dyestuffs produced in 1980 along with the percentage of the total direct dye production that each color category represents.

| Color Category | Percent of Total Directs |
|---|---|
| Direct Yellows | 45.7% |
| Direct Blues | 20.9% |
| Direct Reds | 19.2% |
| Direct Blacks | 8.9% |
| Direct Oranges | 4.2% |
| Direct Brown | 0.9% |
| Direct Violet | 0.8% |
| Direct Green | 0.5% |
| | 100.0% |

6.3.1.2 Outstanding Volume Products. The following are the direct dyes with the largest 1980 U.S. production volumes reported along with the percentage of the total direct dyestuff production that they represent.

| C.I. Name | Percent of Total Directs |
|---|---|
| Direct Yellow 11 | 15.9% |
| Direct Yellow 147 | 10.1% |
| Direct Red 81 | 6.1% |
| Direct Black 22 | 4.5% |
| Direct Blue 86 | 4.3% |
| Direct Yellow 4 | 3.2% |
| Direct Red 238 | 3.0% |
| Direct Blue 218 | 2.6% |
| Direct Blue 199 | 2.4% |
| | 52.1% |

6.3.2 Application Properties of Direct Dyes

Direct dyes in textile usage are primarily for cotton and other cellulosic fibers. These include linen, hemp, jute, rayon, and viscose.

All of these fibers except rayon require careful pretreatment such as scouring and desizing to obtain a quality dyeing. The purpose of pretreatment is to remove impurities in the fabric such as lubricants added to facilitate knitting, sizing materials applied to cotton to add fiber strength in knitting, and other naturally occurring impurities. These impurities are removed so the dye will adhere to the fiber substrate rather than to the impurities on the fiber.

Although many variations of this procedure are used, a typical cotton yarn dyeing process would begin with preparing of a dyebath containing salt. The textile is introduced into the cold dye bath and worked for a fixed period of time. The dyebath temperature then is raised to some characteristic exhaustion temperature (up to 100°C) and dyeing continues.

The criteria for dyestuff selection would include its shade, its dyeing rate, degree of exhaustion, and water solubility. The two most important process control factors to consider are the dyeing rate and exhaustion which in turn are controlled by time, temperature, salt concentration, liquor ratio, dyebath volume, dye concentration, and the inherent compatibility of the dyestuff and fiber-type. Dyeing time exhibits exponential behavior in that dyeing rate is very accelerated initially and then begins to level off. An equilibrium is usually reached within 45 minutes. At that point, extra time is allowed for the dye to level, that is, come to a uniform color over the textile (Shenai, 1973).

Dyeing rate and dye exhaustion are proportional to dyebath temperature, however, increasing both of these properties to accelerate the dyeing is not always desirable. Salt concentration also influences the progress of the dyeing process in an exponential fashion. Salt is either added before dyeing or in increments to the hot dyebath. As the ratio of fabric to the volume of the dyebath increases, the dyeing will take longer to reach equilibrium and less total color is exhausted. Next the temperature of the dyebath is slowly raised to 50-60°C and common salt is added in the range of 10-40% of texile weight. Although considerably less important than the other factors, the concentration of the dye also influences the rate of exhaustion, in an inverse fashion (Francolors, 1982). Exhaustion and leveling of the dye are indeed complex processes and are determined by inherent qualities of the textile and dyestuff as well as interrelationships among the process parameters.

Direct dyes usually have reactive groups, such as amines ($R-NH_2$), which react with the hydroxyl (R-OH) groups on the cellulose macromolecule; they attach by weak hydrogen bonds. Direct dyes penetrate the physical structure of the fiber excellently but do not penetrate the chemical structure of the cellulose macromolecule (Shenai, 1973). Therefore, the dye molecules adhere quickly to the surface of individual fibers and diffuse only slightly into the fiber owing to their large molecular size.

Direct dyestuffs are dissolved in water and dissociate into positive sodium cations and negative organic anions. The commercial powdered dyestuff is frequently dissolved in cold water to form a paste and then soda ash and hot water then are added to solubilize the dyestuff. The dye cannot be directly dissolved in hot water because insoluble lumps will form and cause a "flecky" dyeing (Shenai, 1973). The dyestuff in solution exists as an equilibrium mixture of single dyestuff anions and molecular aggregates. However, only the single dyestuff molecules are substantive to the textile and for that reason the dyebath has to be heated, since increased temperature shifts the equilibrium in favor of the single molecules. On the other hand, direct dyed textiles cannot be washed in boiling water, especially in the presence of soap, since this causes the weak physical bonds to break and the dyestuff to be stripped from the textile. Also, if the temperature is too high, the dye molecules attach to the textile so quickly that the dyeing obtained has very poor leveling. In practice, the dyebath is slowly heated from room temperature to a predetermined temperature. The heating rate and final temperature are determined by the kinetics of the forward reaction, transfer of the dissolved dye to the fiber, and the reverse reaction or the stripping of the dyestuff. Upon reaching this final temperature the rates of the former and latter reactions are equal and in dynamic equilibrium: equal amounts of dye going onto and off the fabric over a period of time.

A particular dyestuff is characterized by its temperature of maximum exhaustion and dye-equilibrium absorption - the amount of dye in grams - taken up by a kilogram of fabric once dynamic equilibrium is reached. Note that even though the dyeing rate accelerates at very high temperatures, the dye-equilibrium absorption value decreases. Another implication of this phenomenon is that when direct dyestuffs are mixed to achieve custom shades (a common practice), they must have more or less equivalent temperatures of maximum exhaustion and similar equilibria. For every 30°C of temperature increase, the dye-equilibrium absorption is halved.

Normally, direct dyes do not exhaust completely; the extent of exhaustion is governed by temperature and/or salt concentration. Direct dyes that exhaust more completely show poorer qualities of leveling. This means that a significant amount of the dyestuff added initially will remain in the dyebath after the textile completes coloration. The dye uptake is expressed as percentage exhaustion of the dyebath and follows the following formula (Shenai, 1973):

$$\text{Percentage exhaustion} = \frac{(\text{gm/L Dye})\ \text{initial} - (\text{gm/L dye})\ \text{final}}{(\text{gm/L dye})\ \text{initial}}$$

When salts such as sodium sulfate (Glauber's Salt) and sodium·chloride (often termed exhausting agents) are added to the dyebath, they have a profound effect on the uptake of the dyestuff. This effect is unique for each particular dye and, with increasing salt concentration, rises to a maximum beyond which dyestuff uptake begins to decrease or level off. Because of this reaction, direct dyestuffs are commonly called "salt colors." When cellulosics are immersed in water they develop a substantial negative charge which electrostatically repels the negatively charged dyestuff anions. The sodium cations of the salt associate with the negatively charged cellulose substrate and effectively shield the dyestuff from these repulsion forces. This allows the dye molecule to approach the substrate closely enough to hydrogen bond. Since the anionic groups of the dye are the sulfonic acid groups (or sulfonates) themselves, the more of these groups present, the more pronounced the effect of salt addition (Shenai, 1973). In addition, sodium sulfate also acts to convert some remaining free sulfonic acid groups in the direct dyestuff to sodium sulfonate. The manufacturer reacts the sulfonic acid groups to convert them into their sodium salt forms since free sulfonic acid is much less water soluble. However, a significant amount of unsalted sulfonic acid containing dyestuff typically is found in the dye product. Being less water soluble, the free acid form will not enter into the dyeing equilibrium and ends up as wasted dyestuff.

In the textile dyeing process, the shade of the dyeing is expressed as a percentage of weight dye to weight fabric. However, since exhaustion of direct dyes is not complete, this does not equal the dye uptake onto the fabric. The material to liquor ratio is also a unique quantity. This represents the weight of the textile divided by the weight of the dyebath liquor. In other words, the percentage shade and amount of material quantify the amount of dyestuff and the material-to-liquor ratio which reflects the concentration of the dyebath liquor.

The Society of Dyers and Colourists (SDC) have designated the direct dyes application groups according to their use of salt concentration, temperature, or other variables to control application (AATCC, 1981).

| Class | Leveling | Salt used | Exhaustion |
|---|---|---|---|
| A | Good | Variable | Excellent, but not salt controlled |
| B | Poor | Variable | Salt controlled |
| C | Poor | None | Temperature controlled |

Dyes belonging to Class A have superior migration properties and therefore are highly self-leveling dyestuffs; they can be used even with high concentrations of salt, although they are not salt controlled. Dyeings with Class A dyes are initially very uneven but colors level with continued dyeing. Dyes of the Class B are salt controlled and must be exhausted at a very slow rate initially since any unevenness in shade cannot be corrected. Dyes of the Class C variety are influenced by salt to such a degree that salt is not useful to control exhaustion. Exhaustion of Class C dyes is controlled by the rate of dyebath temperature increase (SDC, 1971) (AATCC, 1981).

The fastness properties of direct dyes are too varied to allow many generalizations other than the fact that most have limited wet fastness and many require chemical aftertreatment. The SDC describes six after-treatment subcategories for direct dyes: "fast-to-light" direct dyes, direct dyes with average fastness some of which may be aftertreated, dyes that must be developed (reacted on the fiber) with CI Developers, dyes which must be developed with p-nitroaniline (C.I. Developer 7), dyes which must be copper or chromium complexed, and finally dyes which must be aftertreated with formaldehyde. Only dyes in the first two subcategories can be used without aftertreatment. Frequently, direct dyeings are also aftertreated with cationic complexing agents to improve wet fastness, but at the expense of lowering the fastness to light. Most of the previously mentioned aftertreatments are employed to increase the molecular weight of the fiber-afixed dye molecule and thereby to increase its wet fastness (SDC, 1971). Another useful application is the topping of a direct dye with basic dyes. Basic dyes have no affinity for cellulosics but do have appreciable affinity for the fiber-afixed direct dye. An insoluble direct-basic complex precipitates out and allows brighter shades of the basic dyestuff with even less basic dyestuff. This technique is limited by the fact that only acid-stable direct dyestuffs can withstand the required processing.

Table 9 presents many of the generalized characteristics of direct dyestuffs for textiles.

### 6.3.3 Chemical and Physical Properties

Direct dyes fall mainly into the dis-, tris-, and polyazo chemical classes, but some are also monoazo, stilbene, oxazine, thiozole, and phthalocyanine types. Direct dyes are anionic in nature and contain solubilizing groups (sulfonic acid, carboxylic acid, or hydroxyl) as the acid dyes do. The chief chemical distinction between acid and direct dyes is the tendency of the direct dyes to possess long coplanar aromatic rings rather than the compact structures of the acid dyes (Steadman, 1977) (Bomberger, 1981) (Shenai, 1973). This property allows the dye molecule to lie parallel to the surface of the fiber and hydrogen bond to the hydroxyl groups of the cellulose macromolecule (spaced at 10.8 A°) with hydrogen bonding groups such as amino groups, amide groups, and reactive resonance hybrid structures of azo functionalities. The occurrence block structures are typically linked at parapositions to the rest of the molecule. See Figure 2 for examples of some typical chemical structures.

Table 10 summarizes the relevant chemical and physical properties of direct dyes.

## 6.4 AZOIC DYES

### 6.4.1 General Description

Azoic dyes (also called naphthols or "ice colors") are produced through an in-situ process which creates the colored material directly on the fabric by coupling a C.I. Azoic-Diazo Component and a C.I. Coupling Component. The cloth first is impregnated with the coupling component

TABLE 9. APPLICATION PROPERTIES OF DIRECT DYES

| | | Reference |
|---|---|---|
| Fabrics dyed | Mostly cotton and other cellulosic (including rayon, jute, linen, hemp), also wool, silk and bast. | SDC, 1971 |
| Fabrics printed | Mostly cotton, also other cellulosics, silk, wool, nylon. Usage is declining. | SDC, 1971<br>Clarke, 1977 |
| Leather dyeing | Benzidine-based direct blacks and browns have been the mainstay of leather dyeing until recent years. See Note 1. | SDC, 1971<br>AATCC, 1981 |
| Fabrics stained | Acetate and nylon (varies from dye to dye). | SDC, 1971 |
| Disposable fabrics | | |
| Leveling | Class A dyes good leveling. Class B and C dyes poor leveling. | |
| Exhaustion | Normally do not exhaust completely and exhaustion is salt or temperature controlled. Exhaustion usually approaches or exceeds 90% with the addition of salt within 1 hour at boiling. | Kirk-Othmer, 1971 |
| Migration | Class A dyes good migration. Class B dyes poor migration. Class C dyes poor migration which is affected by temperature. | AATCC, 1981 |
| Dischargeability | Poor to very good using formaldehyde reagent. C.I. Reducing Agent 2. | SDC, 1971 |
| Water solubility | Salt forms are used to enhance solubility. Many are very soluble and ionize in water. 20-80 gm/L. | AATCC, 1981 |

(continued)

TABLE 9. APPLICATION PROPERTIES OF DIRECT DYES (continued)

| | | Reference |
|---|---|---|
| Acid fastness | Highly variable. Poor to good. Index 1-5. | SDC, 1971 |
| Alkali fastness | Highly variable. Poor to good. Index 1-5. | SDC, 1971 |
| Heat resistance | Fair to good. Indexed 2-5 for hot pressing. | SDC, 1971 |
| Light fastness | Highly variable. Poor to excellent. | SDC, 1971<br>AATCC, 1981 |
| Chlorine fastness | Highly variable. | |
| Wash fastness | Highly variable. Poor to moderate (Index 1-4), unless aftertreated. | SDC, 1971 |
| Peroxide fastness | Highly variable | |
| Perspiration fastness | Highly variable. | |
| Useful colors | Full color range. | |
| Bonding mechanism | Anionic dyestuff hydrogen-bonded to hydroxyl groups of cellulose. | Shenai, 1973 |
| Rate of dyeing | Dye specific. | |
| Pretreatment | Dye specific. | |

(continued)

TABLE 9. APPLICATION PROPERTIES OF DIRECT DYES (continued)

| | | Reference |
|---|---|---|
| Aftertreatment | Often require such reagents as bichromate, copper sulfate, formaldehyde cationic fixing agents, coupling with developing agents and/or combination of these reagents. | SDC, 1971<br>AATCC, 1981 |
| Dyeing process | Exhaust process. Dye applied from neutral aqueous brine suspension. | |
| Typical equipment used | Package, beck, jig, paddle, jet. | Horning, 1978 |

Note 1: Benzidine blacks and browns for leather are slowly being replaced by newly developed non-benzidine acid browns and blacks, direct blacks, and especially the highly wetfast reactive dye colors. However, no extremely good color substitutes have been found when considering color value and cost.

Index Values:

Gray scale: 1 - very poor, 2 - poor, 3 - fair, 4 - good, 5 - excellent.

Lightfastness scale: 1 - very poor, 2 - poor, 3 - fair, 4 - fairly good, 5 - good, 6 - very good, 7 - excellent, 8 - outstanding, 9 - superlative.

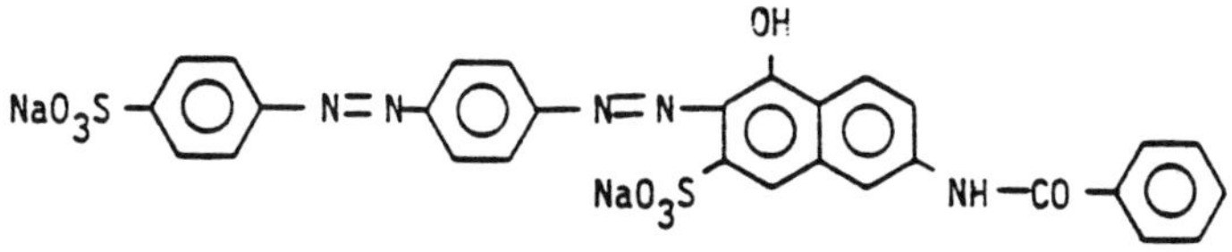

C.I. Direct Red 81 - Disazo dye

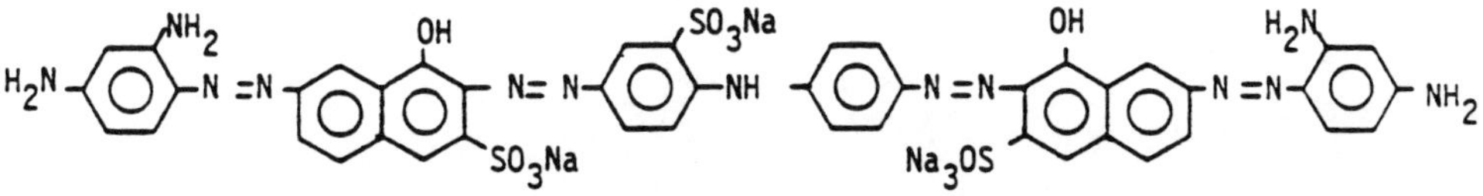

C.I. Direct Black 22 - Tetrakisazo dye

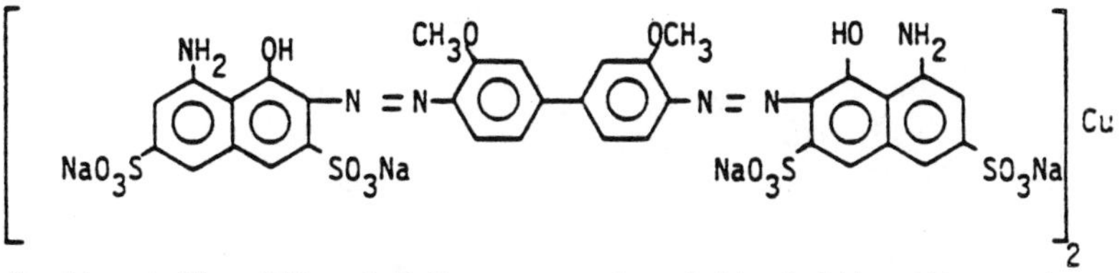

C.I. Direct Blue 218 - 1:2 Copper complexed Dianisidine disazo dye

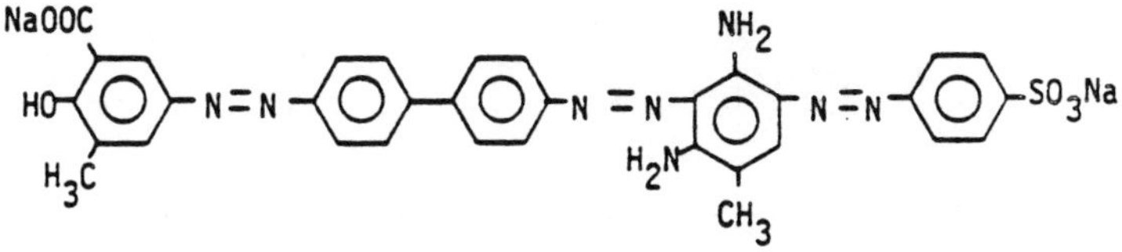

C.I. Direct Brown 154 - Trisazo benzidine dye

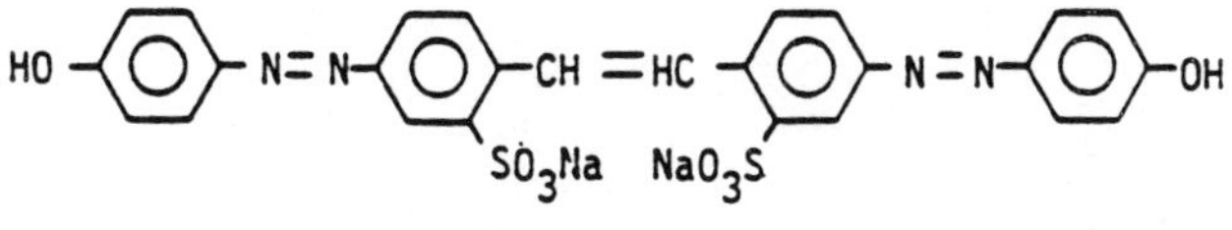

C.I. Direct Yellow 4 - Stilbene disazo dye

C.I. Direct Yellow 11 - Indeterminate stilbene mixture

Figure 2. Chemical structures of various direct dyes.

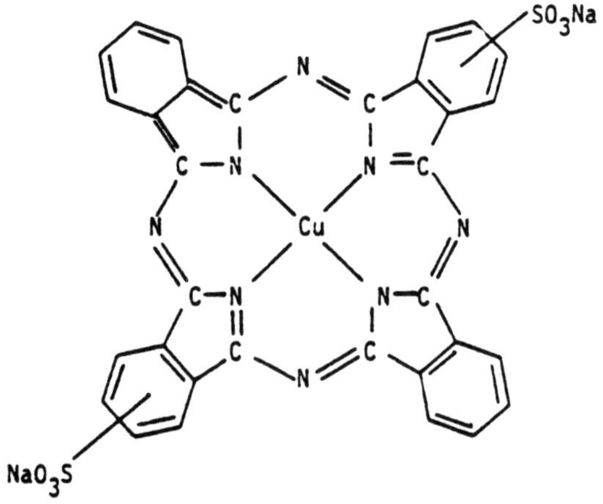

C.I. Direct Blue 86 - Phthalocyanine dye

Figure 2. (continued)

TABLE 10. PHYSICAL/CHEMICAL PROPERTIES OF DIRECT DYES

| | | Reference |
|---|---|---|
| Chemical structure | Mostly polyazo sulfonates. Minor classes include monazo, stilbene, oxazine, thiazine, and phthalocyanine. | SDC, 1971 |
| Physical state | Usually sold as water soluble sodium sulfonate salt form. | |
| Particle size | Dye specific - depends on manufacturing process. | |
| Mole weight | Ranges 350-1600 for a number of dyes observed and averaged 800. High molecular weight is required to yield colloidal solutions. | SDC, 1971 |
| Density | Dye specific. | |
| Melting point | Most direct dyes melt only at temperatures well over 300°C (with probable decomposition to some extent). | Aldrich, 1979 |
| Boiling point | Probably decompose before boiling. | |
| Vapor pressure | Dye specific. | |
| Water solubility | Most are soluble sodium sulfonate salts. Solubility ranges 20-80 gm/L. | Aldrich, 1979 |
| Other solvents | Most insoluble in organics. Some dissolve in cellosolve. | |
| Hydrolysis | Sodium sulfonate salts ionize in water. | |
| Effect of salts | Copper and iron salts affect the hue of the dyestuff. | SDC, 1971 |

(continued)

TABLE 10. PHYSICAL/CHEMICAL PROPERTIES OF DIRECT DYES (continued)

| | Physical/chemical properties | Reference |
|---|---|---|
| Partition coefficient | Dye specific. | |
| Soil adsorption/desorption | Dye specific. | |
| Dissociation constant | Dye specific. | |
| Spectra | Dye specific. | |
| Toxicity | Many direct dyes for cotton have been derived from the carcinogen benzidine and its congeners, although its use is diminishing. See Note 1. | |

Note 1:

Benzidine: OSHA: Carcinogen
NIOSH: Positive human carcinogen
AQTX: TLm 96: 10-1 ppm

o-Dianisidine: NIOSH: Positive animal carcinogen

o-Tolidine: NIOSH: Positive animal carcinogen
Criteria Doc: std-air: CL 20 $mg/m^3/1H$

Dichlorobenzidine: NIOSH: Positive animal carcinogen
OSHA: Carcinogen

Proven Carcinogenic Direct Dyes: Direct Blue 6, Direct Blue 14, Direct Black 38, Direct Violet 1, Direct Brown 95. Twelve other direct dyes have been found to be bioconverted back to the corresponding benzidine congener but have not been proven carcinogenic.

and then immersed in an ice water solution of the diazonium salt prepared from the azoic-diazo component. In the printing process, both ingredients are added simultaneously in an unreactive form and then activated and reacted with acid and steaming. In many references these dyes are more correctly referred to as azoic pigments since the final colored product is, by necessity, water-insoluble (Shenai, 1973).

### 6.4.2 Products

The 1980 International Trade Commission Report on Synthetic Organic Chemicals includes 15 Azoic Coupling Components, 18 Azoic-Diazo Components (free bases and salts) and 11 Azoic Compositions, which are mixtures of the two components yielded temporarily unreactive (until after application). The listing of these products signifies that 1980 production volumes exceeded 2,268 kilograms (5,000 pounds) or $5000 in sales. However, no specific product volumes are given at the request of the producers supplying the information. The compositions included yellow, red, orange, violet, brown, and black shades (ITC, 1980).

The 1982 AATCC Buyer's Guide lists 25 C.I. Azoic Coupling Components available and 25 C.I. Azoic-Diazo Components. Additionally, 19 C.I. Azoic Compositions are included. Four (4) of these are red shades and another five (5) are blues (AATCC, 1981).

### 6.4.3 Application Properties of Azoic Dyes

Azoic dyes are produced in relatively small amounts today and are most popular for bright red shades, although yellows, oranges, browns, and violets are still produced. A variety of other colors and shades can be obtained from azoic dyes. Their use has been largely discontinued due to environmental concerns, OSHA regulations, and replacement with fiber-reactive dyestuffs. The naphthol bright reds are favored because of their light fastness and chlorine resistance (Kirk-Othmer, 1978). Azoic dyes have superior chlorine and light fastness to direct dyes. In a technique termed "developed dyeing," textiles are first dyed with direct dyes and then coupled with amines or phenols to deepen the color and improve wash fastness by increasing the molecular weight. The overall fastness properties of azoic dyes on cellulose are second only to those of vat dyes. Azoic red and violet shades are used to complement vat dyes which offer only dull colors. Disadvantages of azoic dyes include poor abrasion resistance and poor sublimation fastness (Shenai, 1973).

Azoic dyes can be used to dye most cellulosic fibers including linen, jute, hemp, polyester, rayon, and cotton. They are applied both by continuous and exhaust processes. Their simple application is a main advantage along with the fact that rinsing or, at the most, soaping is the only aftertreatment required. Azoic dyes are unique in that the user selects the C.I. Azoic Coupling Component to suit his fastness requirements and the C.I. Azoic-Diazo Component to provide the desired hue, within the limited range of the empirically determined compatible combinations.

Impregnation Process

The impregnation process consists of separate additions of the coupling component ("Naphthol") and diazo component ("Azoic base"). The commonly used term Naphthol was once a tradename for a group of coupling components, and is not necessarily synonymous with the chemical, Naphthol.

Azoic coupling components are sold as liquids or paste-like dispersions and are inherently insoluble in water. The free Naphthol is also less substantive to cotton than its salts; they are usually converted to their sodium salts prior to use in either of two methods. In the hot dissolution process, the Naphthol is pasted with Turkey Red Oil. Caustic soda and boiling water are added and the mixture boiled until it is clear and then is cooled. In the cold process, the Naphthol is stirred in cellosolve or alcohol, caustic soda, and cold water. Although use of the organic solvent gives rise to added expense, the cold process is simpler and is generally used unless the hot process is mandatory. Free Naphthols also are unable to couple with diazonium salts. Atmospheric carbon dioxide tends to produce the free Naphthol from its sodium naphtholate salt, so formaldehyde is added to the coupling agent bath to prohibit this (except for acetoacetylarylamide coupling agents). Any free coupling agent present will eventually become waste. An addition of 3-5 ml/L of Turkey Red Oil is also needed to keep some naphtholates from precipitating from the dyebath. Naphthols have varied substantivity to cotton; affinity is controlled by salt addition. Usually about 30 gm/L of common Glauber's salt is added for the more highly substantive Naphthols and 50 gm/L for the less substantive ones (Shenai, 1973). The coupling component itself largely determines the affinity and in turn, the fastness of the final dyeing (Lubs, 1955). Again, the less substantive the coupling agent, the greater the amount that will be left in the final dyebath as waste.

The critical factors which determine how much coupling component will be taken up are (SDC, 1971):

1) Impregnation bath temperature - temperature is raised to promote penetration yet the rate of exhaustion decreases with temperature.

2) Impregnation time - except for continuous dyeing, 30 minutes is needed.

3) Concentration of the coupling component.

4) The amount of salt electrolyte added.

5) The liquor-to-goods ratio.

6) The inherent substantivity of the C.I. Azoic Coupling Component itself.

Azoic-Diazo components or "fast bases" are usually sold as hydrochloride salts or other stabilized forms. Some - usually powders - are sold as their free bases. If the insoluble free base is purchased it is water solubilized by using concentrated hydrochloric acid to prepare its hydrochloride salt prior to use. These fast bases are the color determining fraction of the final azoic dye molecule. Azoic bases themselves have little affinity for cellulose which is why the substantive Naphthol is applied first. During immersion in the coupling component bath, the textile is first impregnated with the substantive Naphthol. The Azoic base is diazotized (if not originally purchased as the stabilized diazonium salt) and the textile is then immersed in the bath of diazotized amine. There, the diazonium salt undergoes a coupling reaction directly with the Naphthol to form an insoluble pigment-type colored substance affixed to the textile. The concentration of the diazonium chloride must be at least 0.5 gm/L to expedite this coupling reaction.

The diazonium salt is prepared by reaction of the free amine at 8-12°C with hydrochloric acid and sodium nitrite. First the base (as a powder) must be pasted with hydrochloric acid and water. This diazotization usually requires 20-30 minutes and gives off toxic and corrosive nitrogen dioxide ($NO_2$) fumes. The resultant diazonium salt is very sensitive to water and decomposes on metal surfaces so nonmetallic vessels are required (Shenai, 1973).

The diazo coupling is a pH controlled reaction; alkali binding agents must be added for production of azoic dyes. In general, the red colored bases couple much faster than the blues. The unreacted nonsubstantive Naphthols must be removed by washing and/or soaping to preserve the fastness of the final dyeing.

Printing Processes

The various printing processes used with azoic dyes are variations of the basic process. Diazo component paste is applied to Naphthol impregnated fabric using a roller engraved with the desired pattern. The print is then steam treated to develop color and the unreacted coupling component is washed off and discarded. This technique has been modified to eliminate waste products by preparing the diazonium salt as a passive sodium aryldiazotate mixed with the "Rapid Fast" type Naphthols and simultaneously printing them onto unimpregnated fabric. Alternatively, the textile can be printed with a commercially available azoic composition. The components are activated and reacted upon steam treatment with dilute acid addition. This technique both minimizes wastes and offers simple application and fast brilliant colors. However, it is not suitable for diazo components with positively charged substituent groups since the diazotate cannot be formed. Other azoic dyeing schemes use the reversibly formed triazine and sulfonate stabilized derivatives of the diazonium salt to produce the commercial "Rapidogen" and "Rapidazole" colors (Lubs, 1955). C.I. Azoic Compositions are similarly used.

A separate type of temporarily solubilized azoic pigments are prepared from the azoic "dye" and m-(chlorosulfonyl) benzoic acid paste. The paste is printed onto the textile and steamed for penetration. Finally, caustic brine is used to desolubilize the color (Lubs, 1955).

Table 11 summarizes the application properties of azoic dyes.

6.4.4 Chemical and Physical Properties

Azoic dyes have the azo chemical functionality (-N=N-) and are similar in chemical composition to azo dyes in other application classes. The two main distinctions are 1) other azo dyes are coupled prior to the dyeing process, and 2) only coupling components that yield water-insoluble dyestuffs are useful for producing azoic dyes.

C.I. Azoic Coupling Components are largely derivatives of beta-Naphthol. Several hundred derivatives of the original and very successful Naphthol AS have been prepared by condensing naphthoic acids with naphthylamines, anilines and benzidine congeners (diaminobiphenyls). A second and smaller class of coupling components consists of arylamides formed by condensation of substituted anilines with the hydroxycarboxylic acids, anthracene, carbazole, benzocarbazole, and diphenylene oxide. These are used mostly for green, brown, and black shades. A third chemical group is comprised of acylacetarylamides which are reacted by diazo coupling of azoic bases onto its active methylene groups. These are used chiefly for yellow shades.

As earlier mentioned, the fastness properties of the final azoic dyeing are dependent on the substantive properties of the Azoic Coupling Component since the Azoic-Diazo Components have no affinity for cellulose. The substantivity of the coupling component and its attachment to the textile fibers has been found to be related to the occurrence and spacing of hydrogen-bonding groups in the component. However, no completely satisfactory model has been delineated.

TABLE 11. APPLICATION PROPERTIES OF AZOIC DYES

| | | Reference |
|---|---|---|
| Fabrics dyed | Chiefly cellulosics, especially cotton, but also linen, rayon, jute, hemp, and also furs, silk, nylon, polyester, and acetate. | AATCC, 1981 |
| Fabrics printed | All of the textiles listed above. | Clarke, 1977 |
| Leather dyeing | | |
| Fabrics stained | | |
| Disposable fabrics | | |
| Leveling | | |
| Exhaustion | Many azoic components exhaust only 10-12% while others almost completely exhaust. Rate of exhaustion decreases with increased temperature. Note that temperatures are slowly raised from ice bath temperatures to promote penetration. | AATCC, 1981 |
| Migration | | |
| Dischargeability | Particularly suitable for discharge printing. | SDC, 1971 |
| Water solubility | Formed from solubilized components onto the fabric, but the ultimate colored product is always an insoluble pigment. | |
| Acid fastness | | |
| Alkali fastness | Poor-good. Index 2-4. | SDC, 1971 |

(continued)

TABLE 11. APPLICATION PROPERTIES OF AZOIC DYES (continued)

| | | Reference |
|---|---|---|
| Heat resistance | Good. Index 3-4. | SDC, 1971 |
| Light fastness | Poor-very good. Index 2-7. Superior to direct dyes. | SDC, 1971 |
| Chlorine fastness | Poor-good. Index 2-5. Superior to direct dyes. | SDC, 1971 |
| Wash fastness | Very good. Second only to vat dyes. | SDC, 1971 |
| Peroxide fastness | Poor-good. Index 1-5. | SDC, 1971 |
| Perspiration fastness | | |
| Useful colors | Chiefly reds and especially bright reds. | AATCC, 1981 |
| Bonding mechanism | Mechanical retention of insoluble dye molecule within fiber structure. | Shenai, 1973 |
| Miscellaneous | Poor fastness to crocking. | AATCC, 1981 |
| Rate of dyeing | Equal to direct, vat, and reactive dyes on cotton but slower on blends. | AATCC, 1981 |
| Pretreatment | Fabric must be simply bleached and/or scoured. | AATCC, 1981 |
| Aftertreatment | Simple soaping and rinsing to remove unreacted ingredients. | |
| Dyeing process | Pad batch, exhaust, and printing. | Horning, 1978 |

(continued)

TABLE 11. APPLICATION PROPERTIES OF AZOIC DYES (continued)

| | | Reference |
|---|---|---|
| Typical equipment used | Continuous process, pad-jig, beck, jig. Low liquor ratio is the most economical and reproducible. | AATCC, 1981 |
| Miscellaneous | Colored azoic pigments are formed directly on the textile in situ from coupling of a C.I. Coupling Component and a C.I. Azoic-Diazo Component. | |

Index Values:

Gray scale: 1 - very poor, 2 - poor, 3 - fair, 4 - good, 5 - excellent.

Lightfastness scale: 1 - very poor, 2 - poor, 3 - fair, 4 - fairly good, 5 - good, 6 - very good, 7 - excellent, 8 - outstanding, 9 - superlative.

These coupling components or "Naphthols" show varying degrees of substantivity. They also show increased substantivity when salt is added to the impregnation bath where they are introduced into the fabric prior to coupling with the Azoic-Diazo Component or "azoic base." In their pure state, Naphthols are water-insoluble and so are applied via their water-soluble sodium salts or sodium naphtholates, which are prepared by treatment with caustic soda. Formaldehyde is frequently added to inhibit carbon dioxide decomposition of the naphtholate back to the free Naphthol. The reason for this is that the free Naphthols have less substantivity and cannot undergo the coupling reaction with the diazotized azoic base.

Some generalizations can be made about the relationship between the chemical features of the Naphthol and the application properties of the resultant dye (Lubs, 1955). Of the smallest chemical category of products, anthracenes usually yield greens, heterocyclics yield browns and active methylene compounds yield yellows. For the various 3-hydroxy-2-naphthoic arylamide coupling components, moving any substituent from ortho to meta to para gives rise to a bathochromic effect or a shift of the resultant color away from the yellow end of the spectrum toward the blue. Also, in the following series the bathochromic effect increases from left to right for a fixed substituent site: OR, H, R, Cl, $NO_2$. Substantivity and wash fastness are unrelated when associated with azoic dyestuffs. The wash fastness is only a function of the number of solubilizing sulfonate, carboxylate, or hydroxyl groups. The amide coupling groups found in some coupling components enhance substantivity yet decrease chlorine resistance. Substitution of groups onto the nitrogen of the amide destroys the substantivity. Adding three substituent groups to the 2, 4, and 5 positions of the 3-hydroxyl-2-naphthoic arylamides increases light fastness.

C.I. Azoic-Diazo Components or "azoic bases" are all diazotizable amines or diamines and contain no solubilizing groups. Most of these azoic bases are substituted anilines, toluidines, anisidines, azobenzenes, or diphenylamines. The majority are of the general structure 2-(+)-3-(-)-

aniline where (+) represents a positive substituent and (-) represents a negative group. Frequently occurring substituent groups include: nitro, cyano, trifluoromethyl, halogen, alkyl sulfonyl, anilino, and benzanilides (Lubs, 1955). The azoic base largely determines the shade of the final product. The free bases of these compounds are water insoluble, so the hydrochloride salt must be formed to obtain a water soluble ingredient for dye formation.

The azoic bases prepared from o-anisidine, p-nitroaniline, β-naphthylamine, and chloroaniline are useful for preparing quality red shades (Shenai, 1973). p-Nitroaniline, chloroaniline, and β-naphthylamine are all listed as EPA priority pollutants and in Appendix VIII of FR 45, May 1980 as hazardous pollutants.

Some relationships between chemical features of the azoic bases and properties of the ultimate azoic pigment have been described (Lubs, 1955). The presence of trifluoromethane substituents on the molecule leads to greater light fastness. Moving a single group from ortho to meta to para on the aromatic nuclei of the azoic base gives rise to a bathochromic shift and the hue changes from yellow toward the blue end of the color spectrum. This bathochromic effect increases in the following progression: H, $NO_2$, Cl, RO. The 2-(+)-5-(-)-aniline type azoic bases have far superior brilliance and fastness properties.

The hydrochloride of the azoic base must be diazotized for subsequent coupling with the coupling component (Naphthol). This reaction generally involves adding hydrochloric acid and sodium nitrite to a solution of the amine base at 8-12°C. The reaction usually takes 20-30 minutes and liberates toxic and corrosive nitrogen dioxide ($NO_2$) fumes. An alternative to preparing the diazonium salt from the azoic base is to purchase stabilized diazonium salts singularly or combined in C.I. Azoic Compositions.

Stable diazonium salts are prepared by precipitating the diazonium species as its chloride, sulfate, or zinc chloride or boron fluoride complexes. These fast salts are very important commercially because they are convenient to use, simple to apply (removes several process steps), and reduce exposure to toxic arylamines and aryldiamines as well as toxic $NO_2$ fumes.

The coupling reaction essentially consists of immersing the coupling-agent-impregnated textile in a solution of the diazonium salt. Since diazonium salts decompose in water and on metal surfaces, so a nonmetallic vessel must be employed. Careful control of the reaction pH (4-5) must be maintained and alkali binding agents added. The diazonium salt must be present in a concentration of 0.5 gm/L to expedite the coupling reaction (Shenai, 1973). If the pH is incorrect or diazonium concentration too low, side-reactions will dominate and hamper the dyeing process. Aftertreatment soaping removes the unreacted and loosely bonded coupling components and so improves the crocking fastness and abrasion fastness of the final product. This final soaping also improves the fastness properties by causing agglomeration of the azoic pigment.

Table 12 presents a summary of the chemical and physical properties of azoic dyes. See Figure 3 for example chemical structures of various azoic dye constituents.

## 6.5 DISPERSE DYES

### 6.5.1 General Description

Disperse dyes, as their name implies, are colloidal in nature and have very low, but finite, water solubilities owing to the absence of sulfonic acid functionalities (Noller). In the pure state, they are crystalline materials which must be ground with dispersing agents to produce powders, and mixed with water to make near-colloidal aqueous suspensions and pastes. Regardless of the marketed form, disperse dyestuffs are made into a very dilute aqueous dispersion prior to use.

The majority of the disperse dyes produced are used for three textiles: polyester, acetate, and triacetate. Dyeing or printing with disperse dyes is the only practical means of coloring these synthetics (AATCC, 1981).

TABLE 12. PHYSICAL/CHEMICAL PROPERTIES OF AZOIC DYES

| | | Reference |
|---|---|---|
| Chemical structure | All are azo compounds. The majority have naphthoic acid amide, benzidine, toluidine, anisidine, and aniline functionalities in the dye molecule. | AATCC, 1981 |
| Physical state | C.I. Coupling Components are sold as liquids or paste-like dispersions, while C.I. Azoic-Diazo Components are usually powders (hydrochloride salt or free base). | AATCC, 1982 |
| Particle size | Dye specific. | |
| Mole weight | Estimated mean molecular weight of final dyestuff is 560 gm/mole. See Note 1. | Lubs, 1955 |
| Density | Dye specific. | |
| Melting point | The melting point of coupling components ranges from 105-350°C and averages 240°C for the number observed. | Lubs, 1955 |
| Boiling point | Dye specific. | |
| Vapor pressure | Many of the final dyeings have poor sublimation fastness. | AATCC, 1981 |
| Water solubility | The two components used may or may not be soluble, but the ultimate colored product is always insoluble (i.e., a pigment). See Note 2. | |
| Other solvents | Azoic coupling components can be dispersed in alcohol, cellosolve, or Turkey Red Oil. | SDC, 1971 |

(continued)

TABLE 12. PHYSICAL/CHEMICAL PROPERTIES OF AZOIC DYES (continued)

| | | Reference |
|---|---|---|
| Hydrolysis | Dye specific. | |
| Partition coefficient | Dye specific. | |
| Soil adsorption/ desorption | Dye specific. | |
| Dissociation constant | Dye specific. | |
| Spectra | Components specific. | |
| Toxicity | Many Azoic Coupling Components may have toxic properties (naphthols and phenols). Many Azoic-Diazo Components are hazardous, especially nitroaniline, chloroaniline, and beta-naphthylamine. All of these are used in the commercially important red shades. See Note 3. | |
| Miscellaneous | The substantivity (%) for the Azoic Coupling Components observed ranged 11-87% and for red shade components 16-38% except for a red-black yielding component which has a substantivity of 87%. The percentage substantivity is percentage of total Naphthol, a 5 gm/L solution, that is transferred to cotton. | Lubs, 1955 |

(continued)

## TABLE 12. PHYSICAL/CHEMICAL PROPERTIES OF AZOIC DYES (continued)

Note 1: The average molecular weight of 32 Azoic Coupling Components observed was 352 gm/mole. of which eight (8) are known to be useful for red shades and averaged 342 gm/mole. The average molecular weight of 45 Azoic-Diazo Components, which have over the years been of commercial importance, ranged from 140 to 360 and averaged 207 gm/mole. Of these, 21 have been used for red shades and ranged from 140 to 280 gm/mole with an average of 186 gm/mole. The reactive species formed from stable diazonium salts have comparable molecular weights to Azoic-Diazo Components after removal of the complexed metal or nonmetal salts.

Note 2: Azoic components are inherently water insoluble, but are prepared as water soluble liquids or dispersions of their sodium salts. The free bases of the Azoic-Diazo Components have substantially lower water solubility than their marketed forms - hydrochlorides or sulfates.

Note 3: beta-Naphthylamine: OSHA - carcinogen
NIOSH - positive human carcinogen
AQTX - $TL_m$ 96: 10-1 ppm

p-Nitroaniline: TLV - air: 1 ppm (skin)
OSHA STD - air: TWA 1 ppm (skin)
DOT - Poison B

p-Chloroaniline: AQTX: $TL_m$ 96: 100-10 ppm
NCI bioassay test candidate

CI Azoic-Diazo Component 48 (o-Dianisidine): NIOSH: Positive animal carcinogen

5-Nitro-o-anisidine: NCI: Positive animal carcinogen

4-[O-tolylazo]-o-toluidine: NIOSH: Positive animal carcinogen

5-Nitro-o-toluidine: NCI: Positive animal carcinogen

4-Chloro-o-toluidine: DOT - Poison B
NCI - Positive animal carcinogen

5-Chloro-o-toluidine: NCI - Positive animal carcinogen

2-Biphenylamine: NCI Bioassay test candidate

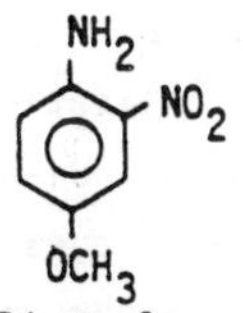

$NH_2$ / $NO_2$ / $OCH_3$

C.I. Azoic Diazo Component 1
Fast Bordeaux, GP

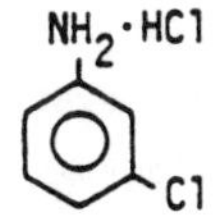

$NH_2 \cdot HCl$ / Cl

C.I. Azoic Diazo Component 2
Fast Orange GC, CG

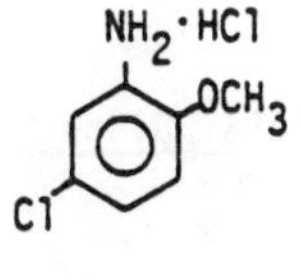

$NH_2 \cdot HCl$ / $OCH_3$ / Cl

C.I. Azoic Diazo Component 10
Fast Red RC

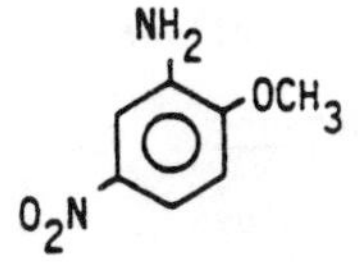

$NH_2$ / $OCH_3$ / $O_2N$

C.I. Azoic Diazo Component 13
Fast Scarlet R, RC

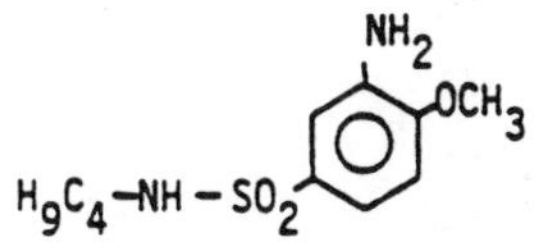

$NH_2$ / $OCH_3$ / $H_9C_4$–NH – $SO_2$

C.I. Azoic Diazo Component 28
Fast Red PDC

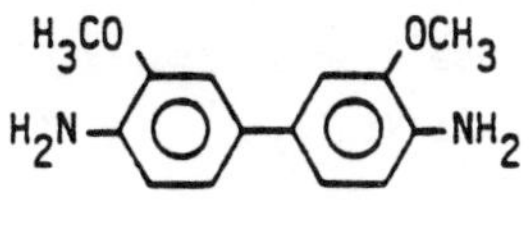

$H_3CO$ / $OCH_3$ / $H_2N$ / $NH_2$

C.I. Azoic Diazo Component 48
Fast Blue B, o-Dianisidine

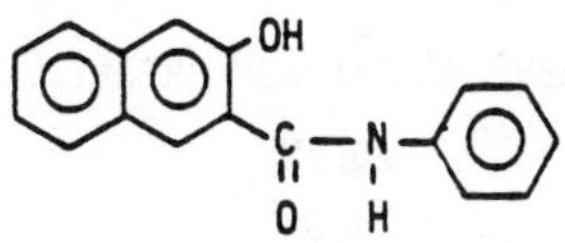

OH / C — N / O H

C.I. Azoic Coupling Component 2
Naphthol AS

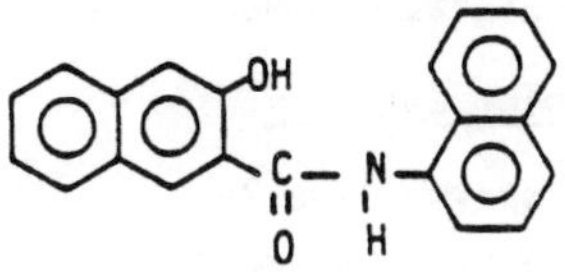

OH / C — N / O H

C.I. Azoic Coupling Component 7
Naphthol AS-SW

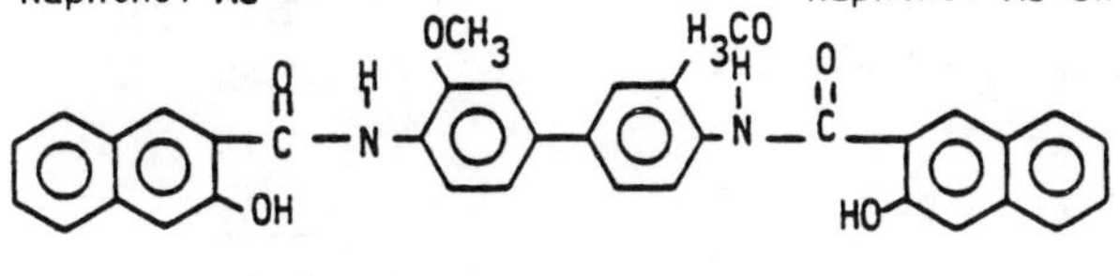

$OCH_3$ / $H_3CO$ / O H / C — N / H O / N — C / OH / HO

C.I. Coupling Component 3
Naphthol AS-BR

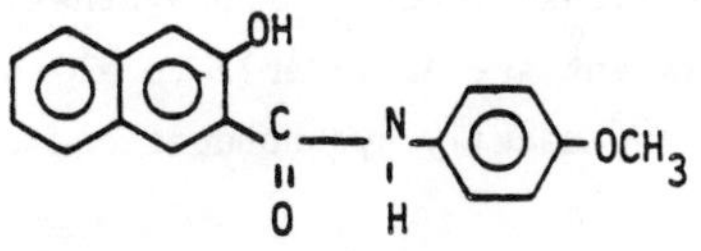

OH / C — N / O H / $OCH_3$

C.I. Coupling Component 11
Naphthol AS-RL

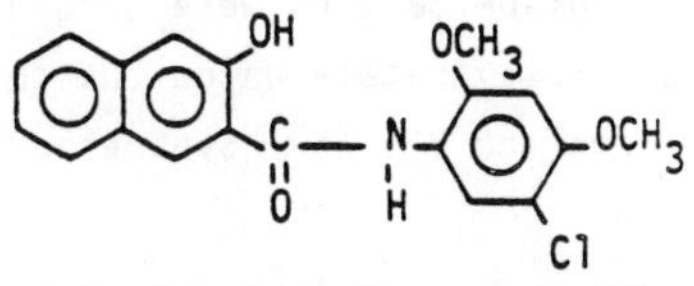

OH / $OCH_3$ / C — N / O H / $OCH_3$ / Cl

C.I. Coupling Component 12
Naphthol AS-ITR

Figure 3. Chemical structures of various azoic dye constituents.

Disperse dyes constituted 19% of the total 1980 U.S. production volume of organic dyes and was the largest volume application class at 21.2 million kilograms (46.7 million pounds) produced. Disperse Blues alone were 8.9% of the total U.S. production volume of dyes (ITC, 1980).

6.5.1.1 Color Categories of Disperse Dyes. The percentage of total U.S. disperse dye production represented by each color category for 1980 is as follows.

| Color Category | Percentage of Total Disperse Dyes |
|---|---|
| Disperse Blues | 46.9% |
| Disperse Reds | 22.8% |
| Disperse Yellows | 11.6% |
| Disperse Oranges | 11.0% |
| Disperse Blacks, Browns, Greens | 5.7% |
| Disperse Violets | 2.0% |
| | 100.0% |

6.5.1.2 Large Volume Products. The seven products below represent over one-third of the total volume of disperse dyes produced in the United States in 1980.

| Color Category | Percentage of Total Disperse Dyes |
|---|---|
| Disperse Blue 79 | 20.7% |
| Disperse Yellow 3 | 4.3% |
| Disperse Red 60 | 3.2% |
| Disperse Blue 3 | 2.6% |
| Disperse Brown 1 | 1.8% |
| Disperse Red 177 | 1.7% |
| Disperse Yellow 54 | 1.5% |
| | 35.8% |

### 6.5.2 Application Properties of Disperse Dyes

Disperse dyes were originally developed to color the synthetic cellulose acetate rayon but to some extent are applicable to all synthetic fibers and blends. Synthetic fibers are usually hydrophobic and can develop a large negative surface potential in water which tends to repel ionic dyestuffs. Disperse dyes are nonionic, hydrophobic materials of low water solubility. They are prepared as aqueous dispersions for application, however, and either diffuse into the fiber directly or from the fiber surface-water interface. The fact that they actually penetrate the molecular structure of the fiber molecules, rather than just the physical structure, distinguishes them from other dye application classes.

Disperse dyes are substantive to hydrophobic fibers: cellulose acetate, triacetate, polyamide (nylon), nitriles; these dyes are especially useful for polyesters since this synthetic is frequently blended with other fibers. The resulting blends are still colorable even for hydrophylic fibers. The majority of disperse dyes are used to dye homopolymer polyester, which is the largest volume synthetic fiber produced (AATCC, 1981). Polyester requires a higher application temperature and therefore sublimation fastness becomes a more critical factor. Disperse dyes are sometimes useful in masking barre patterns of acid dyed nylon textiles. Some shades of disperse dyes can be applied to acrylics where they show limited buildup and they may or may not be very colorfast.

The affinity of the dyestuff for hydrophobic textiles can often be related to chemical and physical properties. Dye affinity is often directly proportional to the basicity of the dye molecule, which is determined by the number and substituents of the amine groups. At the extreme, very strong amine bases tend to be so insoluble as to be unuseable (Shenai, 1973). The affinity and dye buildup are inversely proportional to molecular complexity and aggregate tendency. The high molecular weight molecules and molecular aggregates have a reduced ability to penetrate the physical structure of the fiber and in turn even less chance to diffuse into the molecular structure of the fiber.

Disperse dyes are applied by high temperature aqueous exhaust processes (40-70°C), steaming processes, heat transfer, and solvent dyeing/thermofixation processes. The application of disperse dyestuffs can be generalized into three groups (Dawson, 1972):

1) Aqueous application at or below 100°C may be used for all fibers, but dye carriers are required for polyester and often desirable for cellulose triacetate.

2) Application at 120°-140°C under high pressure for polyester is useful when fabric/fiber shape-distortion is of no concern.

3) Application by dry heat at 180°-220°C for polyester and polyester-cotton blends.

Use of anionic dispersants is required in commercial products and usually 1-2 gm/liter is added to the dyebath. Since many disperse dyes are unuseable in extremely acidic or basic dyebaths, a pH in the range of 5-6 is generally used (SDC, 1971). For many processes, use of 2-10 gm/liter organic solvent type carrier is also required. Dye carriers act by swelling the fabric and opening up the fiber structure to accelerate the dyeing process. They also serve as dye migration aids (Shenai, 1973). Other frequently used dyebath additives include nonionic surfactants and antifoaming agents (AATCC, 1981).

The successful dyeing of synthetic fibers like polyester and its blends using exhaust dyeing with disperse dyes involves careful consideration of such factors as the energy level, hydrolysis, pH stability, solubility, cost, use limitations, effects of metals, effects of dye carriers, leveling, and sublimation, as well as other physical characteristics of the dyestuff. Some interrelation between dye energy, leveling, and sublimation fastness exists, but is more easily handled using a rating system that has been developed for these properties using E, L, and S values. The "E" value (range 1-6) indicates the energy required to exhaust the dye considering such factors as the temperature required, the time required, and the concentration of dye and dye carriers (which act to increase the kinetic energy of the dyestuff). The "L" value (range 1-5) stands for leveling and is controlled by the same factors that determine the dye energy. The "S" value (range 1-5) for sublimation fastness is similarly but inversely controlled and includes an additional dependence on afterscouring. As a rule-of-thumb, sublimation fastness increases with energy level; at the same time, the quality of leveling tends to decrease. There are, however, many exceptions. Extremely low energy dyes have sublimation fastness too poor for use with polyester. Extremely high energy dyes are useful only for continuous dyeing because of their large molecular weight and particle size. Hydrolysis of the dyestuff is determined by the particular pH sensitivity of the dyestuff which is a function of the chemical constitution of the dye, dyeing time, pH, and the reduction potential of the dyebath (note that cotton and wool blends are mild reducing agents). The above mentioned properties of the dyestuff, the physical dispersion of the dye, and the effects of such chemicals as dye carriers (see Table 5), dyeing retardants, salts, metal ions, antifoaming agents, dispersants, and trimers/obligomers, all must be considered in the dyeing "recipe" (Neal, 1982). The chemical system that is best suited for each particular dye is complex and therefore is best determined by using empirically obtained "recipes" as given on the manufacturers' shade cards. A typical polyester-exhaust dyeing procedure for disperse dyes is given in Section 7.1.1.6.

Improvements in solvent dyeing techniques, chiefly for disperse dyes, recently have attracted interest. Interest in these techniques has grown slowly because of the cost of organic solvents, the problems of disposal and/or reuse, and the fact that most existing equipment is designed for aqueous processes. The French STX process and an adaptation of the duPont Thermosol process overcome some of these limitations and make solvent dyeing more feasible.

In the Thermosol/thermofixation process, chemically modified disperse dyes are dyed or printed on polyester/cotton blends in a single thermal fixation step, using existing equipment. The dye is dispersed in nonvolatile polyethylene glycol derivatives which swell the fabric. The fabric is dryed with thermal fixation as the dye is passed from the aqueous phase to the hot glycol saturated fabric. Water is evolved from the thermosol oven. When the fabric is subsequently washed, the dye precipitates into the fiber structure and the solvent is washed out

(AATCC, 1981). In the pilot scale STX process, the miscible solvents, methanol and perchloroethylene, have been used to dye nylon carpet material. This solvent combination has been shown to have penetration properties superior to water, improve these fastness properties and decrease the energy utilized to complete the dyeing process. This occurs because of reduced dyeing time, bath heating, liquid pumping, and circulation. Dye exhaustion is complete and no other auxiliary chemicals are required. Furthermore, the process generates no wastewater and both solvents are reclaimed and recycled (Wommack and Favier, 1978).

Disperse dyes also are used in pressure or steam developed conventional printing procedures. The dischargeability of disperse dyes is basically the chemical reduction of highly-colored substituted amine groups into colorless free amines. Many disperse dyes are dischargeable in color by an additional printing step employing C.I. Reducing Agent 2 (SDC, 1971).

Transfer printing of disperse dyes, another recently popularized process, is applicable to most synthetic fibers. The disperse dyestuff, without dispersing agents, is printed onto paper and dry-heat transferred to the textile by sublimation. This process is unique in that many inexpensive but previously unusable, low sublimation fast dyes may now be readily employed (SDC, 1971) (Dawson, 1972) (AATCC, 1981).

Some of the disadvantages of disperse dyes include limited wash fastness, gas-fading, the necessity of multi-step fiber pretreatment, the problem of flocculation of the dyestuff, the additional costs of the required additives, and the environmental concern over many of the aromatic solvent dye carriers employed. Barre effects do occur but can be controlled by extending the dyeing cycle and slightly increasing the dyebath temperature.

Table 13 summarizes many of the application characteristics of disperse dyestuffs.

Table 14 presents the application properties of some selected disperse dyes for polyester. See Figure 4 for examples of chemical structures of various disperse dyes.

TABLE 13. APPLICATION PROPERTIES OF DISPERSE DYES

| | | Reference |
|---|---|---|
| Fabrics dyed | Majority used for polyester. Also cellulose acetate, nylon, acetate, and triacetate. Often the best dyes for acetate, polyester, and triacetate. (See Note 1.) | SDC, 1971<br>AATCC, 1981 |
| Fabrics printed | All of the above, but use for nylon is declining. | SDC, 1971<br>Clarke, 1977 |
| Leather dyeing | Not used for leather, but can be applied at 40-60°C to sheepskins and furs. | SDC, 1971 |
| Fabrics stained | Stains cotton in blends with polyester. This cannot be avoided so attempts are made to make "cross-staining" as even as possible. Also stains protein. | Thomas, 1982<br>NCSU, 1982 |
| Disposable fabrics | | |
| Leveling | Moderate to very good. Most are good. A function of particle size and solubility. | AATCC, 1981 |
| Exhaustion | Controlled by concentration of dye carriers, dyeing time, and dyebath temperature for aqueous exhaust procedure. | |
| Migration | Migration is controlled by addition of dye carriers. | |
| Dischargeability | Some are dischargeable using C.I. Reducing Agent 2. | SDC, 1971<br>AATCC, 1981 |
| Water solubility | Very low as a rule, but controlled by addition of dispersing agents. Less soluble than acid or basic dyes, yet more soluble than vat dyes. No solutions of usable strength are obtainable. | SDC, 1971<br>AATCC, 1981<br>Shenai, 1973<br>Patterson, 1972 |

(continued)

TABLE 13. APPLICATION PROPERTIES OF DISPERSE DYES (continued)

| | | Reference |
|---|---|---|
| Acid fastness | Most are good. Index 3-4. | BASF, 1969 |
| Alkali fastness | Most are good (Index 3-4), while a few are fair (Index 2). | SDC, 1971 |
| Heat resistence | Good unless it is a dye that sublimes. Index 2-5. Most are 4-5. | SDC, 1971 |
| Light fastness | Ranges poor to very good. Index 2-6. | SDC, 1971 |
| Chlorine fastness | | |
| Wash fastness | Poor to good. Index 2-5. Altered by after treatment. Most are good (4-5). | SDC, 1971<br>AATCC, 1981 |
| Peroxide fastness | | |
| Dry cleaning | Good fastness. Indexed 3-4 toward trichloroethylene and Indexed 4-5 toward perchloroethylene. | BASF, 1969 |
| Perspiration fastness | Fair to good. Index 3-5. | SDC, 1971 |
| Useful colors | Full color range except on acrylics. Especially useful for pastels. Blue and violet shades are chiefly anthraquinones. Anthraquinone products usually brighter than azo products of the same shade. See Note 3. | SDC, 1971<br>AATCC, 1981 |
| Bonding mechanism | Nonionic. Colors diffuse into, dissolve into, the fabric forming a solid solution in the fiber. | AATCC, 1981<br>Lubs, 1972 |
| Rate of dyeing | From slow to rapid. Many azos tend to dye faster than anthraquinone (see Note 2). | |

(continued)

TABLE 13. APPLICATION PROPERTIES OF DISPERSE DYES (continued)

| | | Reference |
|---|---|---|
| Pretreatment | Surfactant/alkali multistep scouring and heating. | AATCC, 1981 |
| Aftertreatment | Rinsing and after-scouring. | AATCC, 1981 |
| Associated metals | Colors are unaffected by iron salts and only dulled by copper salts. | BASF, 1969 |
| Dyeing process | High temperature exhaust, exhaust, atmospheric exhaust, and heat transfer, all at elevated temperatures or pressures. | SDC, 1971<br>AATCC, 1981<br>Horning, 1978 |
| Typical equipment used | Beck, package, skeins, jigs, thermosol-pad-steam, continuous kuster. | SDC, 1971<br>Horning, 1978 |

Note 1: 30-200 gm of dye used per kg of cellulose acetate dyed (AATCC, 1981).

Note 2: Dyeing rate is controlled by the concentration of dye carriers and solubility, which is in turn a function of concentration of carrier, temperature, and particle size. Particular dyestuffs also show enhanced solubilities for specific dispersing agents (Shenai, 1973).

Note 3: The strength of commercial disperse dyes is controlled to within 2.5% of a preferred color value determined spectrophotometrically (Thomas, 1982).

Index Values:

Gray scale: 1 - very poor, 2 - poor, 3 - fair, 4 - good, 5 - excellent.

Lightfastness scale: 1 - very poor, 2 - poor, 3 - fair, 4 - fairly good, 5 - good, 6 - very good, 7 - excellent, 8 - outstanding, 9 - superlative.

TABLE 14. POLYESTER WORKHORSE COLORS[a]

| Dyestuff | Money value G F P | Tinctorial value strong/ weak | Leveling G F P | Light-fastness G F P | Sublimation | Wet fastness | Other comments |
|---|---|---|---|---|---|---|---|
| Low energy | | | | | | | |
| Yellow 54-64 | Good | Strong | Good | Good | Poor | Fair | |
| Red 60 | Good | Strong | Fair | Good | Poor | Fair | Sensitive to metals |
| Blue 56 | Fair | Strong | Poor | Good | Poor | Fair | |
| Medium energy | | | | | | | |
| Yellow 114 | Good | Strong | Good | Good | Good | Good | Not pH sensitive |
| Orange 30 | Good | Medium | Good | Good | Good | Good | |
| Red 91 | Poor | Weak | Good | Excellent[b] | Good | Good | |
| Red 73 | Good | Medium | Good | Good | Up to 1.5% | Fair | |
| Blue 73 | Fair | Medium | Fair | Good | Good | Good | Covers Barre well |
| High energy | | | | | | | |
| Yellow 42 | Fair | Weak | Good | Excellent[b] | Good | Good | Pulls off in alkali bath |
| Red 313 | Good | Medium | Poor | Good | Good | Good | |
| Blue 60 | Poor | Weak | Good | Good | Good | Good | Needs 265°F to develop shade |
| Navy-Blacks | --- | --- | Poor | Good | Good | Good | |

[a]This table is reproduced from "Dyeing Textured Woven Polyester" by Joe J. Belcher (Belcher, 1982).

[b]Use disperse Blue 27 GLF with these two for maximum lightfastness on light shade.

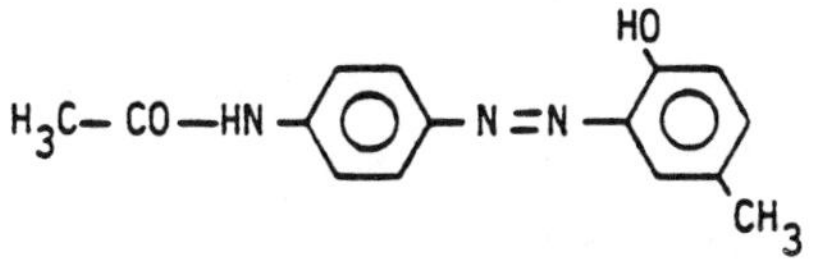

C.I. Disperse Yellow 3/Solvent Yellow 77 - Monoazo dye

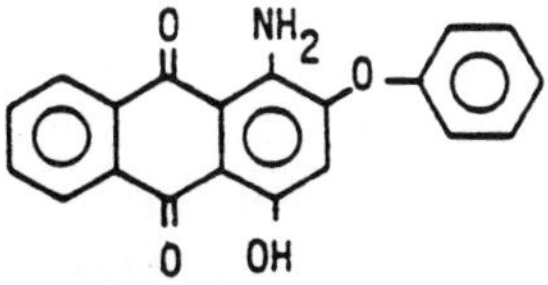

C.I. Disperse Red 60 - Anthraquinone dye

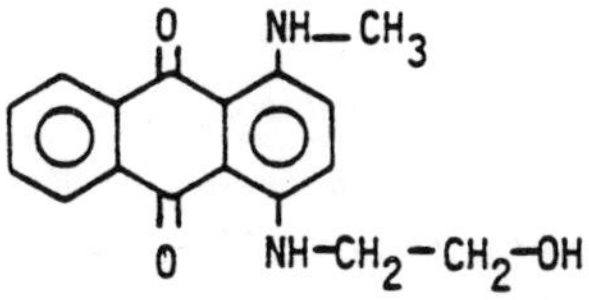

C.I. Disperse Blue 3 - Anthraquinone dye

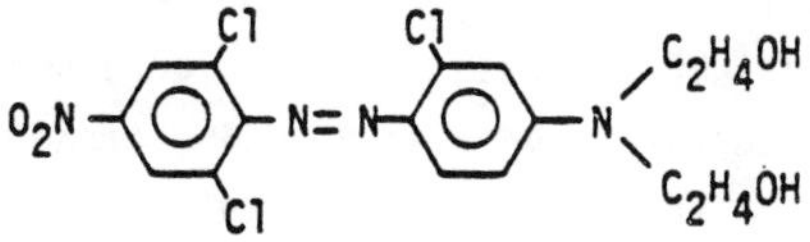

C.I. Disperse Brown 1 - Monoazo dye

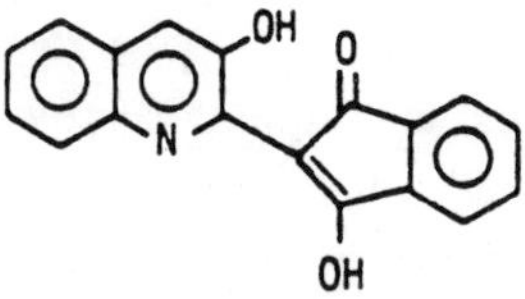

C.I. Disperse Yellow 54 - Quinoline dye

Figure 4. Chemical structures of various disperse dyes.

6.5.3 Chemical and Physical Properties

The two principal chemical classes of disperse dyes are azo [mainly aminoazobenzenes (60%) and anthraquinone (25%)]. Other minor chemical classes include: benzanthrone, azomethine, and nitroarene. For the most part, disperse dyes exhibit a total lack of ionic groups and sulfonate solubilizing groups and, in fact, sulfonate groups even hamper dye affinity for some fiber substrates. However, partial sulfonation has been used to slightly raise the solubilities of some extremely insoluble compounds. Disperse dyes containing free amine groups can also be developed using C.I. Developing Agents after dyeing the textile. A large number of the commercially available disperse dyestuffs are ring substituted and N-substituted derivatives of amino and diaminoanthraquinone and amino and diaminoazobenzene. Substitutes that produce useful dyestuffs include: alkyl, aryl, alkoxy, hydroxyl, and mercapto groups. From 1967-1971, disperse and reactive dye experimentation dominated the patent literature on new dyestuffs (Dawson, 1972).

The monoazo and disazo compounds are useful for the yellow, orange, and blue shades while the violet and blues have substantially diminished light fastness. There has been significant patent literature on the development of colorfast blue azo dyes. A large number of the azo orange and red dyestuffs are derived from 4-nitroaniline and 2-chloro-4-nitroaniline, while the browns are typically derived from 2,6-dichloro-4-aniline, and reds and violets from 2-cyano-4-nitroanilines (Dawson, 1972). A multitude of substituent groups have been tried on these conventional chemical starting materials. The groups are designed to increase shade depth and fastness by increasing the polarity and weight of the dye molecule. Yellow and orange anthraquinone dyestuffs are chiefly hydroxyl, alkoxy, and mercapto ring substituted anthraquinones or alkyl and aryl N-substituted monoaminoanthraquinones. The red to bluish-red shades are usually monoaminoanthraquinones and 1,5-diamino and 1,8-diaminoanthraquinones. Since the azo blue shades are of limited use, the blues and violets prepared from 1,4-diaminoanthraquinones are especially valuable (Shenai, 1973) (Lubs, 1972). Unlike certain azo and styryl disperse dyes, anthraquinone disperse dyes are not subject to reduction and hydrolysis in the dyebath. They are, however, hindered by their multi-step synthetic route which makes them expensive to use. The recent patent literature has concentrated on increasing the sublimation fastness of anthraquinone dyes by adding polar substituent groups (Dawson, 1972).

Of the minor chemical categories of disperse dyes, a relatively small amount of inexpensive yellow and orange dyes are produced from nitrodiphenylamine. These dyes are easy to manufacture and very lightfast on polyester, but do have limited buildup. New varieties have aimed for better sublimation fastness and color variety by adding large substituent groups, especially colored azo moieties. A few styryl dyes are used for greenish-yellows on secondary acetate. Some new complex heterocyclic disperse dyes have been developed for yellows and greens. A select number of methine dyes are used for brillant fluorescent greenish-yellow on nylon (Dawson, 1972).

Disperse dyes have low molecular weights (200-400 gm per mole) and are nonionic which is necessary for preparing stable dispersions. The fact that disperse dyestuffs must be able to be prepared in freely divided states is important. This determines the dissolution rate, uniformity of coloration, and ability to sublime for those processes in which the dye is actually diffused into the textile in the gaseous state. There is a tradeoff, however, between the sublimation fastness of the dyed textile and the quality of leveling, which seems to be a function of molecular weight. To achieve level dyeing the particle size must be maintained below 4 microns and preferably 0.5-3 microns (1 micron = $10^{-9}$ meters). Naturally the particle size also must be as uniform as possible. Since disperse dyestuffs are crystalline in the pure state, it is frequently difficult to grind them to meet the above requirements. Dye particles of over 4 microns produce "specky" colorations. Often 16-60 hours of grinding are necessary and even then the highly crystalline compounds must be precipitated from acid solutions before grinding. In this instance, dispersing agents serve a secondary role as grinding aids.

Useful disperse dyestuffs must have low water solubilities, but at least soluble to the extent of 0.1 mg/liter of water. In liquid phase applications, the disperse dyestuff is believed to be taken up by the fabric from the aqueous phase. It follows then, that the low but finite water solubility of these dyes is a critical factor in determining the leveling properties and dyeing rate. It has been shown that for some dyes their normally low solubility rises appreciably at the high temperatures at which they are applied (Shenai, 1973).

Table 15 presents general chemical and physical properties of the disperse dyes as a class.

## 6.6 SULFUR DYES

Sulfur dyes are largely indeterminate complex heterocyclic molecules or mixtures formed by melting or boiling organic compounds with sodium polysulfide and/or sulfur. The organic intermediates used typically have amine or nitro groups which are reacted with sulfur.

Application of sulfur dyes involves carefully planned transformations between the water-soluble reduced state of the dye and the insoluble oxidized form. The dyestuff is normally applied to the textile in its reduced form in sodium sulfide solution. After diffusing into the fiber, the dye is oxidized into the insoluble form either by air bubbling or by using chemical oxidation. Sulfur dyes are used primarily for cotton and rayon, though sulfur dyes sometimes are used in nylon coloration. Both batch and continuous dyeing processes are in use, but continuous application dominates by far. The chief advantages are low cost, fair to good light fastness, and high water fastness. Disadvantages include the lack of bright shades and sensitivity to chlorine bleaches. It is also necessary to add chelating agents when applying sulfur dyes to certain fibers to prevent imparting a harsh texture to the textile. New research is focused on developing additional colors and brighter shades.

Today there are only a few producers of sulfur dyes. Traditionally there have been a number of sulfur dyes that have been very successful because of their extremely low price. In recent years (1966-1976),

TABLE 15. PHYSICAL/CHEMICAL PROPERTIES OF DISPERSE DYES

| | | Reference |
|---|---|---|
| Chemical structure | Most are azo (60%) and anthraquinones (25%), including alkyl, aryl, hydroxyl, alkoxy, and mercapto N-substituted derivatives as well as the corresponding free amines. They lack ionic groups and contain few, if any, solubilizing groups. Dye affinity can be many times related to basicity with disperse dyes. | |
| Physical state | Crystalline in pure form. Ground with dispersing agents to yield pastes and powders (except printing inks). Sold as non-dusting preparations. | Shenai, 1973<br>BASF, 1979 |
| Particle size | 0.5-3 microns is desirable, below 4 microns is necessary for level dyeing. (1 micron - $10^{-9}$ meters). | Shenai, 1973<br>AATCC, 1981<br>Kirk-Othmer, 1978 |
| Mole weight | Generally low (220-400 grams-per-mole, typically). | |
| Density | Dye specific. | |
| Melting point | Most melt at or above 150°C or sublime. | Shenai, 1973 |
| Boiling point | Many sublime readily, although, certain newer, higher molecular weight dyes are stable to 200°C. | SDC, 1971 |
| Vapor pressure | | |
| Water solubility | Very low but must be at least 0.1 mg/liter. Less soluble than acids or bases but more soluble than vats. See Note 1. | Shenai, 1973<br>Patterson, 1972 |

(continued)

TABLE 15. PHYSICAL/CHEMICAL PROPERTIES OF DISPERSE DYES (continued)

| | | Reference |
|---|---|---|
| Other solubility | Some are soluble in organic solvents (benzene, ether, acetone). | Shenai, 1973 |
| Hydrolysis | Largely only the free-amine azo and styryl type hydrolyze in boiling acid or base. Anthraquinone types do not hydrolyze. | Shenai, 1973 |
| Partition coefficient | Dye specific. | |
| Soil adsorption/ desorption | Dye specific. | |
| Dissociation constant | Dye specific. | |
| Spectra | Dye specific. | |
| Toxicity | Dye carriers such as chlorobenzene, phenols, o-phenylphenol, butylbenzoate, trichlorobenzene, and biphenyl are of concern with regard to exposure and environmental release (see Note 2). These carriers are used in dyeing polyester fibers with disperse dyes. | Shenai, 1973; NIOSH, 1979 |

(continued)

TABLE 15. PHYSICAL/CHEMICAL PROPERTIES OF DISPERSE DYES (continued)

Note 1: Typical solubilities are 0-10 mg/L for azos and 0-1 mg/L for anthraquinones at 25°C; at 80°C those dyes that exhibit solubility over 0.2 mg/L increase appreciably. At 80°C some azo dyes exhibit solubilities of 1-250 mg/L while anthraquinones are generally still under 20 mg/L. Addition of dispersing agents may increase anthraquinone dyestuff water solubility two or three-fold while azo solubilities may increase ten or one hundred-fold. Still only particular dispersing agents-dyestuff combinations show the more dramatic increases in dyestuff solubility (Shenai, 1973)

Note 2: Chlorobenzene:
TLV - air: 75 ppm
OSHA/STD - air: TWA 75 ppm
AQTX - TLm 96: 100-1 ppm
NCI study candidate

Phenol:
OHSA/STD - air: TWA 5 ppm
AQTX - TLm 96: 100-10 ppm
NCI candidate
DOT - Poison B
Criteria Exposure: TWA 20 $mg/m^3$; CL 60 $mg/m^3$/15m

o-Phenylphenol - NCI study candidate

Trichlorobenzene:
TLV - air: 5 ppm
AQTX - $TL_m$96: 10-1 ppm

Biphenyl:
TLV - air: 0.2 ppm
OSHA/STD - air: TWA 0.2 ppm

however, the cost of sulfur dyes has increased to the point where they no longer have a large competitive edge with regard to price, and their disadvantages are more of a consideration. Also only a relative few new developments have encouraged their success (Wood, 1976).

Until about 20 years ago sulfur dyes were used only for corduroy, denim, and other 100% cotton fabrics, but in recent years they have found acceptance in the dyeing of "no iron" finished polyester/cotton blends. In these blends, only the cellulosic portion is colored by the sulfur dye. For this type of dyeing they have been found to deliver shades of suitable fastness and reduced cost. Recently, brighter shades of blue, green and red have appeared for apparel dyeing. Also the poor chlorine resistance of sulfur dyes has become less of a detrimental factor owing to the widespread and growing popularity of reactive dyes which also are chlorine sensitive. These new dyes have lead to new non-chlorine consumer bleach products. Improvements in chlorine stability have occurred with the advent of new protective reactive resins for sulfur-dyed polyester/cotton blends (Martin-Marietta, 1982). The decreasing price advantage of sulfur dyes probably has been offset by their increased flexibility with regard to available colors and dyeable fabrics. Additionally, when considering current textile industry economics, any cost advantage, whether in terms of energy or dyestuff prices, becomes more significant and probably will keep the usage of sulfur dyes at a stable level.

### 6.6.1 Products

The 1980 International Trade Commission Report on Synthetic Organic Chemicals includes 34 sulfur dyestuffs in three forms: sulfur dyes, leuco sulfur dyes, and solubilized sulfur dyes. These include yellows, oranges, reds, blues, greens, browns, and blacks. Browns and blacks represented the two most numerous color categories. The listing of these products signifies that they are all produced in volumes exceeding 5,000 pounds or $5,000 sales in 1980; no specific product volumes are given at the request of the producers supplying the information.

The 1982 AATCC Buyers Guide lists 31 sulfur dye products, many of which are not listed in the Trade Commission Report.

Through the years the sulfur blacks have been the most commercially important sulfur dyes. The various forms of two dyes, C.I. Sulfur Black 1 and C.I. Sulfur Black 11 represent the largest amount of sales of sulfur black dyes. Sulfur Black 1 is one of the most important and least expensive sulfur dyes produced.

In recent year sulfur dyes have been replaced in many applications by stable anthraquinone vat, insoluble azo direct, and reactive dyes.

### 6.6.2 Application Properties of Sulfur Dyes

Sulfur dyes are used for creating most popular shades on cotton and rayon textiles and blends. Sulfur dyes are particularly applicable where good fastness is more important than shade brightness. Especially suitable goods would include work clothes, tarpaulins, furniture upholstery, and inexpensive dress materials (Lubs, 1955). Sulfur dyes are not applicable to wool or silk since the strongly alkaline dyeing conditions of the leuco compound damages such fibers (Laptev, 1973). A few bright shades are available, but for the most part sulfur dyes are dull in shade and show decreasing wash fastness with increased brightness of shade (AATCC, 1981). Although red sulfur dyes are advertised, these are not true red shades, but are actually brownish or bluish red shades. One disadvantage peculiar to blue and black shades is a bronzing effect which is caused by too highly concentrated dyebaths. Another disadvantage peculiar to black shades is the hydrolysis and release of mineral acids which attack and "tender" the textile. The sulfur dye group as a whole offers good to excellent fastness to washing and light at lower costs than colors in other application classes.

The washfastness of sulfur dyes is fair to good and sulfur dyes usually have better washfastness than direct dyes, but worse than vats (Kirk-Othmer, 1978). Light fastness is fair to good in general. Heat and chemical resistance (including acid and base) is usually moderate to good. The three limiting properties are the crocking fastness, availability of bright shades, and the resistance to chlorine bleaches.

Sulfur colors are usually sold in three chemical forms: sulfur dyes, leuco sulfur dyes, and solubilized sulfur dyes. The latter two categories are sold as pre-reduced solutions or sulfur liquids. The sulfur dye forms contain the oxidized form of the dyes and thus are intrinsically insoluble in water. When the oxidized forms are applied, an alkaline reduction of the dyestuff must preceed the dyeing to render the dyestuff water-soluble and substantive to cellulose (AATCC, 1981). Solubilized sulfur dyes are the water soluble thiosulfonic acids of the corresponding C.I. sulfur dye and frequently have separate C.I. numbers. These are converted to the leuco sulfur form before application. A small new class, C.I. condensed sulfur dyes, has been added and is applied similarly to solubilized sulfur dyes. The leuco sulfur dyes are the parent dyestuff dissolved in a mixed sodium sulfide and hydrosulfide solution. Leuco sulfur dye is the form that is both substantive to cellulose and water-soluble. Leuco forms are particularly sensitive to atmospheric oxygen. These forms are sometimes sold as powders. In this case, the leuco dye is prepared by grinding the parent dye with either sodium sulfide or sodium formaldehyde sulfoxylate (SDC, 1971). Although prereduced sulfur liquid dye products are stable up to a year on the shelf if unopened, manufacturers recommend using them within six months for maximum quality. Sulfur dyes in paste form (dispersions) are also quite stable and may be used within six months of purchase. Longer shelving results in viscosity and concentration changes (Martin-Marietta, 1982).

Although a few sulfur dyes are classified as C.I. vat dyes, most differ from the vat dyes in application properties even though applied in a similar vatting process. The main difference in fastness properties is the pronounced sensitivity of sulfur dyes to chlorine bleaches, but this problem is being overcome by using finish curing techniques. Sulfur dyes also are much easier to reduce, while at the same time much more difficult to oxidize than vat dyes (AATCC, 1981). Another dissimilarity with vat dyes is that with sulfur dyes, final soaping does not induce crystallization within the fiber. This is because vat dyes are highly crystalline materials while sulfur dyes are almost exclusively amorphous.

Sulfur dyes are suitable for widespread use in the dyeing industry because they can be applied by both continuous and batch processes on all types of existing dyeing equipment. The Colour Index describes six dyebath formulas for the various subgroups of the three main sulfur dye chemical forms (SDC, 1971). Only normal fabric pretreatment is required, with the exception being that polyvinyl alcohol cannot be used in sizing of greige fabrics. Mercerizing of cotton goods prior to sulfur dyeing is very advantageous because it causes an increased color yield of 30 to 40% (AATCC, 1981). Although exhaust dyeing processes are possible, almost all sulfur dyes are presently applied by continuous processes (Kirk-Othmer, 1978).

A dyebath for continuous dyeing (normally by a pad-steam process) with sulfur dyes contains the dyestuff, water, sodium sulfide solution, and a penetrant. The sodium sulfide ensures that all of the dye is tranformed into the soluble and substantive leuco form. Preliminary reduction of commercial sulfur dyestuffs is intentionally left incomplete as over-reduction yields a dye that does not exhaust well, lacks color depth, and is hard to reoxidize after dyeing (Lubs, 1955). The penetrant disperses the dye in the bath and aids in wetting of the fabric. After they go through the dyebath at an elevated temperature (100°C), the goods are briefly steamed, washed, and then oxidized to fix the dyestuff as its insoluble oxidized form. The comparatively low dyeing temperature allows a low exhaustion rate and improves dyeing quality. The steaming step helps to diffuse the dye into the fabric before fixing. Excess reducing agent is washed from the fabric. Typical oxidants used to desolubilize the dyestuff are sodium dichromate, sodium perborate, sodium bromate, potassium iodate, and hydrogen peroxide. This converts all of the mercapto groups in the leuco form dyebath to intermolecular and intramolecular disulfide bridges which increase the molecular size and fastness of the dyestuff. Finally the textile is hot water washed, dried, and finished (AATCC, 1981).

A dyebath for batch dyeing of goods with sulfur dyes contains the dyestuff, sodium polysulfide solution, calcium-free salt, a penetrant, and EDTA chelating agent. The addition of salt aids in the exhaustion of the dyestuff similar to what it does with direct and azoic dyeings. EDTA is added to chelate any metal salts extracted from the cotton goods and effectively remove these ions from the dyebath. In batch dyeing with sulfur dyes, chelating agents are necessary to prevent a harsh texture forming on the textile (Kirk-Othmer, 1978). Sulfur dyes may be applied to yarns on package and beam machines or to fabrics by beck, jet, or jig dyeing machines. Rawstock is dyed in kiers or on skein dyeing equipment. Prior to dye application, the fabric is wetted with a solution of the previously mentioned dyebath additives. The dye is then applied during two passes of the fabric through the dyebath to yield a more uniform shade. Since sulfur dyes have a fast strike rate, salt must be added after the initial surge of dye onto the fabric (AATCC, 1981). In some instances sodium bisulfite, Glauber's salt, or ammonium sulfate offer deeper shades than common salt when used as exhausting agents (Shenai, 1973). However, use of these agents produces noxious ammonia and hydrogen sulfide gases. After dyeing, the bath temperature is dropped and the fabric is rinsed and then oxidized. The preliminary washing improves washfastness and resistance to crocking. The textile is then soaped (except for jig process) and soda ash added for suflur black dyes. In all, up to 22 passes through the dyebath or treating bath are required (AATCC, 1981).

The lightfastness of sulfur dyeings is sometimes improved by aftertreatment using copper sulfate and acetic acid with or without potassium dichromate. Potassium dichromate also acts to slightly increase the washfastness.

Table 16 presents application properties of sulfur dyes.

### 6.6.3 Chemical and Physical Properties

Sulfur dyes are prepared by one of several high temperature baking, boiling, or melting processes (known as sulfurization or thiolation), in which sulfur, sodium polysulfide, or other thiolating agents are heated with organic compounds. Sulfur yellow, orange, and brown dyes are mostly prepared by the baking process, while green, blue, and black dyes are mainly prepared by the boiling process (Laptev, 1973). The organic compounds that go into sulfur dyes can be grouped into seven categories (Shenai, 1973).

TABLE 16. APPLICATION PROPERTIES OF SULFUR DYES

| | | Reference |
|---|---|---|
| Fabrics dyed | Mostly cotton and rayon, but also some use for nylon/cotton and polyester/cotton blends. See Note 1. | AATCC, 1982<br>Clarke, 1977 |
| Fabrics printed | Occasionally cotton, linen, and rayon are direct printed with sulfur dyes. | SDC, 1971 |
| Leather dyeing | Select leuco and solubilized sulfur dyes are useful for coloring alkali-resistant leathers. | SDC, 1971 |
| Fabrics stained | | |
| Disposable fabrics | | |
| Leveling | | |
| Exhaustion | Very good but not complete. | SDC, 1971 |
| Migration | Dye specific. | |
| Dischargeability | Dye specific. | |
| Water solubility | Insoluble unless treated. See Note 1. | SDC, 1971<br>AATCC, 1982 |
| Acid fastness | Good. Index 4-5. | SDC, 1971 |
| Alkali fastness | Moderate to good. Index 3-5. | SDC, 1971 |
| Heat resistance | Moderate to good. Index 3-5. | SDC, 1971 |

(continued)

TABLE 16. APPLICATION PROPERTIES OF SULFUR DYES (continued)

| | | Reference |
|---|---|---|
| Light fastness | Good to very good. Index 5-8. | SDC, 1971 |
| Chlorine fastness | Particularly poor, but improved by curing finishes over the dyed substrate. Also improved in recent years by using protective reactant resins. | Clarke, 1977 |
| Wash fastness | Good to very good. Index 4-5. Improved by use of reactive resins. | SDC, 1971<br>Clarke, 1977 |
| Peroxide fastness | | |
| Perspiration fastness | Good. Index 5. | |
| Useful colors | Particulary heavy shades of brown, black, and blue. No "true" reds. Also most shades are dull in color. Newer green, "red", and blue shades are brighter colored. See Note 2. | Clarke, 1977 |
| Bonding mechanism | Mechanical retention of insoluble dye molecule within fiber structure. | Shenai, 1973 |
| Miscellaneous | Many sulfur dyes have poor resistance to abrasion. | |
| Rate of dyeing | Moderate. | |
| Pretreatment | Normal fabric preparation. Mercerizing cotton improves color yield 30-40%. | AATCC, 1982 |
| Aftertreatment | Treatment with acetic acid, peroxides, chrome and copper salts. | |

(continued)

TABLE 16. APPLICATION PROPERTIES OF SULFUR DYES (continued)

| | | Reference |
|---|---|---|
| Dyeing process | Continuous. Pad; Package and Beam for yarn; Beck, Jig, and Jet for fabric. See Note 2. | AATCC, 1982<br>Horning, 1978 |

Note 1: Sulfur dyes can be purchased or prepared in water soluble reduced forms. They are eventually precipitated into the textile by oxidation back to their insoluble forms or "vatting."

Sulfur liquid dyes are used in concentrations ranging from 4 oz./gal. for light shades to 40 oz./gal. for heavy shades (Clarke, 1977).

Note 2: Most extensively applied in pad-steam batch processes. Solubilized sulfur dyes are seeing increased pad-jig application.

Sulfur dyes are prepared to within 5% of the desired accepted color standard as determined spectrophotometrically (Clarke, 1977).

Index Values:

Gray scale: 1 - very poor, 2 - poor, 3 - fair, 4 - good, 5 - excellent.

Lightfastness scale: 1 - very poor, 2 - poor, 3 - fair, 4 - fairly good, 5 - good, 6 - very good, 7 - excellent, 8 - outstanding, 9 - superlative.

1) Amino and nitrobenzenes
2) Nitro and aminobiphenyls
3) Substituted phenols
4) Substituted naphthalenes
5) Condensed aromatics
6) Indophenols
7) Miscellaneous (azine, oxazine, thiazone, etc)

These dyes are thought to be complex mixtures primarily of thiazole, phenothiazine, and 9,10-dithiaanthracene ring systems. The actual chemical composition varies among manufacturers of the same product and probably even among batches. Several possible structures for these dyes and their active chromophores have been postulated (SDC, 1971) (Laptev, 1973). In most cases, even the molecular weights of these products are impossible to determine.

The thiolation process forms substituent mercapto groups on, and cross-linking disulfide groups between, the polymeric chains of the dye molecules. To these two functionalities is attributed the solubilization-desolubilization properties of sulfur dyes. The manufacturing process ends with the oxidation of the reaction mixture which converts all of the mercapto groups to intramolecular and intermolecular disulfide linkages and the dye precipitates. The dyestuff contains a considerable amount of loosely bound sulfur as polysulfide. In this final oxidation of the reaction mix, the content of loosely bound sulfur is decreased, the shade of the dye is modified, and the exhaustion properties of the dyestuff onto textiles are altered. It also has been shown that after-oxidized dyes reach their final oxidized form faster upon application. The filtrate is then washed to remove chemical impurities and dried (Lubs, 1955).

Almost all sulfur dyes are amorphous masses. A select few show crystalline forms, but the majority exhibit no crystalline structure even with x-ray diffraction analysis. Sulfur dyes are soluble in sulfuric acid and sodium sulfide; attempts to use these two solvents in purification of the final dyestuff led to changes in the chemical structure and tintorial strength. Water filtration also is ineffective since the ability to filter sulfur dyes depends on the presence of inorganic salts. Most sulfur dyes are purified by multiple dilute acid and dilute alkali washes. When the salts are finally removed by dialysis or exhaustive extraction, the dyestuff swells, retains water, and exists as an unfilterable mass (Lubs, 1955).

The type of organic starting compound used to manufacture a sulfur dye may be determined by the final shade. Generally, sulfur blacks are derived from nitrophenols, aminophenols, and benzidines. Sulfur blues are prepared from indophenols, diphenylamines, carbazoles, and p-nitrosophenols. The corresponding greens are prepared by addition of copper sulfate to melts of the blue dyes. The yellows, oranges, and browns are prepared from nitrotoluidines and m-toluene diamine derivatives with reactive "meta" groups (Lubs, 1955). The addition of copper sulfate to brown sulfur dyes provides reddish hues. Sulfur browns are also prepared from naphthalenes, biphenyls, and anthracenes. Sulfur dyes with violet hues are prepared from azines. Sulfur greens prepared from copper phthalocyanine have fastness properties exceeding all other sulfur dyes.

Table 17 presents general chemical and physical properties of sulfur dyes.

## 6.7 FIBER REACTIVE DYES

Fiber reactive dyes were introduced to the market in 1956 by ICI. They derive their name from the fact that they react chemically to form covalent bonds with the fiber molecules. This contrasts with the binding forces prevalent in other dyestuffs (i.e., Van der Waals, ionic, and hydrogen-bonding). Chemically, fiber reactive dyes are much simpler than the complex molecules of direct dyes. Fiber reactive dyes include colored acid chlorides, vinyl sulfones, and the vinyl sulfone and triazine derivatives of anthraquinones. Upon fixation, these dyes react with the amine groups of wool and the hydroxyl groups of cellulosic fibers. Silk and polyamide (nylons) also can be colored.

TABLE 17. PHYSICAL/CHEMICAL PROPERTIES OF SULFUR DYES

| | | Reference |
|---|---|---|
| Chemical structure | Complex mixtures of heterocyclic aromatic products of which thiazine ring type structures are thought to dominate. Actual structures are indeterminant. Empirical formula for sulfur Black 1 is $C_{24}H_{16}N_6O_8S_8$. | SDC, 1971 |
| Physical state | Usually sold as paste, amorphous powder, or solution. Sulfur dyes all exist as negatively charged colloids. | SDC, 1971<br>Lubs, 1955 |
| Particle size | Colloidal particle size increases with concentration of inorganic salts. | Lubs, 1955 |
| Mole weight | High molecular weight extended heteroaromatic structures. Molecular weight for Sulfur Black 1 is 772 gm/mole. | |
| Density | Dye specific. | |
| Melting point | Dye specific. | |
| Boiling point | Dye specific. | |
| Vapor pressure | Dye specific. | |
| Water solubility | Final form of dye is insoluble. See Note 1. | |
| Other solubility | Insoluble in alcohol. Usually dissolved in sodium polysulfide. | |
| Hydrolysis | Many sulfur dyes hydrolyze under high temperature and humidity releasing mineral acids which degrade the fabric over time. | AATCC, 1982a |
| Partition coefficient | Dye specific. | |

(continued)

TABLE 17. PHYSICAL/CHEMICAL PROPERTIES OF SULFUR DYES (continued)

| | | Reference |
|---|---|---|
| Soil adsorption/ desorption | Dye specific. | |
| Dissociation constant | Dye specific. | |
| Spectra | Absorption bands of similar shades are broad and lie in the same region. No sharp easily-defined maxima are seen. | Lubs, 1955 |
| Toxicity | Many of solvent type compounds used to make sulfur dyes are toxic. Some sulfur dyes are derived from carcinogenic benzidine and toluidine. It is not known to what degree these solvents, if unreacted, may exist in the dye as contaminants, by-products, or decomposition products since sulfur dyes are very difficult to purify. See Note 2. | |
| Biodegradation | Sulfur Black 1 has been found to show only 27% reduction of color over 200 hours in a wastewater photodegradation study. Photodegradation under natural light was thought to be about ten times slower. | Porter, 1973 |

Note 1: C.I. Sulfur Dyes = water-insoluble.
C.I. Leuco Sulfur Dyes = water-soluble.
C.I. Solubilized Sulfur Dyes = water-soluble.

Note 2: "The difficulty in purifying sulfur colors and in establishing accurate and reproducible physical constants has been a great obstacle in all efforts to study their composition" (Lubs, 1955). Sulfur dyes might possibly be contaminated with such hazardous chemicals as benzidines, toluidines, toluenediamine, and nitrophenols due to the cited difficulty in purifying these dyestuffs.

Fiber reactive dyes are applied in an exhaust process or one of several pad-batch processes. Because of their unique chemical bonding they become an integral part of the textile and offer some distinct advantages. A variety of fiber reactive dyes are available for application at almost any temperature above ambient temperature. These dyes rapidly diffuse into textiles as a result of their small molecular size. Reactive dyes are priced between direct dyes and vat dyes. Though more expensive than direct dyes, reactive dyes have some distinct advantages; they offer highly reproducible bright shades and provide very level dyeing. Reactive dyes also have outstanding wet fastness. The simple and quick application technique used with these dyes is an important economic consideration. Reactive dyes are substantially less expensive than vat dyes to use in preparing highly wetfast shades.

### 6.7.1 Products

The annual total production volume of fiber-reactive dyestuffs in 1980 was 2,600,000 kilograms (5,731,000 pounds) or 2 percent of the total production of dyes. There were 66 reactive dye products listed in the 1980 ITC report; the majority (59) represented about equal numbers of yellow, orange, red, and blue colored dyestuffs. The blacks, browns, greens, and violets were represented by only a handful of products (ITC, 1980). The listing of these products signifies that they were produced in quantities exceeding 2,268 kilograms (5,000 pounds) in 1980 or had sales exceeding $5,000.

The 1982 AATCC Buyers Guide advertized 139 reactive dyestuffs in proportions about equal to those listed above.

### 6.7.2 Application Properties of Reactive Dyes

Reactive dyes are marketed as powders, liquids, and printing pastes; they offer extreme ranges of reactivity, color, fiber affinity, and stability in water. When stored under dyehouse drug room conditions, fiber reactive dyes have an almost unlimited shelf life (well over a year) (Kenyon, 1982) and 5 to 10 years of useful life can be expected.

Reactive dyestuffs cover a wide color spectrum and include shades varying from bright to heavy dark on cotton, rayon, linen, cellulosic fibers, and wool. To a much smaller extent, reactive dyes also are used to dye nylons (polyamides), silk, and acetates. Acid reactive dyes are used for wool and nylon. Reactive dyeings are superior to direct dyeings in their ability to reproduce bright shades, high quality of leveling, and wash fastness (AATCC, 1981). The wash and wet fastness of reactive dyes approaches that of vat dyes and the colors obtained are brighter than metallized azo dyes (Noller). The cost of reactive dyestuffs is higher than direct but less than vat dyestuffs (AATCC, 1981), however, cost savings are provided by the comparatively simple and rapid dyeing processes associated with the use of reactive dyes.

Commercial reactive dyes are divided into two application groups based on their inherent reactivity: "hot dyeing" and "cold dyeing" dyes. The "cold dyeing" dyes represent the most reactive dyes. Application using low liquor ratio padding equipment undoubtably offers the most economical and most shade reproducible dyeing. This ratio ranges from 1:10 to 1:1. Reactive dyes of any fiber affinity may be used with this equipment and fewer additional chemicals are required than with the high liquor ratio machines. However, more fresh water is needed for washing with the low ratio machines. Low ratio package beam, jig, jet and beck machines also are suitable. The high liquor ratio application of reactive dyes is used specifically for high affinity reactive dyes and may be done in winch becks or kettles (VPI, 1981). Reactive dyes are exhausted onto wool or cellulose from neutral solutions using salt as an exhausting agent. The cations of the salt shield the anionic dye molecules from negative charges present on the textile and allow penetration. Alkali (sodium carbonate) is added to catalyze the formation of covalent bonds between the fiber macromolecule and the dye molecule. The reactive group of the dye, either a double bond or a replaceable chlorine, thus is reacted with the amino groups on wool or the hydroxyl groups of cellulose to form covalent bonds. The strength of these bonds is directly related to the atoms involved in forming the linkage.

The hydrolysis side reaction of reactive dyes with water during their application is an important consideration. This reaction is unavoidable in reactive dyeing; many of the commercially available dyestuffs hydrolyze to the extent of 15-40%. However, recent advances have been made in producing more water-stable dyes (Shenai, 1973). The hydrolyzed dyestuff becomes affixed to the fiber by very weak intermolecular forces and, if left there, destroys the wetfastness normally exhibited by the covalently bound unhydrolyzed dye molecules. Reactive dyestuffs are intentionally designed to have low substantivity in order to facilitate the removal of this hydrolyzed dyestuff by simple soaping and rinsing. However, substantivity cannot be reduced beyond the point where the buildup of the dye on the textile is degraded (Shenai, 1973). This low substantivity also allows the dye to cover the fabric evenly and to have excellent leveling properties. On the other hand, the low substantivity requires salt concentrations of three to four times those required by direct dyes to exhaust onto cellulose. Use of equipment that allows low liquor ratios does, however, reduce the total amount of salt required (AATCC, 1981). Since alkali also promotes the competing hydrolysis reaction, the dye is allowed to exhaust to its maximum before sodium carbonate is added. This raises the pH and catalyzes the covalent bonding of the reactive moiety in the dye molecule to the substrate macromolecule. The key factors which affect the exhaustion rate are as follows (VPI, 1981).

1) Inherent substantivity of the dyestuff
2) Liquor ratio
3) Dyebath temperature
4) Salt concentration
5) Inherent leveling properties of the dyestuff
6) Inherent chemical reactivity of the dyestuff
7) pH of the dyebath

An alternate group of application processes involve padding the cloth with a cold sodium bisulfite-dye solution and then drying it. The dye is subsequently induced to covalently bond to the fabric (i.e. fixation) by either steaming or oven heating.

Wool is dyed at a pH of 2-3 by so called acid reactive dyes, while a basic pH of 9-12 is generally used for cellulosics (Kirk-Othmer, 1978). It also has been observed that the quality of leveling is enhanced if the preliminary dyeing is commenced at a mildly acidic pH of 5.0-6.5 (Davies, 1972). Whatever the optimum pH for a particular reactive dye may be, it must be carefully maintained throughout the dyeing process. When dyeing wool, it is conventional to use reactive dyes created especially for wool. These wool dyes are based on a chemically reactive species that is especially stable toward hydrolysis. Despite this advantage, reactive dyeing of wool is not as popular as reactive dyeing of cellulosics because highly wetfast dyeings of wool have always been available using other application classes of dyes (SDC, 1971).

Only a couple of dyebath additives, in addition to salt, are used with reactive dyes. Chromate is sometimes used to increase the depth of the resultant color. Fixation agents are used primarily with certain classes of reactive dyes originally developed by BASF and termed Basazol dyes. These agents are fully hydrated (reduced) reactive 1,3,5-substituted triazine derivatives (Davies, 1972). This polyfunctional chemical group is a good carrier for a wide variety of groups. Fixation agents (also called reactive mordants or crosslinking agents) have two or more reactive groups, two of which bond directly to the fiber macromolecule and the reactive moiety of the reactive dye molecule. Dyes which are useful for this type of dyeing must not be deactivated after the first reactive group is reacted (i.e. amino N-monosubstituted sulfonamino, hydroxyl, and mercapto groups, and nitrogen heterocyclics). Additionally, the dyes must have reactive groups which preferentially react with the crosslinking agent as opposed to combining directly with the textile. Effectiveness of the crosslinking agent can be correlated with its molecular mobility. Even though there are theoretically favored side reactions with water and between dyebath ingredients due to the fact that the fixation agent has multiple reactive groups, color yields of 90 percent are obtained under carefully controlled conditions. Another benefit of this type of dyeing is that any hydrolysis that takes place under the usual conditions hydrolyzes the inexpensive fixation agent hydrolyzes rather than the dyestuff. Reactive dyes with 1:2 metal complexed chromogens are particularly suitable for this type of dyeing (Shenai, 1973).

Direct printing of cellulosic fibers with reactive dyes is performed using thickened aqueous pastes containing urea and sodium bicarbonate. The dye is fixed by either steaming, baking, or padding with alkali and the print is washed and air dried. Resist and discharge processes are applicable and composition printing using pigments, azoics, and solubilized vats is possible (SDC, 1971). Most processes today use super-heated steam fixation and employ alkali-metal silicates to aid fixation. Sodium alginate is typically used as a thickening agent (Davies, 1972). Monochlorotriazinyl dyes show especially good stability over time in printing pastes (SDC, 1971).

Increasing demand for leather dyes with improved fastness to water and wet treatments such as dry cleaning have led to the increased use of reactive dyes in such products as leather gloves and coats. This trend is supplemented by the discontinued use of many extensively used benzidine-based direct brown and black dyes. Dichlorotriazine and dichloropyrimidine are the chief reactive constituents of the azo and metal complex chromogens used (Shenai, 1973).

Table 18 presents many of the important application properties of reactive dyes.

### 6.7.3 Chemical and Physical Properties of Reactive Dyes

Reactive dyes are highly water-soluble substances as are direct dyes, but in contrast to direct dyes, are purposefully designed to have low substantivity. Reactive dyes are similar to azoic dyes in that they are comprised of a fiber-substantive chemical moiety, which serves to link the colored part of the dye molecule with the fiber, and the dye moiety or chromogen. However, the similarity ends there; the fiber-substantive part of the fiber reactive dye molecule displays a characteristic that distinguishes it from all other types of dyes – the reactive component covalently bonds to the fiber as well as to the chromogen. The formation of the covalent bond is alkali promoted and

TABLE 18. APPLICATION PROPERTIES OF FIBER REACTIVE DYES

| | | Reference |
|---|---|---|
| Fabrics dyed | Primarily cellulosics and wool. Silk and nylon also are dyeable. | |
| Fabrics printed | Silk, wool, rayon and cellulosics (especially cotton). Popular for printing since even brightest colors are light and wet fast. | SDC, 1971<br>Shenai, 1973<br>Clarke, 1977 |
| Leather dyeing | Especially good for leather goods that will be wet treated or dry cleaned (e.g. gloves). See Note 1. | SDC, 1971<br>Leather Dyeing, 1972 |
| Fabrics stained | Much of the recent patent literature deals with purposefully eliminating the staining properties of reactive dyestuffs. | Davies, 1972 |
| Disposable fabrics | | |
| Leveling | Very good. Self-leveling and more rapidly leveling than other dye types. | AATCC, 1981 |
| Exhaustion | Good. pH and salt controlled. | SDC, 1971 |
| Migration | Extremely good. | |
| Dischargeability | Some are dischargeable to white. | SDC, 1971 |
| Water solubility | Generally water-soluble. | |
| Acid fastness | Dye-fiber bond is hydrolyzed at very low pH except for reactive dyes which bind through stable ether-cellulose bonds. | Shenai, 1973 |

(continued)

TABLE 18. APPLICATION PROPERTIES OF FIBER REACTIVE DYES (continued)

| | | Reference |
|---|---|---|
| Alkali fastness | Fair to good. Index 3-5. Dye-fiber bond is hydrolyzed at very high pH. | SDC, 1971 |
| Heat resistance | | |
| Light fastness | Very good. Index 5-6 | SDC, 1971 |
| Chlorine fastness | Limited, but new non-chlorine bleaches make this less of a disadvantage. | Martin-Marietta, 1982 |
| Wash fastness | Very good. Index 4-5. | SDC, 1971 |
| Perxide fastness | | |
| Perspiration fastness | Good. Index 4-5 | SDC, 1971 |
| Useful colors | Full range of colors from extremely bright to heavy dark shades. No fluorescent shades. As a class, reactive dyes offer the widest color range available to the dyer. | VPI, 1981<br>Kenyon, 1982 |
| Rate of dyeing | Very rapid. | SDC, 1971<br>AATCC, 1981 |
| Pretreatment | Removal of sizing, especially starch sizing, is mandatory since reactive dyes prefer to react with sizings instead of the fabric. It is also critical that all bleaching agents be rinsed free from the textile. | AATCC, 1981 |
| Aftertreatment | Soaping/rinsing to remove hydrolyzed dyestuff. Sometimes alkali or salt fixation. | Horning, 1978 |

(continued)

TABLE 18. APPLICATION PROPERTIES OF FIBER REACTIVE DYES (continued)

| | | Reference |
|---|---|---|
| Dyeing process | Exhaust (salt controlled). | Horning, 1978 |
| Typical equipment used | Continuous pad-batch, beck, pad-jig, pad-thermofix, pad-steam. Low liquor ratio padding is the most widespread and is the most economical and reproducible. | SDC, 1971<br>Horning, 1978<br>VPI, 1981 |

Note 1: Reactive colors are slowly replacing some of the benzidine-based direct browns and blacks. Most of these reactive dyes have monoazo, polyazo, and metal complex chromogens. The 1:2 metal complexes yield olive and browns, and with chromed monoazo, browns and greys. The 1:1 cobalt complexes yield yellow to black shades. Nickel and copper salts also yield useful shade modifications.

Index Values:

Gray scale: 1 - very poor, 2 - poor, 3 - fair, 4 - good, 5 - excellent.

Lightfastness scale: 1 - very poor, 2 - poor, 3 - fair, 4 - fairly good, 5 - good, 6 - very good, 7 - excellent, 8 - outstanding, 9 - superlative.

sometimes reversible. Additional steaming also aids the fixation of the dyestuff. The strength of the covalent bond exceeds that of metal coordination bonds and vastly exceeds the strength of bonds arising from electrostatic attraction (ionic), hydrogen-bonding, and Van der Waals attraction as seen in the retention of dyes in other application classes. As a result, reactive dyes offer superior overall fastness properties with washfastness and lightfastness approaching that of vat dyes.

Reactive dyes are classified generally according to the chemical composition of the reactive group or the degree of inherent chemical reactivity of this group.

6.7.3.1 Reactive Groups. Most of the numerous types of reactive dyes can be grouped into two broad chemical categories: vinyl sulfones and reactive acid chlorides. The most commonly used reactive dye chemical types are listed below in order of decreasing reactivity (VPI, 1981).

1) Dichlorotriazine
2) Dichloroquinoxaline
3) Vinyl-sulfone
4) Monochlorotriazine
5) Chloropyrimidine
6) Acryloylamino types

Any reactive dyeing may be represented by the following scheme:

R—B—X—F

where: R is the chromogen (chromophore)
B is the bridging group (linking group)
X is the reactive group
F is the fiber macromolecule

In this bonding scheme the fiber-dye bond (X—F) is the weakest bond (Shenai, 1973).

6.7.3.1.1 Triazine derived dyes. When wool or cotton is dyed with acid chloride reactive dyes, the dyebath is made alkaline with sodium carbonate and warmed (after salt aided exhaustion). As this occurs, halogen groups (almost exclusively chlorine and fluorine) on the triazine nucleus of these dyes are displaced by amine groups on the wool macromolecule or the hydroxyl groups of cellulose. Hydrogen is lost from the macromolecule and a covalent bond is formed, liberating HCl which is neutrallized by the alkali present in the dyebath. This is a base-promoted nucleophilic substitution reaction forming amide bonds (X—NH—CO—F) with wool and ester bonds (X—O—CO—F) with cellulose (Shenai, 1973).

Reactive systems of triazine ranging in molecular weight from 69-211 gm/mole are useful. In general, the higher the molecular weight the more costly the dyeing because more dye has to be used to produce the same shade (Shenai, 1973).

Originally, many triazine-based fiber reactive dyes were classed as direct dyes for cotton and were observed to be faster exhausting and more substantive than most other direct dyes. Also, some vat dyes contain the triazine moiety. After it was proven that the cellulose macromolecule was indeed reactive and not completely inert as previously believed, these substances were reclassified as reactive dyes.

Most triazine derived dyes are synthesized from cyanuric chloride derivatives (only a select few from cyanuric fluoride) containing from one to three reactive, replaceable halogen atoms on the triazine ring. The majority of modern triazine reactive dyes are of the monochlorotriazine variety. A wide variety of reactivities can be obtained from this chemical system because successive replacement of the three chlorines occurs with a stepwise increase in difficulty. The first chlorine is displaced in adding the chromogen to the reactive nucleus and occurs readily at cold temperatures. The second chlorine group reacts readily at room temperature with the hydroxyl group of cellulose. If two of the chlorines are replaced by either reacting both with dye molecules or by adding other substituent groups to one site, the third chlorine reacts only at reflux temperatures. Thus, this one chemical system can yield both cold dyeing brands of reactive dyes possessing two replaceable chlorines or hot dyeing brands which possess only one reactive chlorine atom (Shenai, 1973).

Triazine reactive dyes react with water to form hydrolyzed species that are unreactive and have very poor fastness. Removing these hydrolyzed molecules requires that the original dyestuff, as well as the hydrolyzed form, have low substantivity such that simple soaping and rinsing can accomplish the desired stripping. Therefore, useful triazine dyes are designed to have low substantivity.

It is common to use a bridging group to link the colored dye molecule (chromogen) to the reactive nucleus when using the triazine-type reactive groups. Other types of reactive entities: vinyl sulfone, epoxide, sulfonyl fluoride, and chloroisopropanol, bond directly to the chromogen without a bridging group. The bridging group often used with triazines is the imino group (—NH—). The oxide and sulfide linkages between chromogen and reactive nuclei are much less stable to alkaline hydrolysis than the imino linkage, and unlike the imino linkage they exhibit undesirable side-reactions. Alkylation of this imino linkage (replacing the hydrogen with organic groups) reduces the reaction rate of the reactive dyestuff formed, but greatly stabilizes the whole molecule toward hydrolytic cleavage (Shenai, 1973).

When the second reactive chlorine is replaced by colored substituent groups, secondary and tertiary shades can be obtained. Furthermore, the reactivity of the remaining chlorine group is affected by the presence of these or other uncolored functional groups. The reactivity of the ultimate dyestuff decreases with the basicity of these functional groups. For example, a substituent hydroxyl yields a dyestuff that is very slow to react with cellulose, while substituent amines yield dyes of intermediate reactivity and alkoxy and phenoxy substituent groups give rise to dyestuffs of high reactivity. Sometimes the reactive chlorine is replaced by the sulfonate group to yield highly reactive dyes with very good solubility (Shenai, 1973).

Tertiary amines such as pyridine, trimethylamine, and N,N-dimethylhydrazine, etc. often are introduced into the dyebath to activate the monochlorotriazines toward fixation. Many times this allows the dyeing to proceed in dyebaths with temperatures as low as 35°C by catalyzing the replacement of the sole remaining chlorine.

The extremely reactive dichlorotriazines are used in cold dyeing. However, a disadvantage associated with using them is that if one of the reactive chlorines gets hydrolyzed, the molecule can rearrange into a ketone-imine. This molecule becomes protonated and immediately hydrolyzes in the acid solution which results in the cleaving of the reactive dye from the fiber (Shenai, 1973).

6.7.3.1.2 Vinyl sulfone dyes. When wool or cellulose is dyed with vinyl sulfone reactive dyes, the dyebath is made alkaline after salt aided exhaustion. The vinyl double bond, which is conjugated with the adjacent sulfone double bond, undergoes a nucleophilic addition reaction forming amino bonds (X—NH—F) with wool and ether bonds (X—O—F) with cellulose, where X is formed from the reactive group ($R—SO_2—CH{=}CH_2$). Salt concentrations of up to 50 gm/L are needed to get good color yields and large liquor ratios up to 20:1 and 30:1 are used. Still, the reaction with cellulose is completely reversible and, under certain conditions, the original vinyl sulfone may reform. However, after the completion of the dyeing process, these ether linkages between the reactive moiety and the fiber are more stable than any of the other types of linkages seen with reactive dyes. These ether linkages are stable to acid and base, whereas the ester linkages are easily hydrolyzed. In the process, the hydrogen from the substrate hydroxyl or amino group is displaced (Shenai, 1973). This reaction is a nucleophilic addition to the beta carbon of the double bond. The site is activated by its conjugation with the sulfone double bond and the reaction proceeds analogously to the well-known Michael addition reaction of alpha, beta-unsaturated carbonyl compounds. Typically the ethylsulfonyl sulfate derivatives of these vinyl sulfone dyes are used instead of the free vinyl sulfone. The corresponding ethylsulfonyl sulfates are very water-soluble without the necessity of adding other solubilizing groups to the dye molecule. They are readily converted to the vinyl sulfone form by mild alkaline treatment in the dyebath. Vinyl sulfones also exhibit the hydrolysis side-reaction and form unreactive hydroxyethyl sulfone species which eventually must be stripped from the dyeing. In addition to hydrolysis, vinyl sulfones also undergo addition reactions with alcohol which yields unreactive species as well (Shenai, 1973).

The reactivity of vinyl sulfone-based reactive dyes lies between those of mono and dichlorotriazines. Reactivity also increases with increasing temperature and increasing pH (i.e. basicity) up to an optimum limit. Typically the dyeing is performed at 60°C using sodium carbonate or trisodium phosphate to catalyze the fixation. Each reactive dye has a unique optimum pH and temperature; if these are exceeded, the dye fiber bond is severed. Some of these dyes give very good yields, but again only at critical pH dyebaths.

6.7.3.1.3 Other reactive groups. Several other nitrogen-containing heterocyclics are used as reactive functionalities in addition to triazine derivatives. Compounds such as trichloropyrimidine, tetrachloropyrimidine, dichlorophthalazine, dichloroquinazoline, and dichloroquinoxaline are used in commercial reactive dyes. The chemical class of pyrimidines may be viewed as a triazine ring in which one of the three nitrogens in the heterocyclic structure has been replaced by another carbon atom. This results in lowered reactivity of the chemical system, or alternatively, higher stability prior to fixation (Shenai, 1973). Figure 5 shows the chemical structures of the above mentioned reactive groups.

Sulfatoethyl sulfonamide reactive dyes are represented by the structure $D\text{-}SO_2\text{-}NH\text{-}CH_2\text{-}CH_2\text{-}Cl$, where D is such chromogens as azo, anthraquinone, or phthalocyanine. This class of reactive dye is more washfast on wool than most other reactive dyes. These dyes contain no solubilizing groups; solubilizing groups act to decrease the substantivity of reactive dyes (Shenai, 1973).

Arylamide reactive dyes display the chemical structure $D\text{-}NHCOCH{=}CH_2$. The vinyl group reacts by nucleophilic addition but is much less reactive than vinyl sulfones. Arylamide dyes are formed by reacting dye molecules (chromogens) with chloroethylamide (Shenai, 1973).

N-methylol dyes such as N-methylol urea are a relatively new series of dyes which are reactive towards cellulose. They exhibit the chemical structure ($D\text{-}NH(CH_2)OH$) and are fixed under acidic conditions in direct

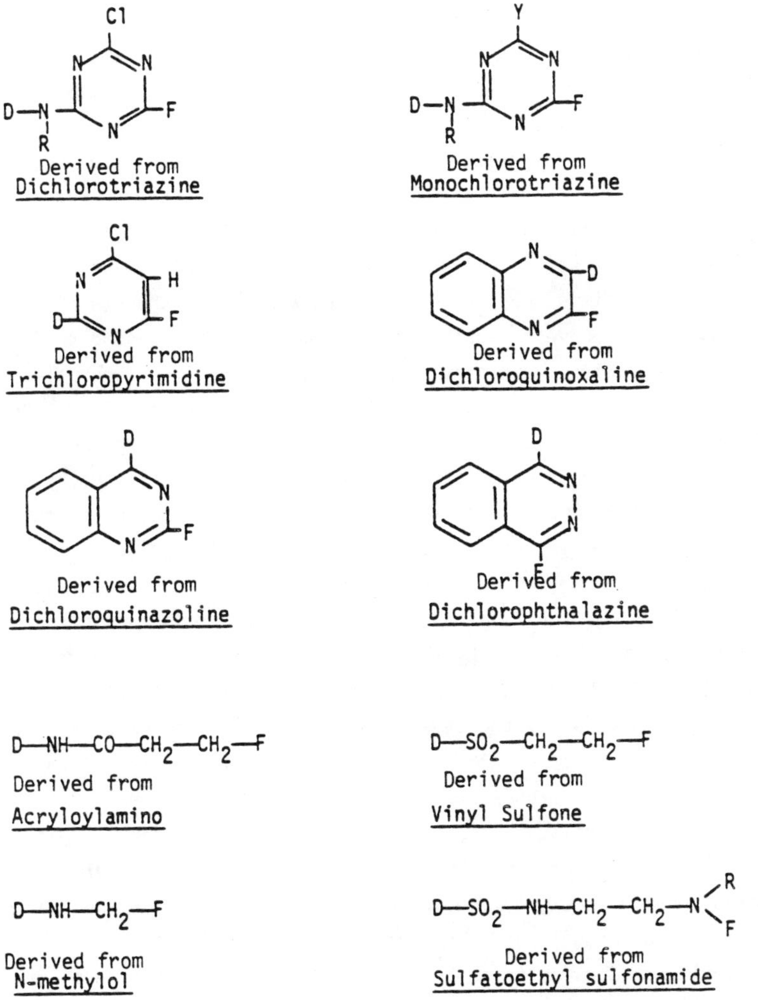

Derived from
Dichlorotriazine

Derived from
Monochlorotriazine

Derived from
Trichloropyrimidine

Derived from
Dichloroquinoxaline

Derived from
Dichloroquinazoline

Derived from
Dichlorophthalazine

D—NH—CO—$CH_2$—$CH_2$—F

Derived from
Acryloylamino

D—$SO_2$—$CH_2$—$CH_2$—F

Derived from
Vinyl Sulfone

D—NH—$CH_2$—F

Derived from
N-methylol

D—$SO_2$—NH—$CH_2$—$CH_2$—N(R)(F)

Derived from
Sulfatoethyl sulfonamide

where: D = Dye molecule F = Cellulose or wool fiber molecule

R = Alkyl substituents Y = Reactive substituents

Figure 5. Chemical structures of fiber-reactive groups.

contrast to most reactive dyestuffs. The quality of fixation is dependent on dyebath temperature, and the amounts of acidic catalyst and reactive dyestuff present. These dyestuffs are stable in aqueous solution and do not undergo the hydrolysis reaction (Shenai, 1973).

Developments of new reactive systems or variations of the ones discussed above have concentrated on decreasing, or otherwise modifying, substantivity; increasing resistance to hydrolysis; and improving fixation to the textile. In recent years, many advances have been made in producing highly-fixed reactive systems and minimizing the staining properties of these dyes. Most new developments center around the chlorotriazine, chloropyrimidinyl and sulfato ethylsulfonyl reactive groups, especially on 1:1 cobalt, chromium, and copper metallized azo chromogens to produce extremely colorfast reds, blues, and greens. Other highly reactive dyestuffs have been obtained by substituting fluorine for chlorine on the triazine ring or by adding other electronegative substituent groups to the ring. Adding sulfonic acid solubilizing groups to the reactive dye molecule has been used as a means of decreasing fiber substantivity. However, these sulfonic acid groups may be cleaved during hydrolysis, resulting in staining problems. A novel means of decreasing the substantivity of reactive dye molecules (as a means of decreasing the same property of the hydrolyzed dye) is to disturb the coplanarity of the reactive dye molecule. This is achieved by adding substituent groups ortho to the point of attachment of the planar reactive group or by N-substitution of nitrogen atoms. This results in lowered substantivity since the property of coplanarity is conducive to alignment with the cellulose macromolecule surface which allows a good opportunity of covalent bonding by proximity. The substantivity of a class of anthraquinone reactive dyes has recently been reduced by preparing a mixture of closely related dye structures (Davies, 1972).

6.7.3.2 Chromagens. A wide variety of azo, diazo, polyazo, metallized azo, acid and aminoanthraquinone, and phthalocyanine chromogens, many of them direct dyes, are used to impart the color to reactive dyestuff. In fact, any chromogen containing an amine group with a replaceable hydrogen can be attached to the reactive nucleus.

Monoazo chromogens are especially useful since they are less reduction prone and less substantive than disazo and other chromogens. Phthalocyanines are used when good water solubility is essential, but the disadvantage associated with using them is that their large molecules are difficult to remove from the textile after hydrolysis. Acid anthraquinones are particularly useful for violets and greens since they exhibit low affinity, excellent lightfastness, and are easy to remove from the hydrolyzed dyestuff. Both triazine and vinylsulfone derivatives of anthraquinones are commercially available. Reactive metal complexed direct dyes, like complexed direct dyes themselves, are highly lightfast and show extended fastness to repeated washing. Unfortunately, they are dull colored and are difficult to remove from the hydrolyzed dyestuff. Complexes of 1:1 and 1:2 are extremely useful for leather dyes (see Table 18) (Shenai, 1973).

6.7.3.3 Printing Products. Reactive dyes suitable for printing must exhibit high fixation and good resistance to hydrolysis, particularly to the presence of strong alkali in the printing paste. Over the years, monochlorotriazines have been popular due to their excellent stability in printing pastes (SDC, 1971). Recent developments have mainly concentrated on reactive dyes containing two or more reactive molecular nuclei. A good number of these have dealt with multiple monochlorotriazine groups with attached azo, metallized azo, phthalocyanine, and anthraquinone chromogens. Another class of highly fixing reactive groups use combinations of monochlorotriazine, chlorodiazine, and chloroethylaminosulfonyl reactive centers. Some new products employ amino groups on the chlorotriazine moiety which can be developed to produce very deep shades by the diazonium coupling reaction (Davies, 1972). Trichloropyrimidines are particularly suitable for printing dyes; they are alkali stable and have low reactivity at 30°C. These dyes are fixed by high temperature steaming after application to the textile (Shenai, 1973).

Table 19 summarizes the physical/chemical properties of fiber reactive dyes.

TABLE 19. PHYSICAL/CHEMICAL PROPERTIES OF FIBER REACTIVE DYES

| | | Reference |
|---|---|---|
| Chemical structure | Mostly triazinyl and vinyl sulfone derivatives of monoazo and acid chloride compounds. Characteristically small and simple molecular structures. Anionic in elctrostatic nature. Much simpler in structure than direct dyes. | SDC, 1971<br>Shenai, 1973 |
| Physical state | Used as solutions; depends on base compounds. | |
| Particle size | Not applicable. | |
| Mole weight | Low generally, but some range up to 775 gm/mole (anthraquinones with phenyl crosslinked triazine reactive group). Small size allows rapid diffusion into the fiber. See Note 1. | AATCC, 1981<br>Shenai, 1973 |
| Density | Dye specific. | |
| Melting point | Not applicable. | |
| Boiling point | Not applicable. | |
| Vapor pressure | Dye specific. | |
| Water solubility | Generally very good water solubility. Sometimes modified to lower solubility. | |
| Other solubility | Dye specific. | |
| Hydrolysis | Dye-fiber bond is hydrolyzed by strong acid or base. The more reactive dichloro- and trichloropyrimidine dyes are especially hydrolysis prone. See Note 2. | Shenai, 1973 |

(continued)

TABLE 19. PHYSICAL/CHEMICAL PROPERTIES OF FIBER REACTIVE DYES (continued)

| | | Reference |
|---|---|---|
| Partition coefficient | Dye specific. | |
| Soil adsorption/ desorption | Dye specific. | |
| Dissociation constant | Dye specific. | |
| Spectra | Reactive dyes have very bright shades owing to their very narrow and high peaked absorption bands which result from their simple structures. | SDC, 1971 |
| Bonding type | Covalently bond to fiber substrate. See Note 3. | AATCC, 1981<br>Shenai, 1973 |
| Toxicity | Information not available. | |

Note 1: The molecular weight of the reactive system ranges from 69-211 gm/mole. The higher the MW the more costly the dyeing because more dye has to be used to produce the same shade (Shenai, 1973).

Note 2: During the application of conventional reactive dyes, as much as 15-40% of the dye is hydrolyzed and must be washed free from the fabric. The use of reactive mordants and less easily hydrolyzed reactive dyes reduces this waste of dyestuff. Reactive dyes for wool are especially stable toward hydrolysis. The stability toward hydrolysis is a function of the chemical dye-fiber linkage (see text).

Note 3: Vinyl sulfones form amino bonds with wool and ether bonds to cellulose. Acid chlorides form amide bonds with wool and ester bonds with cellulosics.

## 6.8 BASIC DYES

### 6.8.1 General Information

Basic dyes were once widely used with tannic acid as a mordant to color fibers such as silk, wool, cotton. They can also color cellulose acetate, nylon, polyester, rayon, and acrylics. Because of their limited wetfastness, the use of basic dyes has declined, with the possible exceptions of coloring leather and paper, use in writing inks, and use of brilliant triphenyl methane basic dyes which are highly substantive to acrylic fibers.

### 6.8.2 Color Categories of Basic Dyes

Basic dyes offer a full range of colors. The color categories and the percentage of the 1980 total production of basic dyes represented by each are listed below.

| Color Category | Percent of Total Basic Dyes |
|---|---|
| Basic Violets | 27.4% |
| Basic Yellows | 24.7% |
| Basic Blues | 17.2% |
| Basic Reds | 15.8% |
| Basic Oranges | 8.2% |
| Basic Browns | 1.7% |
| Other | 5.0% |
| | 100.0% |

### 6.8.3 Outstanding Volume Products

The reported U.S. production volume of basic dyestuffs in 1980 was 6.6 million kilograms (14.59 million pounds) which corresponded to 6% of the total 1980 production volume of dyes. The most outstanding product was Basic Violet 1 which represented 15% of the total production of basic dyestuffs, although less than 1% of the total U.S. dye production.

| C.I. Name | Percent of Total Basic Dyes |
|---|---|
| Basic Violet 1 | 15.0% |
| Basic Yellow 11 | 3.6% |
| Basic Red 14 | 3.6% |
| Basic Yellow 29 | 3.5% |
| Basic Orange 2 | 3.0% |
| | 28.7% |

6.8.4 Application Properties of Basic Dyes

Basic dyes are usually applied in an acetic acid medium to leather, paper, and especially acrylic fibers. Nylon, polyester, and some other synthetics can be copolymerized with small amounts of anionic monomers to make them colorable by basic dyestuffs. However, specific basic dyes generally are different for acrylics as opposed to natural fibers, as are the application procedures. Basic dyes are among the brightest colored dyes available even though their use is declining. The advantages they offer are a wide variety of very bright shades, good fastness to synthetic polymers, and several fluorescing shades. If not applied in excess, they also exhaust very well.

Basic dyes, however, are not very color fast or wash fast to natural fibers and require careful scouring and special pretreatment for some fabrics. Cation retarding agents are also required to achieve level dyeing; they effectively compete for negatively charged sites on the fabric. Leveling difficulty is a chief disadvantage of basic dyes. Furthermore, since basic dyes are chemically competitive, they cannot be relied upon to produce a specific dye shade.

Cellulose may be colored with basic dyes if a tannic acid mordant or synthetic mordant is applied first. Another scheme is to dye the textile first with a direct dyestuff and then top the dyeing with a basic dye. This allows a very bright shade to be obtained with a minimum amount of the basic dyestuff used.

Because of the difficulty in dissolving basic dyes, the dyestuff must be organic pasted and then dissolved in boiling water with filtering to remove specks. Alternatively, liquid dyestuff forms are available commercially. The exhaust rates of basic dyes vary widely but all must be exhausted at boiling. A "K" factor is used to describe the exhaustion rate of basic dyes which ranges from 1 (very fast) to 5 (very slow). Retarders must be employed with the fast exhausting dyes to obtain quality leveling. Use of basic dyes to color acrylics is popular since only with acrylics is the exhaustion process controllable to a useful degree and virtually complete (VPI, 1981).

Table 20 summarizes the important application properties of basic dyes.

### 6.8.5 Chemical and Physical Properties

Basic dyes include such chemical classes of substances as diphenyl methanes, triphenylmethanes, methylidynes, xanthenes, and azines. Basic dyes are cationic in nature usually because of a positively charged quaternary amine group in the dye molecule.

The mildly acidic alpha-hydrogen adjacent to nitrile groups in acrylics accounts for the particular affinity of acrylics for basic dyestuffs.

The organic free base form of basic dyes is insoluble in water, but the commercial forms are generally the soluble salt forms. The later forms include hydrochlorides, oxalates, acetates, sulfates, nitrates, and zinc chloride double salts (Shenai, 1973). Nonetheless, many commercial basic dyestuffs are described as hard to dissolve or as forming sticky masses in water. This is due to a small quantity of the free base form being present. As a result, most basic dyes are applied from pastes created by dispersing the basic dyestuff in acetic acid or alcohol. Another difficulty encountered with basic dyes is the conversion of the colored cationic dyestuff to the colorless free base by a strong alkali solution (Shenai, 1973).

Table 21 summarizes the important chemical and physical properties of basic dyes. Figure 6 presents the chemical structures of various basic dyes.

TABLE 20. APPLICATION PROPERTIES OF BASIC DYES

| | | Reference |
|---|---|---|
| Fabrics dyed | No affinity for cellulose. Can be used for anionic modified nylon, polyester, silk, wool, and acrylics, however, basic dyes for textiles have been almost completely replaced by other dyestuffs except on polyacrylonitrile. Basic dyes are chiefly used for pen inks and paper and leather coloring. | Mayer and Ernst, 1974<br>Ven Kataraman, 1971<br>AATCC, 1981 |
| Fabrics printed | Polyacrylonitrile. | Shenai, 1973<br>Clarke, 1977 |
| Leather dyeing | Basic yellows, blues, and greens are useful for leather coloring. | SDC, 1971 |
| Fabrics stained | | |
| Disposable fabrics | | |
| Leveling | Difficult to obtain, since most basic dyes do not migrate well. The dye must go on evenly initially and only at critically maintained dyebath conditions. | AATCC, 1981 |
| Exhaustion | Good if the dye concentration is not too high. Controllable and virtually complete for acrylics only. | Shenai, 1973<br>AATCC, 1981 |
| Migration | Poor. | |
| Dischargeability | Fair to poor; dye specific. | SDC, 1971 |

(continued)

TABLE 20. APPLICATION PROPERTIES OF BASIC DYES (continued)

| | | Reference |
|---|---|---|
| Water solubility | A few are very soluble in cold or hot water, but most are hard to dissolve. See Note 1. | Patterson, 1972<br>Ven Kataraman, 1971<br>Shenai, 1973 |
| Acid fastness | Not applicable. | |
| Alkali fastness | Sensitive to base and the colorless free base form is liberated. | Shenai, 1973 |
| Heat resistance | Many are heat sensitive and decompose at boiling (100°C). | Ven Kataraman, 1971 |
| Light fastness | Particularly poor lightfastness except on polyacrylonitrile where it is good. | Ven Kataraman, 1971 |
| Chlorine fastness | | |
| Wash fastness | Poor except on polyacrylonitrile where it is good. | AATCC, 1981 |
| Peroxide fastness | | |
| Perspiration fastness | | |
| Useful colors | Almost unlimited number of shades and among the most brilliant colors available. They also have high tinctorial strength. The bright, colorfast colors formed on polyacrylonitrile are particularly important. | Ven Kataraman, 1971<br>AATCC, 1981 |
| Bonding mechanism | Cationic colored molecules have positively charged quartenary amine basic groups which form salt bonds to proteins or to hydrogen-bonded mordants on cellulose. | Shenai, 1973 |

(continued)

TABLE 20. APPLICATION PROPERTIES OF BASIC DYES (continued)

| | | Reference |
|---|---|---|
| Speed of dyeing | Dye specific. | |
| Pretreatment | Fabric must be extensively scoured and some fabrics require special pretreatments. See Note 2. | AATCC, 1981 |
| Aftertreatment | Simple scouring and rinsing. | AATCC, 1981 |
| Processes used | Exhaust, continuous luster. | |
| Equipment | Beck and stock dyeing equipment. | |
| Miscellaneous | Compared to other types of dyes, many additional dyebath additives are required. | AATCC, 1981 |

Note 1: The salt forms of basic dyes are appreciably water soluble but the presence of any of the insoluble free base yields a material that is insoluble or at best forms a sticky mass in water. Usually basic dyes are pasted with ethanol or acetic acid to facilitate their use.

Note 2: Most cellulosic textiles must be mordanted with tannic acid or synthetic mordants before basic dyes become substantive.

TABLE 21. PHYSICAL/CHEMICAL PROPERTIES OF BASIC DYES

| | | Reference |
|---|---|---|
| Chemical structure | Many chemical types: azo, arylmethane, methine, acridine, xanthene azine, oxazine, thiazine, and thiazole. There are many commercially available methine basic dyes. Dissociates into colored cations and colorless anions. | |
| Physical state | Actual form is non-critical, but manufacturers tend to use granulated forms with surfactants added to diminish caking or liquids with stabilizing agents. See Note 1. | Patterson, 1972 |
| Particle size | Dye specific. | |
| Mole weight | Except for the low molecular weight acridine dyes (around 200 gm/mole) the molecular weights of the various classes are similar and range from 270-680 gm/mole averaging 400 gm/mole. | Shenai, 1973 |
| Density | Dye specific. | |
| Melting point | Basic dyes decompose at 190-300°C without melting. A few decompose above 300°C. | Aldrich, 1978 |
| Boiling point | Decompose before melting. | |
| Vapor pressure | Dye specific. | |
| Water solubility | Some are highly soluble in cold water yet most form unusable sticky masses. Comparatively more soluble than disperse, vats, or pigments. See Note 2. | Patterson, 1972<br>Shenai, 1973 |

(continued)

TABLE 21. PHYSICAL/CHEMICAL PROPERTIES OF BASIC DYES (continued)

| | | Reference |
|---|---|---|
| Other solubility | Readily soluble in alcohol or methylated spirit. | Shenai, 1973 |
| Hydrolysis | Some basic dyes decompose when boiled in water; high temperature aqueous exhaust is the usual process. | Shenai, 1973 |
| Partition coefficient | Dye specific. | |
| Soil adsorption/ desorption | Dye specific. | |
| Dissociation constant | Dye specific. | |
| Spectra | Very bright colors are indicative of sharp well-defined absorption peaks. | |
| Toxicity | Basic Yellow 2 (Auramine) is listed in RCRA Appendix VIII as a hazardous substance and by the NIOSH registry as a positive human carcinogen. Basic Yellow 2 is an imino diphenyl methane type dye. See Note 3. | NIOSH, 1979<br>FR, 1980<br>Sax, 1968 |

Note 1: Handling of very fine colorants of high staining value is avoided because of difficulty in weighing, health hazards due to dust, and cross-contamination of dyeings from flying flecks. In their pure state most are shiny crystalline materials.

Note 2: See Note 1 for Table 4-20.

Note 3: Basic aniline dyes are more irritating than acid aniline dyes and allergic reactions have been noted. Dangerous aniline and $NO_x$ fumes are emitted when the dye is heated to decomposition (one example is Basic Green 4).

C.I. Basic Orange 1 - Monoazo dye

C.I. Basic Violet - Triarylmethane dye, methyl-Violet

C.I. Basic Yellow 2 - Ketone Imine dye, Auramine

C.I. Basic Yellow 11 - Methine dye

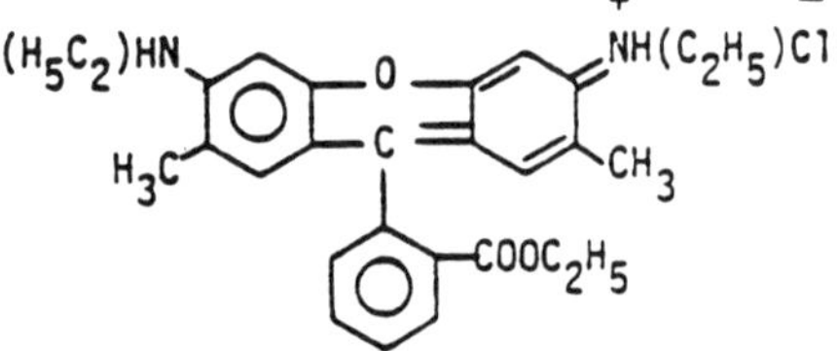


C.I. Basic Red 1 - Xanthene dye

Figure 6. Chemical structures of various basic dyes.

## 6.9 OXIDATION BASES

Oxidation bases are precursors for high molecular weight, water insoluble ingrain colors. Ingrain dyes are, by definition, any water insoluble colors formed in situ (on the fabric) from water soluble intermediates. Phthalocyanines and azoic dyes also could be classed as ingrain colors. Azoic dyes achieve their resultant water solubility from coupling reactions between the water soluble intermediates that yield complex, large molecular weight insoluble species. Oxidation bases, however, offer such water insoluble species by oxidation reactions performed on aromatic amines and diamines. Some use metal salts as mordants. Aniline Black is the most important oxidation base for textile use.

Today oxidation bases are used mainly in a color range from orange to brown for human hair and furs and for black dyeings and prints on textiles. The only oxidation base listed in the 1980 ITC report is C.I. Oxidation Base 21. The AATCC Buyer's Guide lists C.I. Oxidation Base 1.

### 6.9.1 Application Properties of Oxidation Bases

Jet black dyeings on cellulosics are the main use of oxidation bases. To produce the same shade using a vat black would require an expensive 5-10% by weight of dyestuff. Direct black dyeings, on the other hand, have poor washfasteness. Furthermore, sulfur black and vat blacks both tender the textile (Shenai, 1973). Aniline black dyeing and prints produce some of the most intense blacks; these colors are almost completely color stable to acids, bases, and exposure to light. By far, the greatest use of aniline blacks is for dyeing and calico printing of cotton. Silk and wool are dyed only when extensive precautions are taken against tendering (SDC, 1971).

Oxidation dyeing involves first impregnating the textile with a soluble salt of an aromatic amine such as aniline or aminodiphenylamine. Next, the amines are oxidized onto the fabric in an acidic medium using continuous equipment. A vanadium catalyst is very efficient for driving this oxidation reaction and is incorporated into the paste used in the printing process. Along with the dyestuff and catalyst, an acid liberating agent and an oxidizing agent are included in the impregnation bath. Next, the textile is hot air aged with removal of the hydrogen chloride fumes. There are also emissions of volatilized amine. Oxidation occurs during this drying process and the dye becomes fixed (Shenai, 1973).

Good penetration is afforded by oxidation bases since the salt form of the dyestuff has no fiber affinity. Penetration is also aided by the inclusion of formic acid to the dyebath.

The reaction efficiency is greatly improved (nearly 20 percent) if some of the aniline is first diazotized and converted into aminoazobenzene. If this takes place, less unreacted aniline is lost in the fixation drying process.

A wide variety of oxidizing agents have been tried; they impart differing shelf stabilities and evenness of print quality. The printing paste is kept basic during application so fabric tendering by liberated mineral acid can be minimized (Shenai, 1973). Among the oxidizing agents employed in textile coloration with these dyes are vanadium chloride, potassium ferrocyanide, potassium chromate, sodium chlorate, and copper nitrate (SDC, 1971).

Aftertreatment with 5 g/L solution of dichromate or bisulfite is necessary to produce an Aniline Black which will not develop green tint. Also, molecular weight is increased by about 10 percent. However, no afterchroming is required with the Diphenyl Blacks since they do not turn greenish.

Materials dyed or printed by oxidation dyes are characteristically very lightfast and wetfast. The black and brown dyes are also suitable for discharge and resist printing.

Oxidation base colors can be modified by dyeing with chromium, iron, and copper mordants and also by combining them with other oxidation bases. In fact, C.I. Oxidation Base 21 can be added to all other oxidation bases. Addition of chromium salts with or without phenylene-diamine to the dyebath generally yields a better quality dyeing (SDC, 1971).

C.I. Oxidation Base 1 is the original Aniline Black. C.I. Oxidation Base 21 used with a chrome mordant is useful for producing deep reddish browns. C.I. Oxidation Base 3 is probably the diphenylamine sulfamate derivative which is referenced in the literature as Diphenyl Black. Many of the C.I. Oxidation Base products also are listed as C.I. Developers with azoic components being essentially reactive amines (SDC, 1971). Table 22 summarizes the important application properties of oxidation bases.

### 6.9.2 Chemical and Physical Properties

Oxidation colors are obtained by chemical oxidation of aniline, phenylene diamines, p-amino-phenyl-sulfamic acid, aminophenols, o-toluidine, dianisidine, xylidine, p-amino-diphenylamine, 1,4-naphthalene diamine, and various derivatives related to the aforementioned arylamines and diamines.

Browns are obtained from phenylene diamine and aminophenols. Blacks are obtained from aniline and p-amino diphenylamine.

Table 23 summarizes the important chemical and physical properties of oxidation bases. Figure 7 presents the chemical structure of C.I. Oxidation Base 1.

## 6.10 MORDANT (CHROME) DYES

Many classes of dyes use or have used mordant materials to bind to fibers and provide a colorable substrate in cases where the dyes are not otherwise directly substantive to the fabric. Mordant/chrome dyes are those that form coordination chelate complexes with metal ions. It follows then that substantivity increases with increased coordination (i.e., molecular size, stability, and bond strength). Cobalt, copper, and especially chromium are used to treat unmetallized dyes by a variety of methods. Three commonly used procedures with chrome are: 1) prechroming (bottomchroming) - treatment of the fiber with sodium dichromate before adding the dye; 2) metachroming (same bath) dichromate added during the dyeing process; and 3) afterchroming (fresh bath), top chroming (same bath) - adding the dichromation after exhaustion of the dye. Chroming increases the molecular weight of the dyestuff and thereby producing deeper colors with enhanced fastness properties.

TABLE 22. APPLICATION PROPERTIES OF OXIDATION BASES

| | | Reference |
|---|---|---|
| Fabrics dyed | Cellulosics, mainly cotton. | SDC, 1971<br>Shenai, 1973 |
| Fabrics printed | Cotton, linen, rayon by direct, resist, or discharge printing. | SDC, 1971<br>Clarke, 1977<br>Shenai, 1973 |
| Leather dyeing | Not used. | |
| Fabrics stained | | |
| Disposable fabrics | | |
| Leveling | Very good because the dye molecules are small and mobile and penetrate the fabric well since they have no fiber affinity. | Shenai, 1973 |
| Exhaustion | Ideally approaches 100% except when precipitation outside the fiber is not circumvented. | SDC, 1971 |
| Migration | Dye specific. | |
| Dischargeability | Browns and blacks are well suited for discharge printing. | SDC, 1971<br>Shenai, 1973 |
| Water solubility | Dyestuff salt-form is very soluble while free amines are not. | SDC, 1971<br>Shenai, 1973 |
| Acid fastness | Excellent. Aniline Black is virtually unaltered. | SDC, 1971 |

(continued)

TABLE 22. APPLICATION PROPERTIES OF OXIDATION BASES (continued)

| | | Reference |
|---|---|---|
| Alkali fastness | Excellent. Aniline Black is virtually unaltered. | SDC, 1971 |
| Heat resistance | | |
| Light fastness | Excellent. Aniline Black is virtually unaltered if aftertreated to prevent "greening." | SDC, 1971<br>Shenai, 1973 |
| Wash fastness | Excellent. | SDC, 1971<br>Shenai, 1973 |
| Peroxide fastness | | |
| Perspiration fastness | | |
| Useful colors | Jet black and brown only. | |
| Speed of dyeing | Dye specific. | |
| Pretreatment | Scouring required, but neither soaping nor bleaching is allowable. | Shenai, 1973 |
| Aftertreatment | Aniline blacks are afterchromed to prevent "greening." | Shenai, 1973 |
| Processes used | Continuous padding and printing. | |
| Metal salts | Chromium, copper, and iron salts are used as mordants. | SDC, 1971 |

TABLE 23. PHYSICAL/CHEMICAL PROPERTIES OF OXIDATION BASES

| | | Reference |
|---|---|---|
| Chemical structure | Large cationic molecules of phenyl or biphenyl rings linked by amino and diazine groups. The diazine nitrogens hold the cationic change and are N-substituted by additional phenyl rings. | Shenai, 1973 |
| Physical state | Dye specific. | |
| Particle size | Dye specific. | |
| Mole weight | Molecular weight of the Aniline Black ultimate product is 1086.5 gm/mole. Afterchroming increases weight by 10%. | Shenai, 1973 |
| Density | Dye specific. | |
| Melting point | Dye specific. | |
| Boiling point | Dye specific. | |
| Vapor pressure | Dye specific. | |
| Water solubility | Dyestuff is soluble salt while the free amine is not. | SDC, 1971<br>Shenai, 1973 |
| Other solubility | Dye specific. | |
| Hydrolysis | Dye specific. | |
| Partition coefficient | Dye specific. | |

(continued)

TABLE 23. PHYSICAL/CHEMICAL PROPERTIES OF OXIDATION BASES (continued)

| | | Reference |
|---|---|---|
| Soil adsorption/ desorption | Dye specific. | |
| Dissociation constant | Dye specific. | |
| Spectra | | |
| Toxicity | Unoxidized amines and diamines are volatilized during the final heat treatment. Several of these diamines are hazardous: o-dianisidine, toluidine, phenylene diamine; aniline itself has some hazardous properties. The chromium and copper salts used as mordants and also the common practice of adding phenylene diamine to improve dyeing quality are of note. See Note 1. | |

Note 1: Aniline
Phenylenediamine
o-Dianisidine
Toluidine

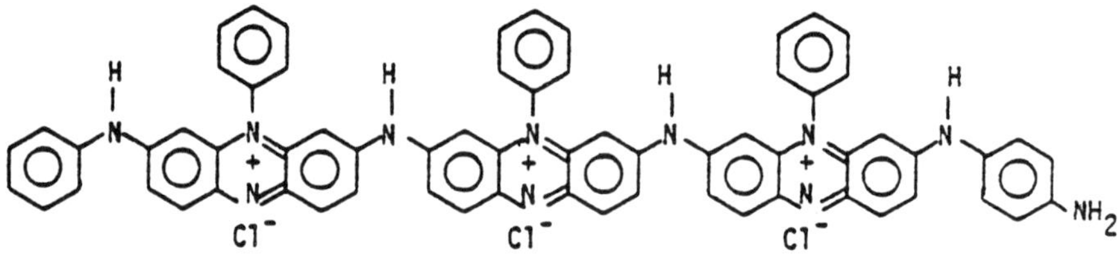

"Ungreenable" Aniline Black

Figure 7. Chemical structure of colored product of C.I. Oxidation Base 1.

The total U.S. production of mordant dyes in 1980 was only 186,000 kilograms (410,000 pounds) or less than 0.2% of the total dyestuff produced. Mordant dyes are being replaced by neutral premetallized dyes which are easier to apply especially when dyeing wool and nylon.

The 1980 ITC Report lists 15 mordant dyestuffs being produced in quantities over 2,268 kilograms (5,000 pounds) per year; these include yellow, orange, red, brown, and black shades. The 1982 AATCC Buyers Guide lists 44 mordant dye products in these same shades plus blue and green products.

Table 24 summarizes the important application properties and Table 25 summarizes the important chemical and physical properties of mordant dyes. Figure 8 presents the chemical structure of various chrome (mordant) dyes.

## 6.11 DEVELOPED DYES

Dyeing with developed dyes is essentially the same as a preliminary dyeing with a substance containing free amine groups. The amine group subsequently is diazotized with hydrochloric acid and sodium nitrite while on the fabric and coupled to other amines, phenols, or naphthols. Thus, a new azo linkage is added to the dye molecule. This allows dyestuffs which are chemically similar to direct dyes but with much higher molecular weights and resultant enhancement of shade deepness and fastness properties.

Initially, developed dyeing was considered an aftertreatment for monoazo direct cotton dyes and produced disazo blacks and blues with conjugated azo groups and disazo yellows, oranges, reds, violets, and greens in which conjugation of the two azo double bonds is blocked by an amido separating group. Developed dyes produced from direct dyes containing two reactive amine groups are moderately lightfast and extremely washfast. Some popular developing groups include: p-toluidine, 2-naphthol, and phenol. These developed dyes were the original ingrain colors (Lubs, 1955).

TABLE 24. APPLICATION PROPERTIES OF MORDANT DYES

| | | Reference |
|---|---|---|
| Fabrics dyed | Chiefly wool, but also nylon and silk. | SDC, 1971<br>Shenai, 1973<br>NSCU, 1982 |
| Fabrics printed | Slight but declining usage on wool and silk. | Clarke, 1977 |
| Leather dyeing | Used for coloring leathers but less so than for dyeing wool. | SDC, 1971 |
| Fabrics stained | | |
| Disposable fabrics | | |
| Leveling | | |
| Exhaustion | | |
| Migration | | |
| Dischargeability | Only a very few are dischargeable to white. | SDC, 1971 |
| Water solubility | Most are very soluble even in cold water. | SDC, 1971 |
| Acid fastness | | |
| Alkali fastness | Good. Index 4-5. | SDC, 1971 |
| Heat resistance | Good resistance to hot pressing. Index 3-5. | SDC, 1971 |
| Light fastness | Very good. Index 4-6. | SDC, 1971 |

(continued)

TABLE 24. APPLICATION PROPERTIES OF MORDANT DYES (continued)

| | | Reference |
|---|---|---|
| Chlorine fastness | | |
| Wash fastness | Very good to excellent (especially useful for heavy shades). | Shenai, 1973<br>NCSU, 1982 |
| Peroxide fastness | Fair to good. Index 2-5. | SDC, 1971 |
| Perspiration fastness | Good. Index 4-5. | SDC, 1971 |
| Useful colors | Lack brilliance but wide range of hues. No good blues, violets, or greens for wool. Largely used for black shades today. | Shenai, 1973<br>NCSU, 1982 |
| Bonding mechanism | Azo, acid, hydroxyl, or carbonyl groups in dye molecule coordinate bond to chromium or other metal ion (i.e. chelation). | Shenai, 1973 |
| Rate of dyeing | Dye specific. | |
| Aftertreatment | Sodium bichromate and also formic acid aftertreatment. | NCSU, 1982 |
| Dyeing process | Apply similarly to acid dyes. | NCSU, 1982 |

Index Values:

Gray scale: 1 - very poor, 2 - poor, 3 - fair, 4 - good, 5 - excellent.

Lightfastness scale: 1 - very poor, 2 - poor, 3 - fair, 4 - fairly good, 5 - good, 6 - very good, 7 - excellent, 8 - outstanding, 9 - superlative.

TABLE 25. PHYSICAL/CHEMICAL PROPERTIES OF MORDANT DYES

| | | Reference |
|---|---|---|
| Chemical structure | Azo, anthraquinone, oxazine, xanthene, triphenylmethane, nitroso, thiazine. Mostly azos for wool. | Shenai, 1973 |
| Physical state | Dye specific; usually solids. | |
| Particle size | Dye specific. | |
| Mole weight | Ranges from 170-720. Chroming subsequently increases the molecular weight about 10%. See Note 1. | Shenai, 1973 |
| Density | Dye specific. | |
| Melting point | The vast majority melts above 300°C; Mordant Red 11 melts at 290°C. | |
| Boiling point | A few dyes decompose at 250-285°C. | Aldrich, 1978 |
| Vapor pressure | Mordant Red 11 (Alizarin) boils at 430°C or may be sublimed. | Sax, 1968 |
| Water solubility | Most are very soluble in cold water. | SDC, 1971 |
| Other solubility | Dye specific. | |
| Hydrolysis | Dye specific. | |
| Partition coefficient | Dye specific. | |
| Soil adsorption/ desorption | Dye specific. | |

(continued)

TABLE 25. PHYSICAL/CHEMICAL PROPERTIES OF MORDANT DYES (continued)

| | | Reference |
|---|---|---|
| Dissociation constant | Dye specific. | |
| Spectra | Characteristics of metals present. | |
| Toxicity | Mordant Orange 1 is rated as an Allergen 1. | Sax, 1978 |

Note 1: Extremely varied molecular weights yet characteristic of their chemical class.

Nitroso: 170-190
Anthraquinone: 240-510
Thiazine: 370
Oxazine: 360-410
Xanthene: 360-490
Triphenylmethane: 460-720
Monoazo: 260-460
Disazo: 515-600

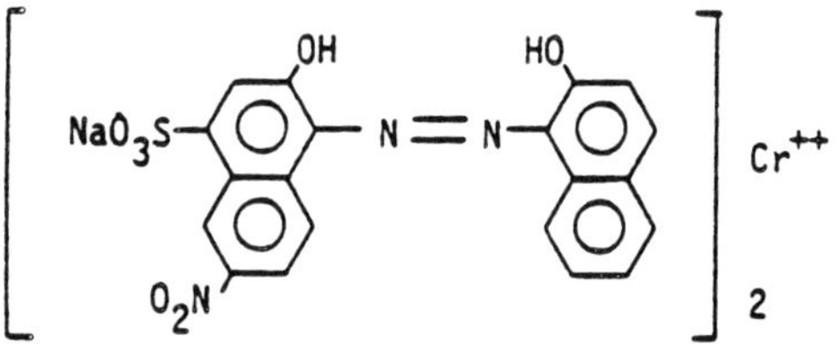

C.I. Mordant Black 11 - Monoazo

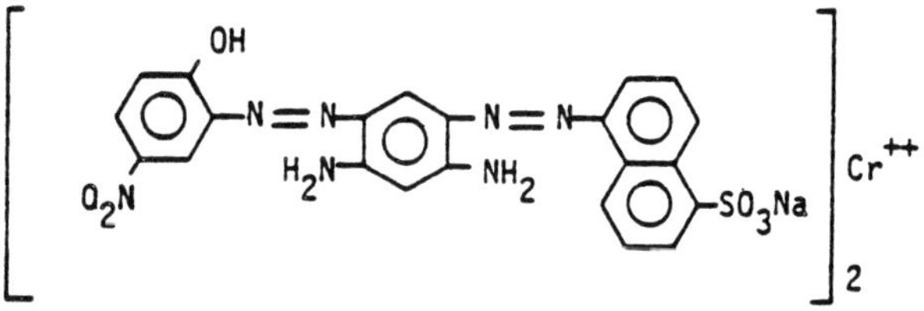

C.I. Mordant Brown 1

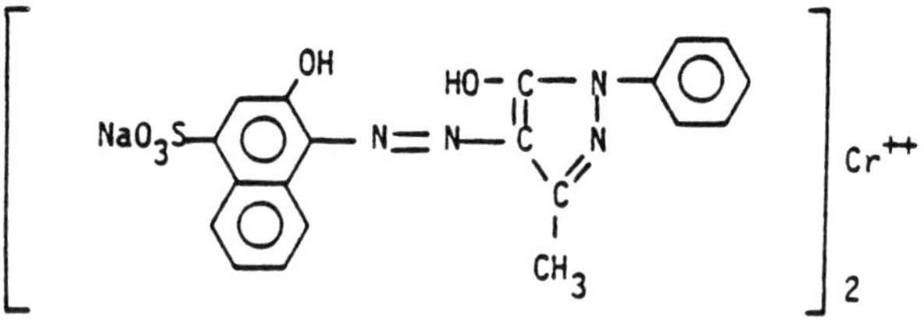

C.I. Mordant Red 7 - Pyrazolone azo

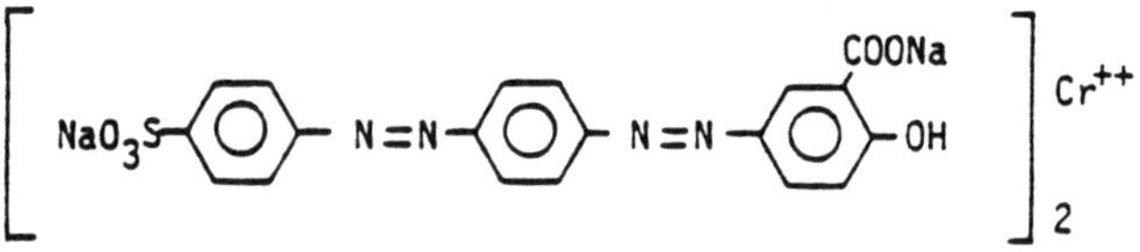

C.I. Mordant Orange 6 - Disazo

Figure 8. Chemical structures of various chrome (mordant) dyes.

Although not as universally applicable as with direct dyes, certain disperse dyes are now being develop dyed. This process renders many disperse dyeings washfast where otherwise they are not (Colour Index, 1971).

Some C.I. Developers are also listed as C.I. Azoic and Diazo Components and as C.I. Oxidation Bases.

Based on the 1982 AATCC Buyer's Guide and other references it appears that the following C.I. Developers are of commercial importance: C.I. Developers 1, 5, 8, 13, 14, and 17. Developer 1 is water soluble and is used to develop yellow, orange, and green direct dyeings. Developer 5 is soluble in aqueous sodium hydroxide and develops all direct dyeings except yellows; it is also used for developing navy and black direct dyeings on leather. Developer 8 is also soluble in aqueous sodium hydroxide and is employed to develop blue, navy, and black disperse dyeings. Developer 13 and 14 are both water soluble and develop direct browns, navys, and blacks. Developer 14 is also Oxidation Base 20 and is used to develop navys and blacks on leather. Developer 17 is nitroaniline (also Azoic Diazo Component 37) and is universally used (SDC, 1971).

Figure 9 shows the structures of these compounds.

## 6.12 VAT DYES

### 6.12.1 General Description

Vat dyes are so called because they are employed in the "vatting" process - a reversible chemical reduction procedure used to solubilize and then precipitate a dye. Vat dyes are naturally water insoluble indigonoids and anthraquinoids. The latter is the most commonly used and has the better fastness properties. A select number of the indigonoids are employed chiefly for their brilliant colors. Vat dyes in general are used for dull shades on cellulosic fibers.

Vat dyes have maintained a significant share of the dye market in the U.S. and are usually the dyestuff of choice for ultimate fastness on cotton and other cellulosics. Their level of usage has reached a stable plateau and is closely tied to the demand for cellulosic fibers (Sollenberger, 1982).

C.I. Developer 1
3-methyl-1-phenyl-5-pyrazolone

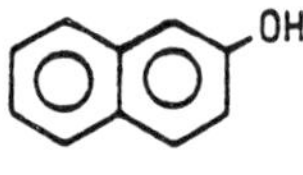


C.I. Developer 5
2-naphthol or (beta-naphthol)

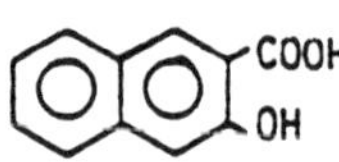


C.I. Developer 8
3-hydroxy-2-naphthoic acid (BON acid)

C.I. Developer 13
p-phenylenediamine

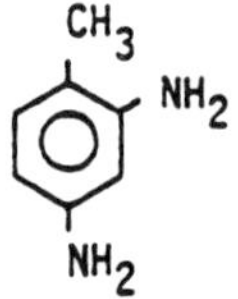


C.I. Developer 14
toluene-2,4-diamine

C.I. Developer 17
p-nitroaniline

Figure 9. Chemical structures of various C.I. Developers.

6.12.2 Color Categories of Vat Dyes

The total U.S. production of vat dyes in 1980 was 18.2 million kilograms (40.2 million pounds) or 16.0% of the total dyestuff production. The vat blues by far dominated in production, but no major products were cited (ITC, 1980). Historically, Vat Blue 6, Vat Green 1, and Vat Green 6 have been the most commercially important products (Klingsberg, 1980). The 1980 ITC report reports vat dye products in the following color categories and proportions.

| Color Category | Percent of Total Vat Dyes |
|---|---|
| Vat Blues | 75.8% |
| Vat Browns | 6.8% |
| Vat Blacks | 5.1% |
| Vat Greens | 4.8% |
| Vat Yellows | 3.1% |
| Vat Violets | 1.7% |
| Vat Reds | 1.5% |
| Vat Oranges | 1.2% |
| | 100.0% |

6.12.3 Application Properties of Vat Dyes

Vat dyes are applied continuously or by exhaust methods to cotton, rayon, cellulosic blends, and to a lesser extent nylon. The exhaust procedure is essentially the same as the continuous except that it is performed in an aqueous medium.

The application of vat dyes is essentially a four-step process. In the first step the vat dye is reduced and solubilized to aid application. In the second step, the textile is dyed with the soluble leuco vat dye in a strongly alkaline bath. Exhaustion is controlled either by retarding or exhausting agents depending on the particular fiber affinity of the dye. Thirdly, the original insoluble vat dye is reformed by oxidation using either air bubbling at the specific location, or oxidation with $Na_2Cr_2O_7$, $NaBO_2$, $KIO_3$ or $H_2O_2$. Finally, the dyeing is aftertreated.

Boiling the dye in soap or detergent solutions aggregates the insoluble dye molecules and influences the shade via the dye particle size (Shenai, 1973).

Vat dyes are available as powders, pastes, and dispersions. The powder forms must be pasted before use, but offer the advantage of stability when long shelf life is needed. These pastes contain 10-30% of the pure vat dye product, plus the critical dispersion agents and additives needed to adjust the pH to 8-9.5 (Sollenberger, 1982).

Vat dyes may be sub-divided into four application groups. The characteristics used to separate the dyes into groups are as follows (Shenai, 1973):

1) Ease of reduction
2) Ease of dissolution of the leuco vat form
3) Inherent affinity toward cellulose
4) Rate and extent of exhaustion
5) Dyeing temperature
6) Alkalinity of dye bath
7) Ease of re-oxidation
8) Chemical stability towards hydrolysis, dehalogenation, over-reduction, and over-oxidation
9) Effect of retarding and exhausting agents
10) Effectiveness of aftertreatment

Vat dyes are particularly well suited for dull shades where extreme wash fastness, extreme chlorine resistance, and shade reproducibility are chief concerns. The anthraquinone types generally have the best fastness properties.

The main disadvantages of vat dyeing are the multi-step process required and the numerous auxiliary chemicals needed. The vat dyestuff must first be reduced to a water soluble form with caustic and then oxidized after being applied to the fabric. Chelating agents, wetting agents, migration agents, and sequestering agents are all required to achieve predictable dyeing.

Table 26 summarizes the important application properties of vat dyes.

TABLE 26. APPLICATION PROPERTIES OF VAT DYES

| | | Reference |
|---|---|---|
| Fabrics dyed | Dull shades on cellulose, particularly cotton and rayon. | AATCC, 1981 |
| Fabrics printed | Cotton, linen, and rayons. | Clarke, 1977 |
| Leather dyeing | Not applied. | |
| Fabrics stained | Some staining results on polyester in cotton blends caused by the presence of impurities in the dyestuff. | Sollenberger, 1982 |
| Disposable fabrics | | |
| Leveling | Widely varied. Those containing pyrene groups level well. Retarding agents improve leveling quality enough to match any other dye class. | Shenai, 1973<br>Sollenberger, 1982 |
| Exhaustion | Widely varied. Most use salt to expedite exhaustion. A few use retarding agents to control exhaustion. | Shenai, 1973 |
| Migration | Exhaustion agents must be used to aid migration during dyeing. The smaller and less crystalline the dyestuff, the better the migration. Antimigration agents also must be used to limit migration during drying. | Sollenberger, 1982 |
| Dischargeability | Variable. | |
| Water solubility | Only slightly soluble. More soluble than pigments yet less than disperse dyes. See Note 1. | Patterson, 1972<br>SDC, 1974 |
| Acid fastness | May depend on final finish. | |

(continued)

TABLE 26. APPLICATION PROPERTIES OF VAT DYES (continued)

| | | Reference |
|---|---|---|
| Alkali fastness | May depend on final finish. | |
| Heat resistance | Dye specific. | |
| Light fastness | Excellent for anthraquinone vat dyes; unsurpassed fastness on cotton. | AATCC, 1981 |
| Chlorine fastness | Fair to good. | |
| Wash fastness | Excellent for anthraquinone vat dyes; unsurpassed fastness on cotton. | AATCC, 1981 |
| Peroxide fastness | Fair. | |
| Perspiration fastness | | |
| Useful colors | Indigonoid types have limited color range and application complications so anthraquinone vat dyes are mainly used. Vat dyes are comparatively dull in shade. See Note 2. | SDC, 1974 |
| Bonding mechanism | Mechanical retention of insoluble dye molecule within fiber structure. | Shenai, 1973 |
| Rate of dyeing | Dye specific; dyeing involves multiple steps. | |
| Pretreatment | Bleaching and mercerizing. | AATCC, 1981 |
| Aftertreatment | Boiling in soap solution to fix the dyestuff is always done. | AATCC, 1981<br>Sollenberger, 1982 |

(continued)

TABLE 26. APPLICATION PROPERTIES OF VAT DYES (continued)

| | | Reference |
|---|---|---|
| Dyeing process | Continuous pad-steaming, exhaust, package, printing. | AATCC, 1981<br>Horning, 1978 |
| Typical equipment used | Package machine, continuous pad-tenter frame. | Horning, 1978 |

Note 1: Anthraquinone vat dyes are water-solubilized by alkaline reduction to their acid hydroxyl derivatives and then re-oxidized to fix them on the fabric. Hydrogen peroxide or sodium perborate is used to oxidize vat dyes after exhaustion. Caustic soda is used to reduce and solubilize dyes prior to application (to their leuco form).

Note 2: All vat dye manufacturers standardize the hue and intensity of their products to within 2.5% of a preferred color value determined spectrophotometrically (Sollensberger, 1982).

6.12.4 Chemical and Physical Properties

Vat dyes are almost always hard to purify, extremely high melting solids. Some new synthetic derivatives melt at or around 130°C but most products melt above 200°C. Although the polynuclear anthraquinone vat dyes are usually very high melting and hard to purify, some decompose with unexpected ease. When ether groups are added to the anthraquinone dye molecule, the resulting products melt at around 200°C and are not recrystallized from nitrobenzene (Klingsberg, 1980).

The synthetically polynuclear, condensed aromatic anthraquinoids are derived from 1) self-condensing diazotized aminonaphthoic acids which are characterized by carbonyl linkages bridging aromatic rings, 2) fusing naphthalimides to other condensed aromatic structures, or 3) the most widely used method - vapor phase oxidation of anthracene to anthraquinone at 150-260°C using oxygen and a vanadium oxide catalyst (Sollenberger, 1982). Indigonoids are derived by ring-closure reactions of aromatic acetanilides.

The solubilization of vat dyes prior to textile application involves first a sodium hydrosulfite reduction of the quinone ketone groups into hydroxyl groups. The resulting weakly acidic but insoluble leuco-form is transformed into soluble vat dye products by using caustic to form the sodium salt of this form. After application, the original quinoid diketone is obtained by air oxidation (Shenai, 1973).

The presence of certain chemical groups in the vat dye molecule may be used to predict such properties as color, affinity, brightness, leveling, exhaustion, dyeing temperature, and stability toward hydrolysis (Shenai, 1973). The commercially important vat blues contain such groups as thiazole, acridone, indanthrone, and perylene. The latter two types require hot alkaline application while the former may be applied under less severe conditions.

Table 27 is a summary of the more important chemical and physical properties of vat dyes. Figure 10 presents chemical structures of various vat dyes.

TABLE 27. PHYSICAL/CHEMICAL PROPERTIES OF VAT DYES

| | | Reference |
|---|---|---|
| Chemical structure | Two main chemical classes: anthraquinone and indigonoid. Most new products are anthraquinones which are much more flexible. See Note 4. | |
| Physical state | Physical form is important since solubility is low. See Note 1. Commercial forms are pastes, powders, and dispersions. | Patterson, 1972<br>Shenai, 1973 |
| Particle size | 0.2-1.0 microns. Particle sizes below 3 microns are much easier to reduce chemically (one-third the reaction time). See Note 2. | Patterson, 1972<br>Sollenberger, 1982 |
| Mole weight | The molecular weights of vat dyes vary widely from 350-1,100 gm/mole. The average is about 670 gm/mole for a 42 carbon structure. | Shenai, 1973 |
| Density | Dye specific. | |
| Melting point | Refractory solids. Most melt above 200°C except for some new synthetic derivatives which melt at around 130°C. | Klingsberg, 1980 |
| Boiling point | Most do not boil. See Note 5. | Noller, 1958 |
| Vapor pressure | Very low except for decomposition products. | |
| Water solubility | Only slightly soluble. More soluble than pigments, less than disperse dyes. See Note 3. | Pattersone, 1972<br>SDC, 1974 |
| Other solubility | Most are insoluble or slightly soluble in alcohol, acetone, and xylene. A few are soluble in xylene, nitrobenzene, or naphthalene. | SDC, 1971 |

(continued)

TABLE 27. PHYSICAL/CHEMICAL PROPERTIES OF VAT DYES (continued)

| | | Reference |
|---|---|---|
| Hydrolysis | Susceptible to hydrolysis, particularly the vats containing acylamino, anthrimide, carbazole, and pyrimidine chemical groups. | Shenai, 1973 |
| Partition coefficient | Dye specific. | |
| Soil adsorption/ desorption | Dye specific. | |
| Dissociation constant | Dye specific. | |
| Spectra | The dull shades of vat dyes are generally indicate very broad and ill-defined absorption peaks. The extended condensed aromatic structures result in high UV absorption. | |
| Toxicity | Many of the high molecular weight polynuclear aromatic (PNA) vat dyes may be of environmental concern. | |
| Biodegradation | Vat Blue 6 has been found to show a photodegradation of 57% in 200 hours in a wastewater photodegradation study. Actual photodegradation under natural light is thought to be about ten times slower. | Porter, 1973 |

(continued)

TABLE 27. PHYSICAL/CHEMICAL PROPERTIES OF VAT DYES (continued)

Note 1: Vat dyes in their final form are technically pigments; once dissolved they behave similarly to direct dyes. The physical form of the dye is a major concern and affects the dispersion qualities, stability, flocculation, ease of reduction, and ease of application.

Note 2: Vat dyes actually aggregate and form fine microcrystals upon final process soaping.

Note 3: Anthraquinone vat dyes are water-solubilized by caustic soda reduction to their acid hydroxyl derivatives and subsequently re-oxidized for fixation on the fabric using oxidizing agents.

Note 4: Three varieties of the important anthraquinone vat dyes exist. Self-condensation products of two to five aminoanthraquinone molecules make up one large group. Another large group consists of six to eleven ring condensed polynuclear aromatics (PNA) with ketone bridges. A third smaller group consists of thiazole, amidizole, and carbazole structures.

Note 5: Vat Blue 4, consisting of two aminoanthraquinone groups, is one of the most stable organic compounds known. It can be heated in air to 470°C, with caustic to 300°C, and with strong hydrochloric acid to 400°C without decomposition. Vat Blue 6 is the dichloro derivative of Vat Blue 4.

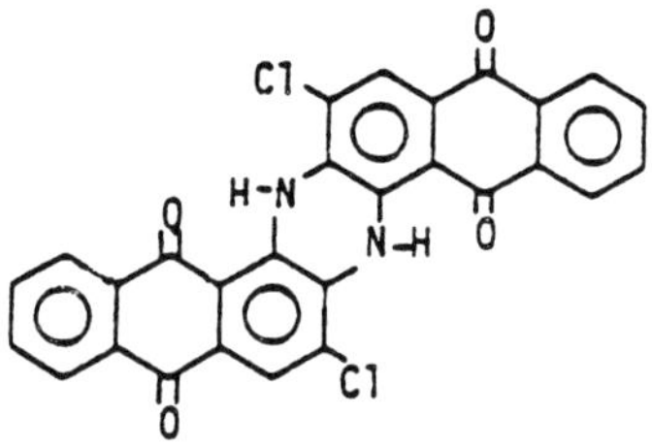

C.I. Vat Blue 6

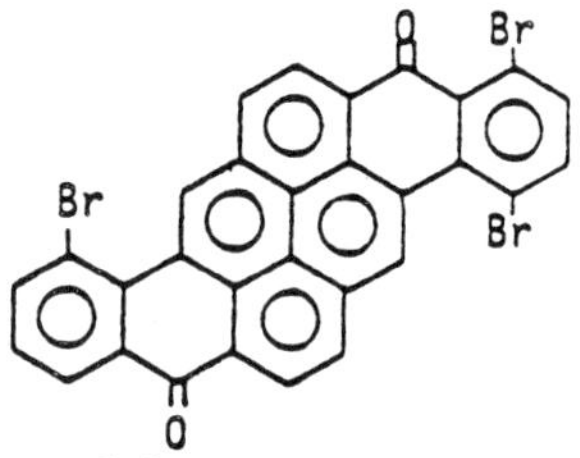

C.I. Vat Orange 2

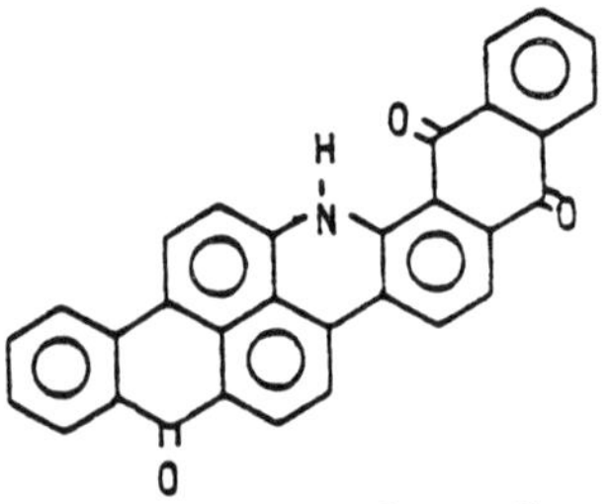

C.I. Vat Green 3

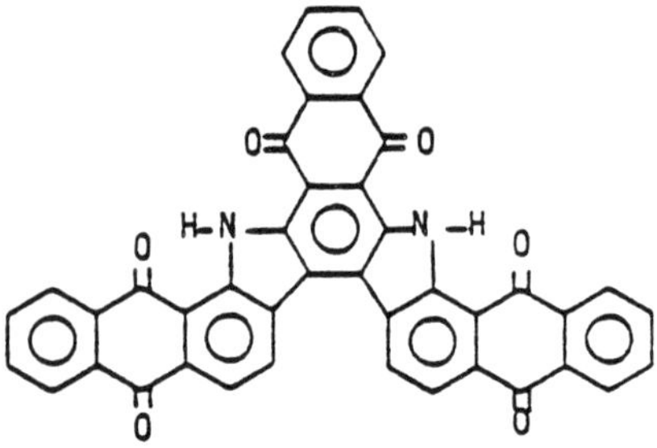

C.I. Vat Brown 1

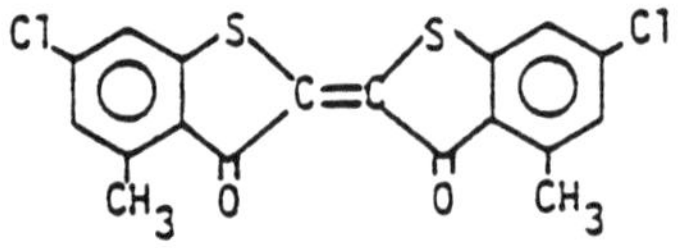

C.I. Vat Red 1 - Thioindigoid

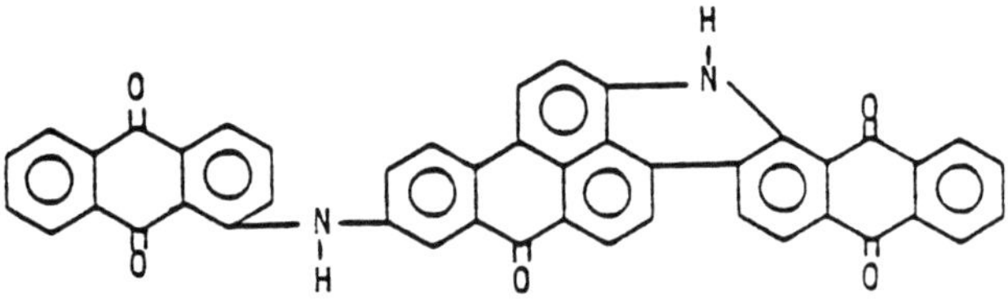

C.I. Vat Black 25

Figure 10. Chemical structures of various vat dyes.

## 6.13 PIGMENTS

Pigments are distinguished from dyes by their general insolubility in water and organic solvents. A number of organic pigments are prepared from dyes by combining the dye with a dye precipitant. This accounts for about one-sixth of the total end use of organic dyestuffs. Total production of organic pigments in the United States was 31.5 million kilograms (69.4 million pounds) in 1980. This included 31.1 million kilograms (68.5 million pounds) in the form of full strength toners and 0.04 million kilograms (0.8 million pounds) of lakes, which are toners mixed with inert inorganic materials. These organic pigments are largely derived from benzenoid chemicals (ITC, 1980). Organic pigments are purer and brighter in color than are the corresponding inorganic pigment colors.

Inorganic pigments include oxides, sulfates, carbonates, silicates, and chromates of many heavy metal elements including: titanium, zinc, barium, lead, antimony, zirconium, calcium, aluminum, magnesium, cadmium, iron, molybdenum, and chromium. Several metal complexes are also important as are naturally occurring oxides and silicates. Inorganic pigments are generally less expensive, more weather resistant, and more chemical resistant then the corresponding organic pigment colors.

### 6.13.1 Pigment Products

6.13.1.1 Organic Pigments. Of the total production of organic pigments, yellow, red, and blue toners accounted for 89% or 27.0 million kilograms (61.7 million pounds) in 1980 (ITC, 1980).

| Color Category | Percent of Total Organic Pigments |
|---|---|
| Red toners | 35.1% |
| Yellow toners | 28.6% |
| Blue toners | 25.2% |
| Green toners | 3.5% |
| Violet toners | 3.3% |
| Orange toners | 2.4% |
| Red lakes | 0.6% |
| Brown toners | 0.4% |
| Black toners | 0.2% |
| Yellow lakes | <0.1% |
| Other lakes | 0.5% |
| | 100.0% |

### 6.13.2 Outstanding Volume Products

#### 6.13.2.1 Organic Pigments.

| CI Name | Percent of Total Organic Pigments |
|---|---|
| Pigment Blue 15, 15:1, 15:2, 15:3 | 13.2% |
| Pigment Yellow 12 | 12.1% |
| Pigment Red 49:1 | 7.4% |
| Pigment Red 57:1 | 5.3% |
| Pigment Red 53:1 | 4.2% |
| Pigment Yellow 14 | 3.6% |
| Pigment Green 7 | 3.1% |
| Other Diarylide Yellows (Pigment Yellow 13, 17, etc.) | 2.9% |
| Pigment Yellow 74 | 1.9% |
| Pigment Violet 19 | 1.8% |
| Pigment Red 48:2 | 1.6% |
| Pigment Red 3 | 1.5% |
| | 58.6% |

### 6.13.3 Application Properties of Pigments

Pigments are sold as 45% ground materials, 40% flushed pigments in oil or shellac, and about 5% filter presscakes (Bomberger, 1981).

Inorganic or organic pigments have no inherent affinity for textile fibers. Recently there have been major developments in the coloration and printing of textiles using resin-bonded pigments. In fact, these materials have a separate listing in the AATCC Buyer's Guide which include 18 such products formulated specifically for application to textiles. The application properties of these resin-bonded pigments are a function of the chemical properties of the binder itself and not as directly related to the actual pigment. Resin-bonded pigments are applied continuously along with binders for printing or pad, dry and cure procedures (AATCC, 1981). The pigment/binder emulsion polymerizes and the resin affixes the pigment to the fiber surface.

Inorganic pigments consist of the salts and oxides of iron, titanium, and chromium, etc. They offer the highest degree of lightfastness available, excellent heat resistance, and insolubility in most organic solvents (Patton, 1973).

Organic azo pigments generally have strong tinctorial strength. Most have good alkali resistance, excellent brightness, and cover a wide range with regard to the other application properties. However, the poor alkali resistance of certain organometallic pigments makes them unsuitable for printing. The diarylide oranges and yellows yield extremely bright colors but are inferior in lightfastness to the Hansa Yellows. The disadvantages of the Hansa Yellows is their migration tendency. Phthalocyanine blues and greens dominate pigment usage for these shades, especially in plastic coloration. They offer low migration, good lightfastness, and good temperature stability. In addition, they are compatible with any resin type except fluorocarbons and provide an antioxidant affect for plastics (Patton, 1973).

Five (5) pigment application systems for textiles (Patton, 1973) include:

1) Aqueous dispersion
2) Solvent dispersion
3) Water-in-oil emulsion (w/o)
4) Oil-in-water emulsion (o/w)
5) Dope dyeing

Pigment dyeing with binders is practiced using padding techniques and yields very washfast and lightfast dyeings. The advantages of this type of dyeing are the fact that potentially any fiber can be colored using a suitable binder and that it can be used to color certain blends that are often difficult to color using other dyeing techniques. Dope dyeing is a special technique in which pigments or solvent dyes are mixed into a melt of the textile polymer before the spinning operation which produces the fiber (Shenai, 1973).

Approximately 75% of all textile printing (usually on cottons) is done with pigments since they are less expensive and more easily applied than other dyes. Another great advantage of pigment printing over dye printing is that with the former there is no change in the hue of the colorant throughout processing. Dye prints frequently come out of final processing with no resemblance to the original color. Water-in-oil emulsions are the most popular pigment dyes (Patton, 1973). Further advantages of pigment printing include: the simplicity of the application process, the fact that no aftertreatment is required, the extensive color range of highly lightfast colors, and the applicability to all fibers, even polyesters, blends, and glass fibers which are hard to print with other dyes. The disadvantages of pigment printing include: the presence of solvent in the emulsions, the gumming up of process equipment, the fact that binders change the texture of the fabric, and the difficulty in obtaining the necessary wet treatment fastness and abrasion resistance with certain products (Shenai, 1973). The requirements for a suitable pigment for printing include (Shenai, 1973):

1) good lightfastness, wetfastness, and abrasion resistance;
2) good resistance to acid, base, perspiration, chlorine, and peroxide;

3) good solvent resistance (i.e. insoluble in $H_2O$, carbon tetrachloride, trichloroethylene, and perchloroethylene);

4) suitable brilliance, hardness, and stability; and

5) suitable characteristics for good dispersion including: particle size and distribution, electrical charge (most are negatively charged particles), specific gravity, purity, and crystalline structure.

Pigments can be printed both by roller and screen methods using discharge, resist, and direct styles of printing. The application steps are (Shenai, 1973):

1) preparation of a pigment paste using dispersion agents and solvents;

2) application of pigment paste and binding resin together onto the fabric;

3) drying at 140-150°C;

4) steam* or dry heat curing to fix the resin-pigment; and

5) washing and hot soaping.

Resin binders with a particle size range of 0.05 to 2 microns usually are available. These contain about 6% by weight of reactive groups for crosslinking the pigment to the textile. The fiber bonding process is acid catalyzed and reversible, but removal of the water or methyl alcohol formed in the binding reaction drives the binding reaction forward. The acrylate co-polymer resins are of particular interest for their high binding power to almost all fabric substrates (Shenai, 1973).

Some important requirements of the resin are as follows (Patton, 1973).

1) should be film-forming
2) should not water swell
3) should not saponify

---

* Dyes are generally fixed (or aged) by steam, not pigments.

4) should not hydrolyze
5) should not be too stiff
6) should not be too thermoplastic
7) should have atmospheric stability

The most important categories of resins used are the following (Patton, 1973).

1) naturally occuring resins (ex. albumen, casein, etc.)
2) synthetic cellulose derivatives
3) acrylate, alkyd, and alkyl resins
4) melamine
5) methacrylate
6) phenol-formaldehyde
7) urea-formaldehyde
8) polyvinyl condensates
9) butadiene copolymers
10) styrene-maleic acids

Each of these resins is suitable for a particular application and has unique advantages (Kent, 1974).

| Resin Type | Advantage |
|---|---|
| Oils | ease of application, solubility in aliphatic solvents |
| Alkyds | all purpose, soluble in most aliphatic solvents |
| Cellulosics | used in fast dry lacquers |
| Acrylics | good durability and color stability |
| Vinyls | good durability and abrasion resistance |
| Phenolics | good chemical resistance; (yellows especially) |
| Epoxies | good chemical resistance |
| Polyurethane | flexibility; abrasion resistance |
| Silicones | good heat resistance |

| Resin Type | Advantage |
|---|---|
| Amino Resins (ureas & melamines) | tough; good color |
| Styrene-butadiene | low cost; alkali resistance |
| Polyvinyl Acetates | low cost; good color stability |

Table 28 summarizes the important application properties of pigments.

6.13.4 Chemical and Physical Properties

Pigments Blue 15 and Green 7 are derivatives of copper phthalocyanine, which is an extremely large molecule resembling the porphin structure of hemoglobin. Pigment Blue 15 is prepared by heating phthalic anhydride with urea and cuprous chloride. Pigment Green 7 is usually prepared by chlorinating Blue 15.

Pigment yellows such as the Hansa Yellows (Pigments Yellow 1, 3, 79, etc.) are monoazo compounds prepared by coupling substituted anilines with acetoacetanilides. The extremely important diarylide yellows such as Pigments Yellow 12, 13, 14, and 17 are disazo compounds prepared by coupling diazotized dichlorobenzidine to acetoaletanilides.

Pigments Red 49 and 1 are monoazo pigments derived from coupling beta-naphthols and naphthalene sulfonic acids.

Table 29 summarizes the important chemical and physical properties of pigments. Figure 11 presents the chemical structures of various pigments.

## 6.14 OPTICAL BRIGHTENERS/FLUORESCENT BRIGHTENERS

6.14.1 General Description

Today the manufacture and application of optical brightening agents is a very dynamic and growing business. These products are also frequently referred to as fluorescent whitening agents (FWA's). Over 340 fluorescent brightening agents are currently listed by the Colour Index and many of those listed are now obsolete, but just as many new products have not yet been cataloged. The 1980 U.S. production volume of fluorescent brighteners was 17.2 million kilograms (37.9 million pounds), a 12.7% rise from 1979. Imports of optical brightners into the United States in 1980 accounted for 313,198 kilograms (690,472 pounds), or approximately

TABLE 28. APPLICATION PROPERTIES OF PIGMENTS

| | | Reference |
|---|---|---|
| Fabrics dyed | Any fiber may be dyed by selecting a suitable binder. See Note 1. | AATCC, 1981 |
| Fabrics printed | Any fiber can be printed by using the appropriate binder, even the hard to print polyester, blends and glass fibers. | Shenai, 1973 |
| Leather dyeing | Not applicable. | |
| Fabrics stained | Not applicable. | |
| Disposable fabrics | Well suited for coloring nonwoven fabrics. See Note 2. | EDANA, 1974<br>Apparel Institute, 1963 |
| Leveling | Applies only to pigment dyeing. | |
| Exhaustion | Applies only to pigment dyeing. | |
| Migration | Migration is considered a detrimental property in pigmentation and is a disadvantage characteristic of the Hansa Yellows. | Patton, 1973 |
| Dischargeability | Some pigments are suitable for discharge printing. | Shenai, 1973 |
| Water solubility | Insoluble for all practical purposes; significantly less soluble than vat dyes. | Patterson, 1972 |
| Acid fastness | | |
| Alkali fastness | Poor for organometallic azo toners. Good for insoluble azo. | |

(continued)

TABLE 28. APPLICATION PROPERTIES OF PIGMENTS (continued)

| | | Reference |
|---|---|---|
| Heat resistance | Extremely varied. Some are stable to 200°C, some up to 300°C. Optimum for inorganic pigments. | AATCC, 1981 |
| Light fastness | Generally very good. Good for azoic reds. Optimum for inorganic pigments. Hansa Yellows better than Diarylides. | AATCC, 1981<br>Morgans |
| Chlorine fastness | | |
| Wash fastness | Generally good to very good. | Morgans |
| Peroxide fastness | | |
| Perspiration fastness | | |
| Useful colors | Diarylide yellows and oranges, Hansa yellows, Azoic reds, Phthalocyanine blues and greens, Carbon blacks, Titanium dioxide whites, violets and browns. | |
| Bonding mechanism | Bound to fabric surface by organic resin binders. | |
| Speed of dyeing | | |
| Aftertreatment | None required. | Shenai, 1973 |
| Processes used | Padding of dyeing. | Morgans |

Note 1: The quality of the dyeing or print depends on the characteristics of the binder used to affix the pigment even more than on the properties of the pigment.

Note 2: Nonwoven fabrics may be colored using pigments and a variety of methods. Disposable nonwoven goods are suitable for pigment printing either by roller or screen printing methods. Also, nonwoven goods may be colored by dope dyeing of synthetic fibers with pigments or by adding pigments to the bonding agents which are used to form the loose fibers into fabric. The newer polyester and polyethylene nonwoven fabrics may be colored as well as the cotton nonwoven fabrics.

TABLE 29. PHYSICAL/CHEMICAL PROPERTIES OF PIGMENTS

| | | Reference |
|---|---|---|
| Chemical structure | 1) Inorganic Oxides<br>2) Inorganic Salts<br>3) Organic Insoluble Azo Compounds<br>4) Organometallic Toners<br>5) Phthalocyanine Metal Complexes | Patton, 1973 |
| Physical state | Physical state is very important since there is no water solubility. See Note 1. | Patterson, 1972 |
| Particle size | Some commercial brands are 99% below 44 microns and size distribution peaks at 5-7 micron (3). See Note 1. | Day-Glo, 1981a<br>Shenai, 1973 |
| Mole weight | Variable; pigment specific. | |
| Density | Specific gravity of phthalocyanines is 1.6. Specific gravities range from 1.14-1.37 for most. | Day-Glo, 1981a<br>NIOSH, 1979 |
| Melting point | Softening points range 110-175°C. Pigment Red 3 melts at 270°C. | Day-Glo, 1981a<br>Aldrich, 1978 |
| Boiling point | Decompose at 195-345°C. Phthalocyanine pigments sublime at 500°C. | Day-Glo, 1981a<br>Woller, 1958 |
| Vapor pressure | Pigment specific. | |
| Water solubility | Insoluble for all practical purposes. Significantly less soluble than vat dyes. | Patterson, 1972 |
| Other solubility | Inorganic pigments are insoluble in most solvents. Azoic reds have poor solvent resistance. Benzidine yellows are more solvent resistant than Hansa Yellows. | Patton, 1973<br>NIOSH, 1979 |

(continued)

TABLE 29. PHYSICAL/CHEMICAL PROPERTIES OF PIGMENTS (continued)

| | | Reference |
|---|---|---|
| Hydrolysis | Pigment specific and usually stable. | |
| Partition coefficient | Pigment specific and pigments are usually insoluble. | |
| Soil adsorption/ desorption | Pigment specific; probably low migration rates. | |
| Dissociation constant | Not applicable. | |
| Spectra | Very strong and high, though not comparatively sharp peaks. | Day-Glo, 1981a |
| Quantum yield | Fluorescent pigments are available which can reflect 200-300% of incident color while nonfluorescing pigments reflect up to 90% the incident light. | Day-Glo, 1981a |
| Toxicity | Pigment specific; a typical pigment shows:<br>Oral toxicity: $LD_{50}$ 10-23 g/kg<br>Dermal toxicity: $LD_{50}$ 10.2-23.0 g/kg<br>Acute dose inhalation: $LC_{50}$ 1.1-8.3 mg/L (air, 4 hours)<br>Some cause mild eye irritation (Day-Glo, 1981g). The diarylide yellows and oranges are produced from dichlorobenzidine which is listed by both OSHA and NIOSH as a positive animal carcinogen. The phthalocyanine pigments may contain traces of polychlorobiphenyls (PCB's) arising from side reactions of trichlorobenzene (TCB) as a solvent in their manufacture (Gaffey, 1977) (Uyeta and Taue, 1976). | NIOSH, 1979<br>Gaffey, 1977<br>Uyeta and Taye, 1976 |

Note 1: When three ranges of particle size were compared it was found that decreasing size yields increasing color value but decreasing hiding power. These particle size ranges studied were 1) 0.4 to 0.8 microns 2) 0.2 to 0.4 microns, and 3) 0.05 to 0.1 microns (Patterson, 1972). One pigment product supplies five series of pigments which have the following average particle size ranges in microns (Day-Glo, 1981a): 3.5-4, 4-5, 3-4, 10-12, and random coarse particles. Another source cites commercial pigment dispersions as being in the range of 0.1 to 1.0 micron, with the maximum tinctorial strength at 0.2 to 0.5 micron and showing increasing color strength with decreasing particle size (Shenai, 1973).

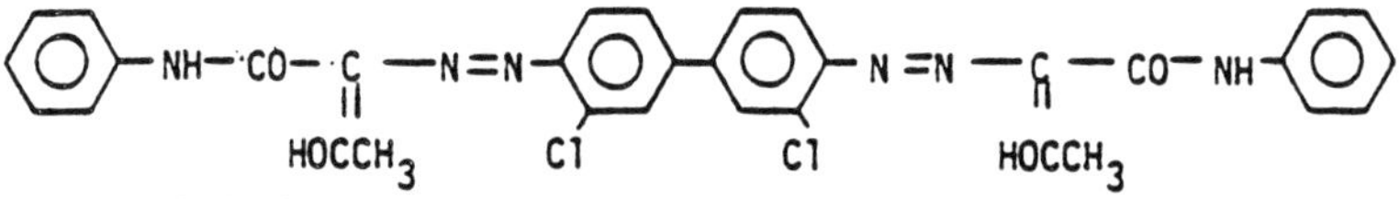

C.I. Pigment Yellow 12 - Dichlorobenzidine-azo type

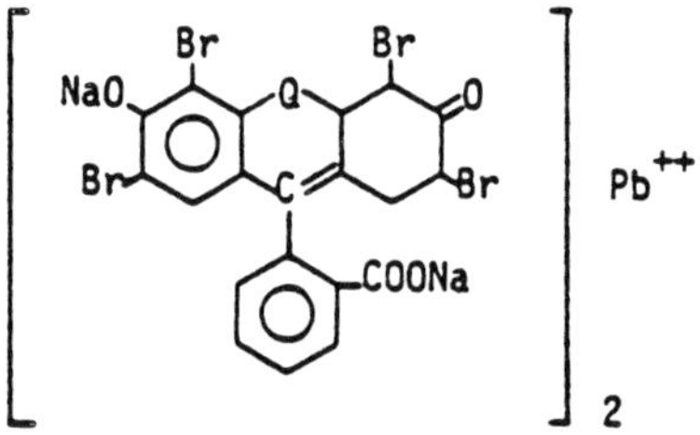

C.I. Pigment Red 90 - Lead complexed xanthene

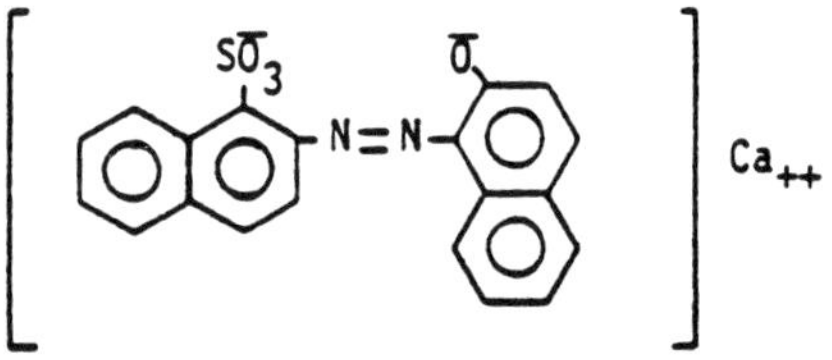

C.I. Pigment Red 49:1 - Calcium complexed azo

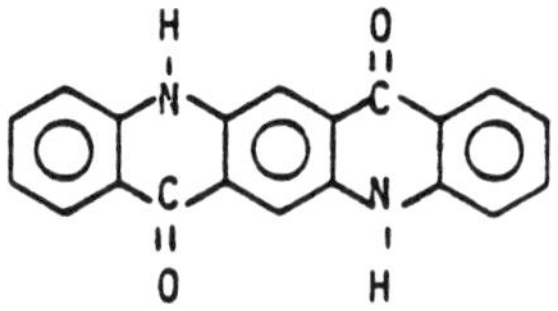

C.I. Pigment Violet 19 - Quinacridone type

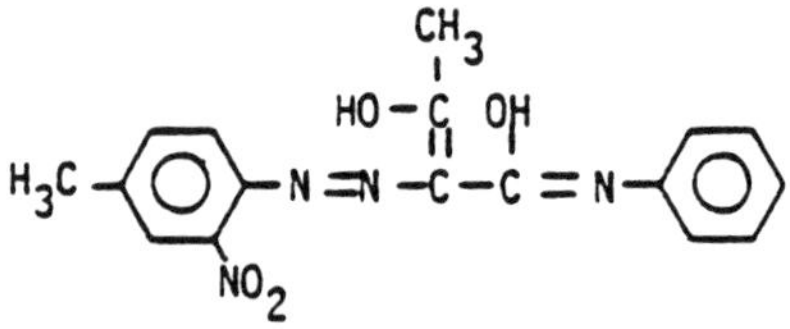

C.I. Pigment Yellow 1 - Hansa Yellow - acetoacetanilide type

Figure 11. Chemical structures of various pigments.

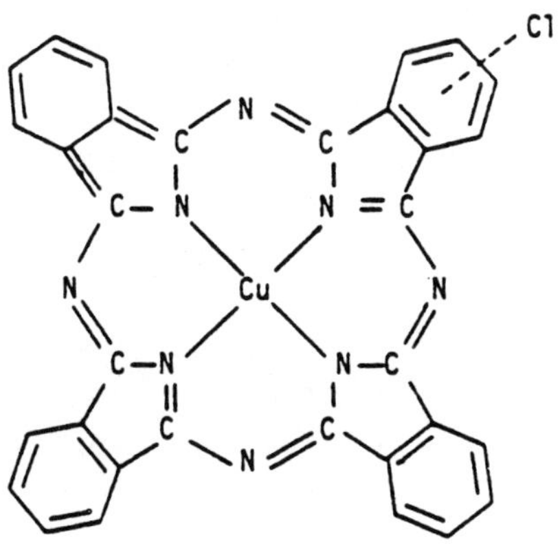

C.I. Pigment Blue 15 - Phthalocyanine type

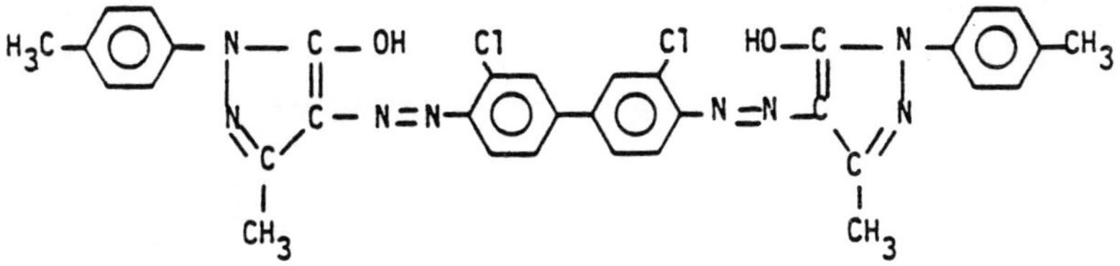

C.I. Pigment Orange 34 - Pyrazolone - dichlorobenzidine - azo type

Figure 11. (continued)

2 percent of the U.S. production volume. Twenty-seven (27) currently available products are included in the 1982 AATCC Buyers Guide and 18 are listed in the 1980 ITC Report.

6.14.2 Application Properties of Optical Brighteners or FWA's

Fluorescent whitening agents (FWA's) were originally employed only for textile finishing, but now have widespread use in paper, detergents, plastics, and paints.

It has been estimated that in 1971, 30% of all the textiles produced in the world were whites; about 20% of the fluorescent brightening agents were used to produce these materials. About 45% of the remaining volume produced were used in detergents (Kirk-Othmer 1978).

Textile fluorescent brighteners can be divided into three application categories. Anionic whiteners containing solubilizing sulfonate groups are used for cotton, wool, and polyamides (nylons). Cationic (basic) whiteners are used mostly for polyacrylonitrile fibers. Nonionic whiteners are used for polyester, acetate, polyacrylonitile, and polyamide (Kirk-Othmer, 1978). Fluorescent brighteners are applied to the textile by exhaust or padding procedures and then fixed by heat treatment.

Anionic FWA's are applied to cellulosics by exhaustion techniques or padding (and sometimes keir). Exhaustion techniques use either acid or salt as exhausting agents and a pH of 8-11 or higher. These products are powders. Products are also available with very high affinity, good light and wetfastness, and stability to peroxide and bleaches (Shenai, 1973). Anionic FWA's are applied to polyamides (nylons) in a similar acidic exhaust procedure and yield very lightfast, bleach and chlorine stable dyeings (Shenai, 1973).

Cationic FWA's are applied to acrylics, including polyacrylonitrite, at 95°C using an exhaust technique and a formic acid catalyst. Sometimes higher temperatures and pressures are required for exhaustion. These FWA's are usually pyrazoline and heterocyclic based chemicals (Shenai, 1973).

Nonionic FWA's are applied with carriers to polyester using exhaustion at boiling temperatures. Thermosol and pad-dry-bake procedures are applicable (Shenai, 1973).

Table 30 summarizes the important application properties of FWA's.

### 6.14.3 Chemical and Physical Properties

Fluorescent brighteners can be roughly classified into six broad chemical types: stilbenes, coumarins and carbostyrils, pyrazolines, naphthalimides, benzoxazolyl substituted systems, and special aromatics and heteroaromatics. These six groups include about 50 individual chemical species and 4000 commercial brands (Anliker and Miller, 1975). Most show partial water solubility and are also dispersible in water.

Table 31 summarizes the important chemical and physical properties of FWA's. Figure 12 presents the chemical structures of various optical brighteners.

## 6.15 SOLVENT DYES

Solvent dyes or oil-soluble colors are used mainly for coloration of petroleum products such as gasoline and brake fluid, and for plastics. These products are not intended for use in textiles. Recent innovations in solvent dyeing technology for textiles focus mainly on organic solvent application of disperse dyes rather than solvent dyes, per se (AATCC, 1981). Some manufacturers do not include a dispersing agent in their solvent dyes. However, many C.I. Disperse Dyes also are useful for coloring petroleum products and plastics and for that reason are cross-listed as C.I. Solvent Dyes. Some acid and basic dyes are also cross-listed (SDC, 1971).

The majority of solvent dye products are azo compounds resembling disperse monoazo dyes. Disazo and anthraquinone products also are produced. Chromium, cobalt, and iron complexed azo dyes, similar to wool dyes, are used. Also included in this category are certain oil-soluble Food, Drug, and Cosmetic (FD&C) dyestuffs. The amount used to color petroleum products is 20 to 50 milligrams per liter (Lubs, 1955). Some basic dyes are also included in this category.

### 6.15.1 Color Categories

The annual production of solvent dyes in 1980 was 4.8 million kilograms (10.6 million pounds) or about 4.3% of the total dyestuff production. Listed below is a breakdown by color category (ITC, 1980).

TABLE 30. APPLICATION PROPERTIES OF OPTICAL BRIGHTENERS (FWA's)

| | | Reference |
|---|---|---|
| Fabrics dyed | Anionic FWA's for cotton, wool, and nylon. Cationic FWA's for acrylics. Nonionic FWA's for polyester, acetate, acrylic, and nylon. | Shenai, 1973<br>Kirk-Othmer, 1978 |
| Fabrics printed | Not applicable. | |
| Leather dyeing | Not applicable. | |
| Fabrics stained | Not applicable. | |
| Disposable fabrics | Paper. | |
| Leveling | | |
| Exhaustion | Various FWA's use either salt or acid promoted exhaustion. | |
| Migration | | |
| Water solubility | Varied, slightly water-soluble. Water dispersible. | Shenai, 1973 |
| Acid fastness | Some FWA's have poor acid fastness. | |
| Alkali fastness | Many of the FWA's have good alkali fastness. | |
| Heat resistance | | |
| Light fastness | Moderate to good. | |

(continued)

TABLE 30. APPLICATION PROPERTIES OF OPTICAL BRIGHTENERS (FWA's) (continued)

| | | Reference |
|---|---|---|
| Chlorine fastness | Varied, some FWA's are extremely resistant. New triazinylaminostilbene FWA's are moderately chlorine stable. | Shenai, 1973<br>Noller, 1958 |
| Wash fastness | Dye dependent. | |
| Peroxide fastness | Poor to good. | |
| Perspiration fastness | | |
| Useful colors | Violet, blue, yellow, and red tinted fluorescent whites. | |
| Bonding mechanism | | |
| Rate of dyeing | Dye specific. | |
| Aftertreatment | Heat fixation. | Shenai, 1973 |
| Dyeing process | Exhaust, padding and kier. | Shenai, 1973 |
| Typical equipment used | Padding, kier. | |

TABLE 31. PHYSICAL/CHEMICAL PROPERTIES OF OPTICAL BRIGHTENERS (FWA's)

| | | Reference |
|---|---|---|
| Chemical structure | Variable; FWA's are based on various chemical classes. | |
| Physical state | Sold as powders and liquids. | Shenai, 1973 |
| Particle size | Dye specific. | |
| Mole weight | Ranges 176-834. See Note 1. | Shenai, 1973 |
| Density | Dye specific. | |
| Melting point | | |
| Boiling point | | |
| Vapor pressure | Dye specific. | |
| Water solubility | Vary, slightly water-soluble. Water-dispersible. | Shenai, 1973 |
| Other solubility | Dye specific. | |
| Hydrolysis | Usually stable. | |
| Partition coefficient | Dye specific. | |
| Soil adsorption/ desorption | Found not to leach from soil at dumpsites, nor to be taken up in plant roots. Believed to concentrate in river-bottom sediments. | Coulston, 1975 |

(continued)

TABLE 31. PHYSICAL/CHEMICAL PROPERTIES OF OPTICAL BRIGHTENERS (FWA's) (continued)

| | | Reference |
|---|---|---|
| Dissociation constant | Dye specific. | |
| Spectra | Stilbenes show absorption peak at 350 nm and emission at 435 nm. | Kirk-Othmer, 1978 |
| Toxicity | Though intensely debated, there exists no direct evidence of toxicity to date. Structural similarity to carcinogenic 4,4'-diaminostilbene gives rise to much speculation. See Note 2. | Shenai, 1973<br>Coulston, 1975 |

Note 1: The ranges of molecular weight are as follows:

stilbenes: 440-834
coumarins: 176-386
others: 237-415

Note 2: In studies performed in Europe (Coulston, 1975) fluorescent whitening agents (FWA's) have been found to be adequately treatable by activated sludge. There has been some concern over FWA's tendency to concentrate in river bottom sediments, but the small accumulations found in fish tissues were both non-toxic and reversible. Only negligable accumulation was seen in plant roots and no soil leaching near the landfills. In laboratory toxicity studies there were no mutagenic or carcinogenic effects, no dermal toxicity, no acute toxicity ($LD_{50}$ mouth >1,000 mg/kg). Also it was shown that FWA's were excreted without metabolism by rats.

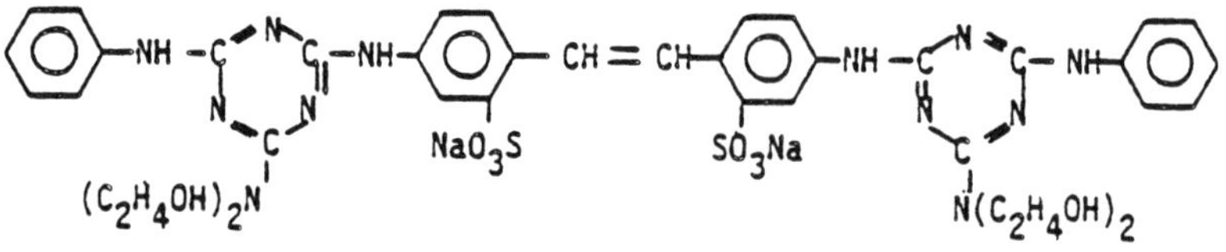

C.I. Fluorescent Brightener 28 - Stilbene type

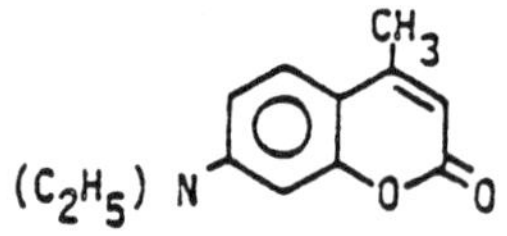

C.I. Fluorescent Brightener 61 - Coumarin type

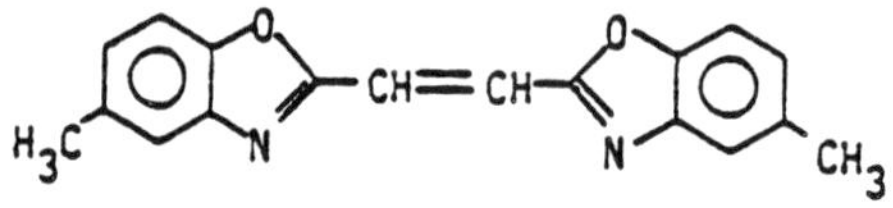

Benzoxazol type - USP 3649623

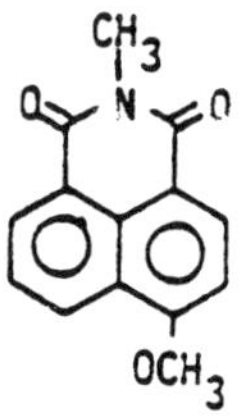

Naphthalimide type - USP 3310564

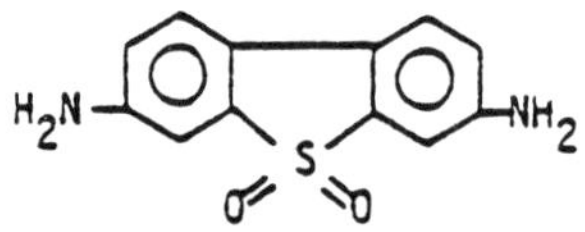

Benzidine Sulfone type - USP 2563795

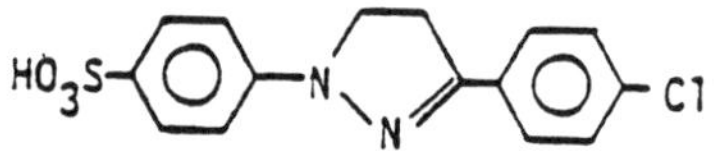

Pyrazoline type - USP 2640056

Figure 12. Chemical structures of various optical brighteners.

| Color Category | Percent of Total Solvents |
|---|---|
| Solvent Blues | 33.3% |
| Solvent Yellows | 12.1% |
| Solvent Oranges | 6.3% |
| | 51.7% |

The 1982 AATCC Buyers Guide lists 121 solvent dye products in liquid and granular form. Of these, 36 are reds, 27 are yellows, 17 are blues, 16 are oranges, and the remaining 25 are violets, greens, browns, and blacks (AATCC, 1982).

6.15.2 Textile Application

The majority of C.I. Solvent dyes are not used in conventional textile dyeing processes. However, a significant number of solvent dyes are used in dope dyeing of cellulose acetate, polypropylene, viscose rayon, and polyester, or in other mass coloration techniques. In dope dyeing the colored material is added to the melted acetate prior to extrusion of the molten mass into fibers. Cellulose acetate molding powders and resins are colored in a similar manner. Products used for mass coloration of cellulose acetate include: Solvent Yellows 17, 25, 35, 62-64, 78, Solvent Red 85, and several others (SDC, 1971).

The C.I. Solvent dyes which are suitable for conventional textile dyeing come from other dye application classes and are cross-listed as C.I. Solvent dyes because of their solubility in organic solvents and polymers. The properties of these dyes have been presented in previous discussions. These textile dyeing products are listed below (SDC, 1971).

Crosslisted Solvent Dye/Textile Products

Solvent Yellow 77/Disperse Yellow 3

Solvent Orange 52/Disperse Orange 13
Solvent Orange 53/Disperse Yellow 9

Solvent Red 47/Acid Red 93
Solvent Red 48/Acid Red 92
Solvent Red 43/Acid Red 87
Solvent Red 49/Basic Violet 10
Solvent Red 111/Disperse Red 9

Solvent Violet 8/Basic Violet 1
Solvent Violet 10/Acid Violet 9
Solvent Violet 26/Disperse Red 1

Solvent Blue 4/Basic Blue 26
Solvent Blue 5/Basic Blue 7
Solvent Blue 6/Basic Blue 11
Solvent Blue 8/Basic Blue 9
Solvent Blue 68/Disperse Blue 19
Solvent Blue 69/Disperse Blue 7
Solvent Blue 36/Disperse Blue 134

Solvent Green 1/Basic Green 4
Solvent Green 7/Acid Green 9
Solvent Green 15/Acid Green 7

Table 32 summarizes the important application properties of solvent dyes.

### 6.15.3 Chemical Classes

More so than with other dye classes, the color of solvent dyes can be directly correlated with their chemical class. Azo dyes are used for the yellow, orange, brown, and red shades, while xanthenes are used for the bright reds. Azine dyes are used for the relatively few solvent blacks. Violets are obtained from azo, anthraquinone, xanthene, and triarylmethane dyestuffs.

Table 33 summarizes the important chemical and physical properties of solvent dyes. Figure 13 presents the chemical structures of various solvent dyes.

TABLE 32. APPLICATION PROPERTIES OF SOLVENT DYES

| | | Reference |
|---|---|---|
| Materials colorable | Polystyrene, ABS, acrylic, nylon, polycarbonate, PVC, gasoline, transmission oil, waxes, shoe polish, stains, leather, and margarine. | Day-Glo, 1981b |
| Fabrics | Sometimes added to synthetic fiber melts before spinning. | Noller, 1958 |
| Leather dyeing | Those solvent dyes which are soluble in alcohols, ketones, esters, and ethers are useful for staining leather. | Lubs, 1955 |
| Disposable fabrics | Copying paper, typewriter ribbons, etc. | |
| Leveling | Good to fair. | |
| Exhaustion | Solvent dependent. | |
| Migration | | |
| Dischargeability | | |
| Acid fastness | Unaltered; good to poor. | |
| Alkali fastness | Unaltered; good to poor. | |
| Heat resistance | Solvent yellows are stable to 580°F for 10 minutes on polystyrene. | Day-Glo, 1981b |
| Light fastness | Basic solvent dyes have poor lightfastness. | Lubs, 1955 |
| Chlorine fastness | Depends on the medium. | |

(continued)

TABLE 32. APPLICATION PROPERTIES OF SOLVENT DYES (continued)

| | | Reference |
|---|---|---|
| Wash fastness | Insoluble; dye specific and may be from poor to good. | |
| Peroxide fastness | | |
| Perspiration fastness | | |
| Useful colors | Yellows, oranges, and blues especially. Also violets, green, browns, reds, and blacks. Many are fluorescent colors. | Day-Glo, 1981b<br>AATCC, 1982<br>ITC, 1980 |
| Rate of dyeing | Dye specific. | |
| Aftertreatment | Usually none. | |

TABLE 33. PHYSICAL/CHEMICAL PROPERTIES OF SOLVENT DYES

| | | Reference |
|---|---|---|
| Chemical structure | Mostly simple azo dyes with amino, hydroxyl, and alkyl groups. Alkyl groups improve oil solubility. Also included are a few pyrazolines (FD&C) and a few anthraquinones (more expensive). | Lubs, 1955 |
| Physical state | Sold as liquids, granular solids, and solid solutions in thermo plastics. | AATCC, 1982 |
| Particle size | Dye specific. | |
| Mole weight | Low molecular weights ranging from 225-460 gm/mole. Some are increased by metal complexation. | Lubs, 1955 |
| Density | Dye specific. | |
| Melting point | Melting points range from 90-200°C. Color stable up to melting point. About half decompose at melting. A select few melt above 300°C. | SDC, 1971<br>NIOSH, 1979 |
| Boiling point | Some sublime. | SDC, 1971 |
| Vapor pressure | Dye specific. | |
| Water solubility | Solubilities range from completely insoluble to very soluble. | SDC, 1971<br>Day-Glo, 1981b |
| Other solubility | See Note 1. | |
| Hydrolysis | Not known. | |

(continued)

TABLE 33. PHYSICAL/CHEMICAL PROPERTIES OF SOLVENT DYES (continued)

| | | Reference |
|---|---|---|
| Partition coefficient | | |
| Soil adsorption/ desorption | Dye specific. | |
| Dissociation constant | Not known. | |
| Spectra | Characteristic of the medium. | |
| Toxicity | Solvent Orange 7 and Red 24 are proven animal carcinogens. Solvent Yellow 7 is an irritant and a NIOSH candidate for cancer bioassay testing. | NIOSH, 1979<br>Aldrich, 1978 |

Note 1: Other solubility (solvent and yellows)

Acetone: 0.7-40 gm/L
Cellusolve: 1.8-42 gm/L
Isopropanol: 0.8-0.9 gm/L
Propyl Acetate: INSOL - 25 gm/L
Toluol: INSOL - 10 gm/L
Mineral Spirits: INSOL
Heptane: INSOL
Methylene Chloride: SL SOL - 300 gm/L

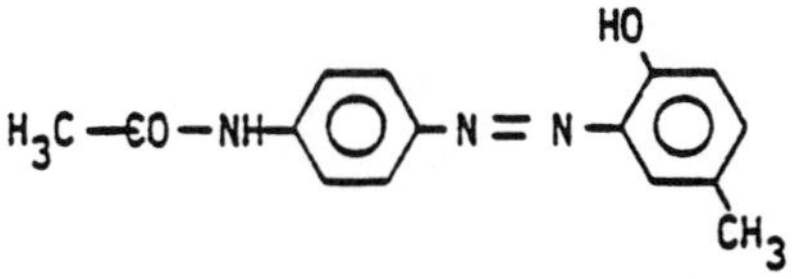

C.I. Solvent Yellow 77/Disperse Yellow 3 - Monoazo

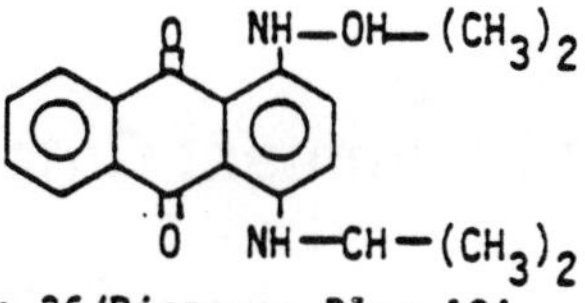

C.I. Solvent Blue 36/Disperse Blue 134 - Anthraquinone

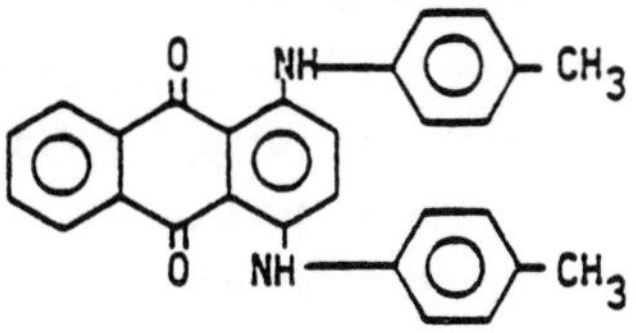

C.I. Solvent Green 3 - Anthraquinone

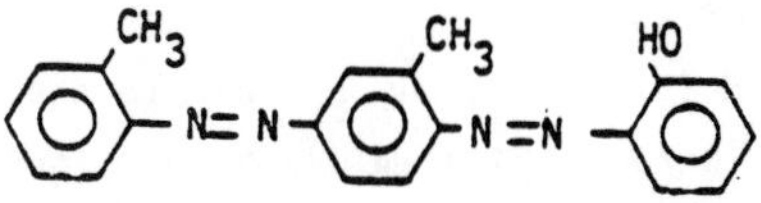

C.I. Solvent Red 24 - Disazo

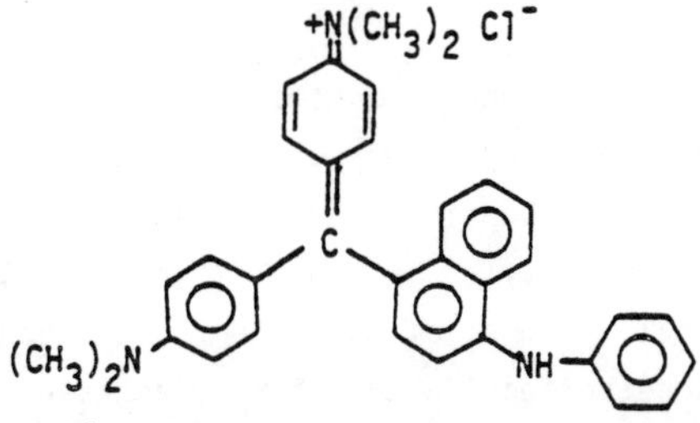

C.I. Solvent Blue 4/Basic Blue 26 - Triarylmethane

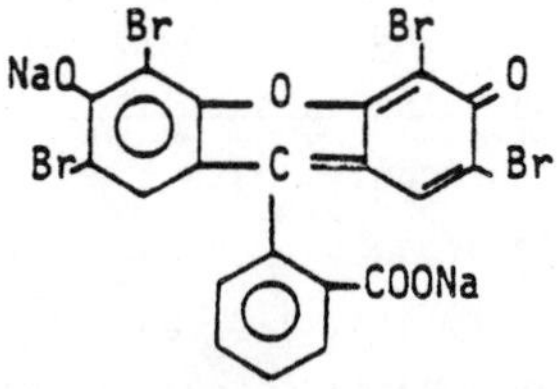

C.I. Solvent Red 43/Acid Red 87 - Xanthene

Figure 13. Chemical structures of various solvent dyes.

# 7. Dyeing Equipment Categorization

## 7.1 OVERVIEW

Modern dye machinery designs are based on one of three basic principles: (1) circulation of the dye through the fiber, (2) circulation of the fiber through the dye, and (3) padding the dye onto the fiber. Principles 1 and 2 apply to the machinery for the exhaust process. Package and beam dyeing machines are based on the first principles. Beck, jet, and jig dyeing equipment utilizes the second principle, and the pad/exhaust machines such as pad-jig and pad-beck, are based on the third principle.

The most frequent procedures used for textile coloration are: pad/batch (semi-continuous) processes, exhaust (batch) processes, printing, and continuous dyeing. Continuous dyeing is used primarily for long runs of a given fabric style. Because of their continuous operation and the relatively small volumes of dye liquor used, continuous processes tend to be more cost-effective than batch processes. Exhaust processes are generally very inefficient in their use of chemicals, water, and energy and generate large volumes of liquid waste which must be treated. Despite these disadvantages, the versatility, ease of control, and short run capability of exhaust processes make them very applicable for coloration of many textile products. A number of different exhaust or batch dyeing processes (beck, jet, jig, package, and beam) are used in the textile industry. Batch processes were used for dyeing an estimated 2.3 billion kilograms (5 billion pounds) of textile fibers and fabrics in 1973 (Lowry, 1977).

TABLE 34. PIECE GOODS DYEING MACHINES IN OPERATION IN THE U.S.[a] (units)

| Year | Jet dyeing machines | Pressure[b] dyeing machines | Atmospheric[b] dyeing machines | Jig dyeing machines | Padder dyeing machines | Continuous dyeing machines |
|---|---|---|---|---|---|---|
| 1960 | | | | | | |
| 1963 | 6 | 34 | 5,000 | 3,800 | 650 | |
| 1964 | 7 | 56 | 4,980 | 3,680 | 648 | |
| 1965 | 12 | 65 | 4,902 | 3,510 | 646 | 200(30)[c] |
| 1966 | 33 | 98 | 4,880 | 3,480 | 644 | |
| 1967 | 67 | 160 | 4,790 | 3,460 | 642 | |
| 1968 | 117 | 230 | 4,750 | 4,208 | 640 | |
| 1969 | 201 | 400 | 4,602 | 2,804 | 638 | |
| 1970 | 374 | 650 | 4,510 | 2,440 | 636 | |
| 1971 | 599 | 750 | 4,350 | 2,208 | 634 | |
| 1972 | 758 | 810 | 4,150 | 2,110 | 632 | |
| 1973 | 858 | 810 | 4,048 | 1,957 | 630 | 295(132)[c] |

[a]Non-carpet machines.

[b]Referenced to Becks and package machines.

[c](Thermosol-pad steam ranges).

Source: Dept. of Treasury, The Textile Industry.

Woven fabrics comprise the largest percentage of printed goods, though in recent years, knitted textile fabrics have increased in importance. Printing can also be done on yarns in skein form, or on warps being passed from a warp beam to another beam, or as yarn strands. Space printing is a process whereby a yarn, temporarily knitted into a loose fabric, is printed and then de-knitted. Carpets can be printed in either woven or tufted constructions. Regardless of the state of the textile material, the printing process makes use of one of the following methods of printing: roller, screen, spray, and transfer printing (Kirk-Othmer, 1978).

Recent developments in man-made fibers and changes in the fashion industry have caused significant changes in the technology used in the dyeing and finishing segment of the textile industry. Because of increased requirements for versatility in dyeing and finishing operations, the dyeing segment has been forced to replace older, relatively simple machinery with modern sophisticated equipment. Table 34 illustrates the decrease in the more traditional methods of dyeing textile products and the increase in newer, higher temperature dyeing methods such as those using the jet and pressure dyeing machines (EPA, 1979).

Table 35 shows the United States production of printed fabric between 1959 and 1973 (Hudak, 1976).

TABLE 35. U.S. PRODUCTION OF PRINTED FABRIC

| Year | Billion linear meters (yards) |
|---|---|
| 1959 | 2.9 (2.1) |
| 1963 | 1.9 (2.1) |
| 1965 | 2.0 (2.2) |
| 1967 | 2.1 (2.3) |
| 1969 | 2.2 (2.4) |
| 1971 | 2.4 (2.6) |
| 1973 | 2.9 (3.2) |

TABLE 36. COMPARISON OF PRINTING METHODS (Hudak, 1976)

| Printing method | Important features and advantages | Limitations and disadvantages |
|---|---|---|
| Roller | Best suited for long production runs of same pattern. | Except for special machines, size of pattern repeat limited to 0.41 M (16 inch) maximum. |
| | Best method for fine line patterns and paisley prints. | Difficult to print weft knits. Requires special handling. Some fabrics cannot be done. |
| | Can produce half tones[a] and fall on effects.[b] | Uneconomical for short runs (less than 5,486 M).[c] |
| | Can print woven fabrics and tricot. | Long production delays in pattern changeovers.[c] |
| | Lowest cost method for large quantity production. | |
| Automatic flat bed screen | Large repeat size up to 2.1 M (84 inches) possible. | Cost of screen preparation and special mountings more costly than hand screen. Not adaptable to low yardage. |
| | Better color definition than roller print; equal to hand screen. | Half tone designs not possible. |
| | Adaptable to all woven and knitted constructions. | Fine line designs and paisley prints not possible. |
| | Rapid changeover of designs possible. | Lengthwise stripes not possible. |
| Rotary screen | Larger repeat size than roller printing is possible, but smaller than that for flat screen methods. | Fine line designs and paisley prints not possible. |
| | Lengthwise stripe effect possible. Fall on designs possible. Adaptable to all woven and knitted constructions. | Half tone effects not possible. |

(continued)

TABLE 36. COMPARISON OF PRINTING METHODS (Hudak, 1976) (continued)

| Printing method | Important features and advantages | Limitations and disadvantages |
|---|---|---|
| Rotary screen (cont'd) | Excellent color definition, but less than with flat screen methods.<br><br>Rapid changeover of designs possible.<br><br>Efficient for long runs and moderately small 914 M (1,000 yards) runs. | |
| Heat transfer | Produces bright, sharp, clear, fine line designs.<br><br>Ability to print cut garment parts and small items. Adaptable to long and short yardage runs.<br><br>Rapid pattern changeover possible.<br><br>Simple low investment installation possible. Steamers, washers, dryers, etc. not required. | Lead time for paper preparation can cause problems in high fashion markets.<br><br>Limited to fabrics having minimum 50% man-made fibers. Cellulosic and protein fibers cannot be printed. |

[a]A half-tone is a gradual shading from light to dark in the same color.

[b]A fall on is two colors of overlapping pattern, which results in a third color. It is thus possible to achieve a three color print with two rollers.

[c]A roller printing machine introduced in the U.S. in the early 1970's eliminates these shortcomings. The newly designed machine is called the Saueressig printer, the name of its West German manufacturer. Production quantities as low as 914 M (1,000 yards) per pattern are feasible with this machine.

The major amount of this growth came during the period from 1967-1973 and was brought about by improved technology. The rotary screen printing method was introduced in 1965 and transfer printing in 1970.

During the 1950-1965 period, almost all printing was done either on roller printing or flat bed screen printing machines. Table 36 gives a comparison of the four printing methods utilized most in the textile industry (Hudak, 1976).

The period 1960-1974 saw a movement from roller printing in 1964 (90% of all United States produced printed fabrics were roller printed in 1964) to an estimated 60% roller/40% screen ratio in 1974, with the rotary screen accounting for virtually all of the growth. The rotary screen's ability to quickly handle a wide variety of fabrics was an important factor in this change. Also, rotary screen printing allowed for high quality printing at reduced unit cost, relative to the existing printing technology, during the 1965-1970 period. As shown in Table 37, the number of flat bed, rotary screen machines in place, rose from 20 in 1965 to 136 in 1973.

Transfer printing accounted for an estimated 69 million linear meters (75 million linear yards) in 1973 which was double the quantity produced in 1971. The number of transfer printing machines grew from zero in 1965 to 77 in 1973. A decline in the number of roller printing machines took place dropping from 450 in 1965 to 394 in 1973. Also, a reduction in flat bed screen printing machines from 300 to 211 occurred.

In general, between 1960 and 1973, few new roller or flat bed screen printing machines were purchased. The majority of the machines retired during this period had been in service more than 20 years. After 1965 almost all new printing machines purchased were either flat bed, rotary screen or transfer printing machines.

One estimate of future trends in printing is the following forecast (Hudak, 1976):

TABLE 37. PRINTING MACHINES IN OPERATION IN THE U.S.[a]

| | 1963 | 1965 | 1973 |
|---|---|---|---|
| Roller printing machines | 460 | 450 | 394 |
| Screen printing machines | | | |
| Flat bed, screen | 310 | 300 | 211 |
| Flat bed, rotary screen | - | 20 | 136 |
| Transfer printing | - | - | 77 |
| Stripe printing machines | - | - | 16 |

[a]Does not include carpet equipment.

Source: Private industry estimates.

U.S. PRINT FABRIC PRODUCTION
IN BILLION LINEAR METERS (YARDS)

| | 1973 | | 1979 | |
|---|---|---|---|---|
| Polyester/cotton | 0.819 | (0.896) | 1.498 | (1.638) |
| Nylon | 0.234 | (0.256) | 0.422 | (0.462) |
| Rayon/acetate | 0.527 | (0.576) | 0.461 | (0.504) |
| Cotton | 0.878 | (0.960) | 0.499 | (0.546) |
| Polyester | 0.351 | (0.384) | 0.730 | (0.798) |
| Glass and other | 0.088 | (0.096) | 0.115 | (0.126) |
| Acrylic | 0.029 | (0.032) | 0.115 | (0.126) |
| | 2.926 | (3.200) | 3.840 | (4.200) |

## 7.2 BECK DYEING

Beck dyeing is one of the oldest forms of mechanized piece goods dyeing. In its basic form, the machine consists of a shallow U-shaped box which has a gradual low curvature in the back and a rather high vertical rise in the front. About 2 meters (7 feet) above the tub is a driven reel which transports the piece goods from the front side and allows them to slide down the back of the beck and then return to the front. This method is referred to in some sources as winch-beck or winch dyeing because of the winch apparatus used to move fabric through the beck.

Jet dyeing machines were introduced to overcome some drawbacks of the pressure beck dyeing machines. Although the functions of the two pieces of equipment are identical (high temperature dyeing of disperse dyes on polyester fibers or blends thereof), these two are distinct pieces of equipment with dissimilar appearances. They operate under different principles of fabric movement, and have diverse fabric capabilities and liquor ratios.

Becks are generally constructed to accept fabrics in either rope forms or open width. The rope form can be threaded as one long spiral which runs as a continuous belt. This type of machine is well suited for woolen knit or woven goods in rope form. The machine consists of a wooden or iron V-shaped vat for holding dye liquor, and an upper driven winch extending the full length of the vat. Fabric is inserted into the machine at one end and threaded into the machine. Successive passages of the fabric over the winch are separated by means of wooden or porcelain pegs in front of the machine. Slack fabric is allowed to lie in the bottom of the vat. Such a machine will hold about 914 meters (1,000 yards) of fabric which is continually drawn out of and into the dye liquor by the upper rotating winch.

The vat is usually has a perforated steam pipe, which enables the dye liquor to be heated as required. In some machines, the guiding pegs are secured to a hinged horizontal rail; when the fabric becomes entangled, this peg rail lifts and thereby operates a lever that automatically disengages the winch drive. Damage to the fabric is thus avoided.

Open-width threading is normally used for heavy weight material such as carpets, twills, and sateens, which would be damaged if crushed into a "rope" form. The machine is simply constructed and consists of an overhead winch placed above a rectangular dye vat. The vat is fitted with a supply of steam and water, and with suitable outlet plugs. Freely rotating wooden or other guide rollers are placed across the ends and bottom of the tank and an endless length of fabric in open width is continuously drawn out of the vat and over the winch. During the dyeing operation, almost all of the fabric is slowly dragged along the bottom of the vat. Such a machine requires some easy means of readily reversing the rotation direction of the winch (Hall 1926).

The two types of winch-beck machines are illustrated in Figure 14 (Haigh 1972). The natural fiber beck generally used is for fabrics which cannot be stretched. When fabric stretching can be tolerated, the shallow-depth synthetic fabric beck is used. In many respects the winch-beck is an inefficient dyeing machine because the liquor/goods ratio can be high (40:1), and the volume of liquor is large with a considerable surface area. This large liquor volume and surface area tend to separate many dyes from the homogenous liquor due to surface tension. To reduce this separation tendency and to improve production volumes, liquor ratios are often in the order of 18 to 25:1.

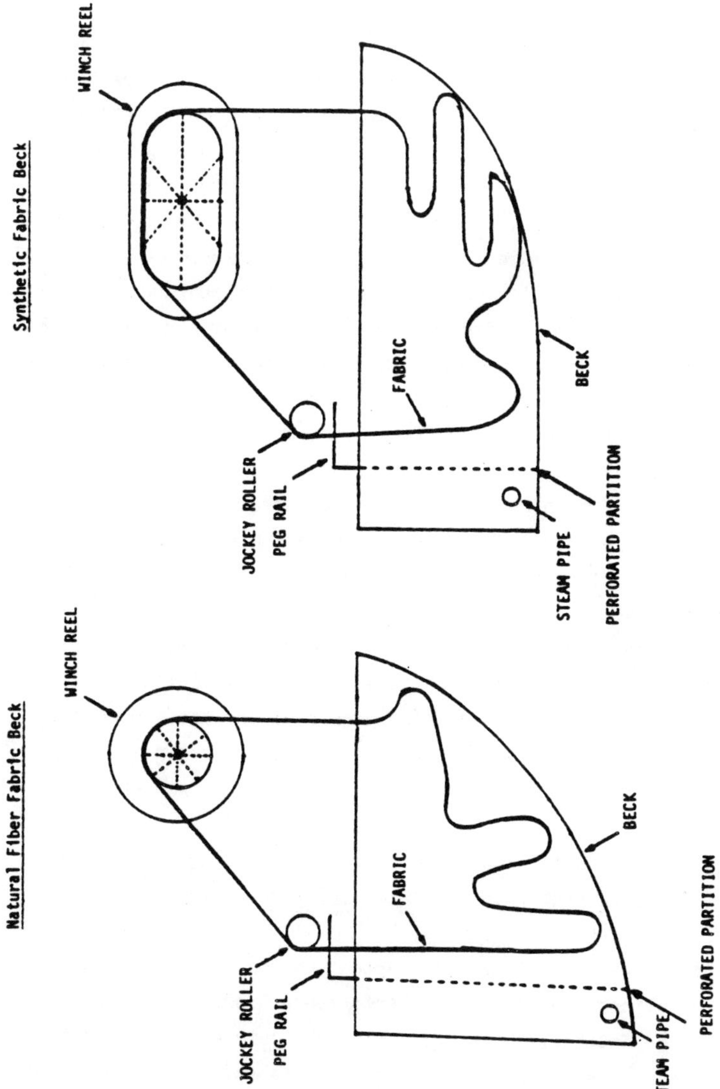


Figure 14. Winch dyeing machines.

Unless the vessel is totally enclosed, steam generated during boiling of the liquor will be lost into the atmosphere. This causes unpleasant, steamy, working conditions, considerable hot wastage, and a dyeing temperature around 95°C (203°F) instead of near 100°C (212°F). Coupled with this may be a significant variation in temperature from the front to the back of the machine or, more seriously, from side to side. Modern machines are enclosed and a uniform temperature near 100°C (212°F) can be obtained by using sliding armour plate glass panels with counterbalances. These panels are fitted at the front and back of the machine to provide easy access for loading and unloading, or easy access in the event that dyed pieces become entangled. Another method that can be used to correct temperature variations within the winch dyeing machine is to incorporate an external calorifier and pump for circulation of the dye liquor (Haigh, 1972).

Pressurized winch machines were slow to be developed and have been largely replaced by jet dyeing machines for dyeing piece goods at high temperature in rope form. Burlington Engineering was the first machine manufacturer to produce low-pressure and high-pressure winch becks. The low-pressure machine resembles a normal winch beck but a metal cover with two retangular ports replaces the glass window, allowing temperatures up to 103°C (218°F) to be obtained. The high pressure machine consists of a winch reel, and jockey roller within a horizontal cylindrical autoclave fitted with two circular portholes for loading and unloading the fabric.

The characteristics of high temperature winch dyeing machines on the market in 1967 are presented in Table 38 (Haigh, 1972).

7.2.1 General Beck Dyeing Procedures

According to the U.S. EPA's "Development Document for Effluent Limitations Guidelines and New Source Performance Standard for Textile Mills Point Source Category," dyeing is the most complex of all textile finishing processes. When textiles are colored, a sufficient amount of a dyestuff is used to make the shade. Additionally, various other chemicals may be used to help deposit the dye, or to develop the color.

TABLE 38. HIGH TEMPERATURE WENCH DYEING MACHINES (1967-1971)

| Manufacturer | Name of machine | Diameter of autoclave | Whether there is internal lid closure | Top temp. | Capacity in kilos | Special features |
|---|---|---|---|---|---|---|
| Bruckner, Germany | | 2 metres | | 140°C | 150 | Metal plate below lid which is heated by coils. Runs any condensate off in grooves. |
| Callebaut de Blicquy, Belgium | Hataspie | 2 metres<br>3 metres | No<br>No | 140°C | 49 - 240<br>98 - 480 | |
| Frauchiger, Switzerland | Hastro 67 | | | 130°C | | Winch beck separate from heated water bath. |
| Ilma, Italy | T/PCP<br>T/PCP 2000 | 2.2 metres<br>2.85 metres | | 140°C<br>140°C | 30 - 240<br>120 - 480 | Special recirculation system. |
| Krantz, Germany | | 2 metres | Yes | 140°C | | Spray system for roof and "fluid expander" for fabric. |
| Leemetals, England | | 2.74 metres | Yes | 135°C | | Top one-third insulated midfeather. Geometrical reel, infinitely variable drive. |
| Longclose (Platt), England | | 2 metres | | 140°C | 100 - 200 approx. | Infinitely variable drive. |
| Mortensen, Denmark | | 3 metres | Yes | 130°C | 110 - 310 | Midfeather. |
| Obermaier, Germany | | 2 metres | | 140°C | | |
| Pegg, England | | | | 140°C | | Winch unit separate from autoclave. Spray system. |
| Scholl, Switzerland | HK14 | 2 metres | Yes | 140°C | 50 - 260 | Infinitely variable drive. |
| Then, Germany | | 2 metres | | 140°C | | Three-speed drive. |
| Thies, Germany | | 3 metres | | 140°C | | Ceiling heated against condensation. |

Dye loading varies widely even within a particular dye class, depending on the weight of the fabrics being treated and the depth of color desired. The range of chemicals employed in dyeing also varies widely from plant to plant and operation to operation, and depends substantially upon the dictates of the market place (EPA 1974).

The beck dyeing process uses a type of exhaustion method. Exhaustion methods use chemical agents and physical conditions to force dyestuffs onto yarn or cloth, so that the fullest value may be received from the dyeing bath. The degree of exhaustion describes the amount of the total dye used which ultimately resides on the fiber rather than in the dye liquors; it is usually expressed as a percentage of the total dye applied. Often in the literature, the term exhaustion rate and degree of exhaustion are erroneously interchanged. The exhaustion rate is of minor importance in assessing release of the dyes to the environment. The degree of exhaustion indicates the amount of dye removed from the dye bath and is quite important in calculating releases. The objective of the dye chemist and the dyer is to achieve reproducible level dyeings in a practical dyeing time with a maximum color yield (AATCC, 1981).

The beck process of applying dyes is always fundamentally the same: dye is transferred from a bath (usually aqueous) to the fiber. Basic dyeing operations include: (1) preparation of the fiber; (2) preparation of the dye bath; (3) application of the dye; and (4) finishing. There are many variations of these operations, depending on the kind of dye being used. The dyeing process is complicated by the fact that single dyes are seldom used. The matching of a specified shade may require from two to a dozen dyes.

Fiber preparation ordinarily includes scouring to remove foreign materials and ensure even surface access to the dye liquor, but varies with the type of product being manufactured and the nature of the goods being dyed. Some natural fibers are contaminated with fatty materials and dirt. Synthetic fibers may have been treated with spinning lubricants or sizing which must be removed. Some fibers also may require bleaching before they are ready for use.

Preparation of the dye bath may involve simply dissolving the dye in water, or more involved operations such as the reduction of vat dyes may be necessary. Wetting agents, salts, carriers, retardants, and other dyeing aids may also be added. Carriers are swelling agents which improve the dyeing rate of very hydrophobic fibers such as polyesters. Two examples are o-phenylphenol and biphenyl. Retardants are colorless substances that compete with dyes for dye sites or complex the dye in the bath and act to slow the dyeing rate. Their use is necessary when a too rapid dyeing rate causes unevenness in the dyeing.

During application, dye must be transferred from the bath to the fiber and allowed to penetrate. In the simplest cases this is done by immersing the fiber in the bath for a prescribed period of time at a suitable temperature. Unless the dye is unstable, the bath is usually heated to increase the rate of dyeing. To ensure an even uptake of dye, it is desirable to stir the bath. This is done by circulating the bath or by moving the fiber. The finishing steps for many dyes, such as the direct dyes, are very simple - the dyed material is merely rinsed and dried. Vat-dyed materials, on the other hand, must be rinsed to remove reducing agent, oxidized, rinsed again, and soaped before the final rinsing and drying steps are carried out. Generally, the finishing steps must fix the color (if this has not occurred during application) and remove any loose dye from the surface of the fiber. Residual dyeing aids such as carriers also must be removed, and aftertreatment is often required. These carriers are often evaporated by heat in drying operations.

The beck operation usually begins with filling the dyeing machine containing the fabric with water and a detergent for scouring. The scour water is dumped and the beck is refilled with water and wetting agent if required. After the fabric is wet out and the temperature raised to set the bath, the dyestuffs are added and the beck brought up to temperature (95°C-205°C in atmospheric machines and higher in pressure units). After dyeing two to four hours, 90 percent or more of the dye has been exhausted, so the dye bath is discharged to the sewer. This dyeing step is followed by one or a series of clear water rinses. Sometimes the rinses are followed with finishing agents and further rinses (EPA, 1974).

For many years beck dyeing machines were the only suitable machine for dyeing knitted goods in fabric form and several types of woolen woven goods. Beck machines are more suitable for elasticized fabrics where tension on the knitted fabric could cause damage. Today, with the emergence of high temperature and pressure becks, the application of dyes by becks is not limited to the knitted fabrics. The following subsections describe general beck dyeing procedures for specific dye classes. Additional dyeing procedures for other fabric/dyestuff combinations are contained in Appendix B of this report.

7.2.1.1 Direct Dyestuff Beck Procedures. Direct dyes can be used on all cellulosics and several polyamides. These dyes are highly water soluble and require large amounts of hot water to form a solution. The beck is advantageous because of the large beck vessel. Direct dyes are classified into three groups (A, B, and C,) according to the leveling and exhaustion characteristics of the dye and the salt addition and control of temperature necessary during dyeing. An example of a winch beck dyeing procedure using direct dyes on cotton after the fiber or fabric has been prepared with desizing, scouring, or bleaching is as follows (VPI, 1981).

1) Set the water as low as possible in the machine and heat to 32-38°C (90-100°F).

2) Add the dyebath and run 15 minutes. Most dyers will use a leveling agent; it is important that this agent be distributed evenly in the fabric before the dye is added.

3) Add the dyestuff and run 10-15 minutes to distribute the dye uniformly.

4) Raise the temperature to 93°C (200°F). Run 20 minutes.

5) Add the first portion of salt and run 20 minutes.

6) Add second salt portion and run 20 minutes.

7) Add the last salt portion and run in a cooling bath to 82°C (180°F).

8) Sample and check shade.

9) Add dye at 82°C (180°F).

10) Raise the temperature to 93-99°C (200-210°F) and run 30 minutes in a cooling batch. When the lot is on shade, washing should be gradual. Flood or overflow washing is recommended down to 60-49°C (140-120°F) before the bath is dropped completely.

11) In short liquor-ratios, such as package machines, drop one-half the dyebath-refill and run 15 minutes - drop again and repeat until the temperature is down to around 54°C (130°F) - wash clean with fresh water. Regardless of which washing method used, it is advisable to avoid any shock treatments--such as dropping a hot bath and refilling with cold water.

7.2.1.2 Acid Dyestuff Beck Procedures. Acid dyestuffs are used on wool, silk, and nylon (polyamide). Chemical bonding is used to adhere the dye to the fiber. Anionic or cationic dyebath auxiliaries are used in acid baths to slow the rate of exhaustion and assist in leveling. There are three classes of acid dyes: (1) true acid, (2) neutral dyeing acid, and (3) pre-metallized. The true acid dyes require acetic or formic acid for good exhaustion. The neutral dyeing acid dyes are applied from a neutral bath with the pH lowered at the end of the cycle to ensure good exhaustion. Pre-metallized dyes contain metals, usually chromium and are applied in a slightly alkaline both to control leveling. Chromium dyes have superior light and wash fastness.

The control of dyebath pH is essential for applying acid dyes to nylon. The optimum pH varies with the fiber(s) being dyed. Some suggested buffered dyebath are (VPI, 1981):

- pH - 4-4.5 - 1.5 grams/liter acetic acid 56%
  0.4 grams/liter sodium acetate

- pH - 6-6.5 - 0.7 grams/liter monosodium phosphate
  0.3 grams/liter di-sodium phosphate
- pH - 7-7.5 - 0.3 grams/liter monosodium phosphate
  0.7 grams/liter di-sodium phosphate

A general dyeing procedure for acid dyes on an exhaustion machine such as a beck is as follows (VPI, 1981):

- Set the bath with the acid donor at 32-37°C (90-100°F). Run 10 minutes and check/adjust pH (usually 6.5-7).
- Add the dyebath chemicals. If an anionic agent is used, run 10 minutes to distribute evenly. If a cationic agent is used, usually one-half is added to the dyebath with the balance being mixed with the dissolved dyestuff. In both cases, uniform distribution in the dyebath and/or on the fiber of fabric is essential.
- Add the dyes and run 10 minutes.
- Raise temperature to boiling at a rate of 1½ to 2 degrees per minute.
- Run at boiling for 60 minutes.
- Check exhaust, pH, and sample.
- If dye additions must be made, cool to 82°C (180°F) before adding. Then raise to boiling.

7.2.1.3 Basic Dyestuff Beck Procedures. The principal use of cationic dyestuffs is for dyeing acrylic fibers. The non-liquid brand of basic dyes is not easily dissolved and requires acetic acid, boiling water, and good mixing before it can be prepared into solution for application. Temperatures above 88°C (190°F) are required to exhaust the dye. Most dye procedures raise the temperature from 77°C (170°F) to the boiling point in stages, holding 10-15 minutes at every 10°F rise in temperature.

Basic dyes are grouped into "K" factors according to their rate of exhaustion (with K1 being very fast and K5 being very slow). The K1-K2 dyes are used for continuous dyeing systems and the K2.5-K3.5 dyes are used in exhaust systems. Cationic dyes have a high affinity for acrylic fiber. The affinity is best at 175°F-212°F and 4.5-5.5 pH. These dyes require large amounts of water for maximum solubility. A typical dyebath will: (1) be chemically buffered to 4-5 pH with sodium bisulfite to remove chlorine and sequestrant to remove trace metals; (2) contain nonionic wetting agents; (3) contain 10% Glaubers salt as a leveling agent; (4) require the addition of acetic acid and sodium acetate to maintain the 4-4.5 pH for dyeing of dark shades; and (5) need retarding agents to slow exhaustion.

An example of a general dyeing procedure for basic dyes is as follows (VPI, 1981):

- Add dyebath chemicals at 49°C (120°F); run for 15-20 minutes; be sure all chemicals are well distributed.
- Raise to 65°C (150°F)
- Add dyestuff (well strained) and run 15 minutes.
- Raise to 77°C (170°F); run 15 minutes.
- Raise to 82°C (180°F); run 15 minutes.
- Raise to 88°C (190°F); run 15 minutes.
- Raise to 93°C (200°F); run 15 minutes.
- Raise to 99-100°C* (210-212°F) and run 30 minutes (60 minutes for dark shades).
- Sample and cool beck the lot slowly to 71°C (160°F). The dyer should also check or sample the dye liquor to determine the extent of exhaustion.

---

*If the critical dyeing temperature is known, the above procedure can be adjusted accordingly. A dyer determines the correctness of dyeing by taking a sample at each of the above temperatures. A comparison of all samples with the final shade will help establish the critical temperature for future lots.

- If dye additions are made, the temperature should be 71-77°C (160-170°F). The temperature is then gradually raised, as before.
- If the lot is on shade, the bath must be cooled back to 60-54°C (140-130°F) before dropping the bath temperature. Washing with warm water is preferred.

  After washing, the fabric/fiber is lightly scoured with a non-ionic surfactant to remove all chemicals and loose dye. A softener may be applied in the last rinse bath.

7.2.1.4 Reactive Dyestuff Beck Procedures. Fiber reactive dyes are used on wool, nylon, and cellulosic fiber such as cotton and linen. Reactive dyes are highly soluble in water and are typed according to degree of reactivity. Reactive dyes have a poor affinity for cellulose, therefore requiring padding onto fabric and the addition of alkali to the dyebath for creating a chemical bond between the fiber and the dyestuff. The best method of applying reactive dyes to cellulosic fibers is to use the low liquor ratio method with a pad/batch system. The batching portion of the process can be performed with a beck, beam, or jig machine.

With a winch beck the exhaustion method can be used as a high liquor ratio system with low or high temperature reactive dyes. A general procedure for using low temperature reactive dyes is as follows (VPI, 1981):

- Set the water as low as possible. Add the dyestuff and be sure the system is running well. A temperature of 27-32°C (80-90°F) is normal for starting.
- Add the salt (usually right at the machine. To help increase dye exhaustion, the temperature can be raised to 38-43°C (100-110°F)).
- Run from 20 to 40 minutes to ensure good uniform exhaustion.
- Add the alkali in 2 or 3 portions at 10-15 minute intervals. After the last portion is in, run 15 minutes and then check the pH. For most dyes, a 10-10.5 pH is recommended.

- Raise the temperature to the required level -- this can vary from 40-60°C (105-140°F).
- Run for 60 to 120 minutes.
- Sample. The sample must be well soaped to determine the final shade.
- If a dye addition must be made, it is best to cool 15-20 degrees before adding dye. Return to temperature and run 30 minutes.
- If the shade is okay, wash the lot clean. A few warm or hot rinses will help to remove the alkali from the cellulose. In some cases a rinse with sodium bicarbonate will help to remove the alkali -- especially when caustic soda has been used.
- Soap off the lot at the boil for 10-15 minutes to remove the unfixed dye. Use either natural soap or a synthetic detergent.

A general procedure for using high temperature reactive dyes is as follows (VPI 1981):

- Set the water as low as possible in the machine. Add the dyestuff and be sure the system is running well.
- Add all the salt (this may vary in amounts from 50 to 200% based on the weight of the lot).
- Raise the temperature to 82°C (200°F) and run for 20 to 40 minutes.
- Cool back to 82°C (180°F) (this depends on the dyestuff and may vary from 88-77°C (190-170°F)).
- Add the alkali in 2-3 portions -- at 10 to 15 minute intervals.
- Check the pH 10 minutes after all the alkali is in. It should be pH 10-10.5
- Run 60 to 120 minutes.

- Sample and shut off the steam. Be sure to soap off the sample very well to develop the true shade. If a dye is added, it should be done at 66°C (150F°).
- If the shade is okay, drop one-half the bath and refill with cold water. Run 5 minutes when refilled. Drop all the dyebath and refill with warm or hot water. Give several warm or hot rinses to remove the alkali and free dyestuff. If caustic was used, a rinse in 1-2% sodium bicarbonate will help to rinse it out.
- When clean, soap at the boil for 10-15 minutes with soap or synthetic detergent.

7.2.1.5 Vat, Sulfur, and Azoic Dyestuff Beck Procedures. The application of vat, sulfur, and azoic dyestuffs is very complicated; it involves forming the insoluble dyestuff inside the fiber. The fundamental steps of these dyestuff procedures are the same (VPI, 1981):

- Converting the insoluble pigment to its soluble form. This is called reducing or vatting.
- Exhausting or padding the dye into the fiber or fabric.
- Converting the soluble dye back to its insoluble pigment form inside the fiber by chemical oxidation.
- Soaping off the dyed fiber or fabric in order to develop the true shade, and removing any loose dye pigment to ensure that the maximum fastness is attained.

Depending on the method of application, the first two steps may be reversed in the sequence.

The dyestuffs can be applied in any type of dyeing machine. However, if an economical method is required, the lower liquor ratio machines are preferred; the pad/batch systems are effective for this type of application. A beck, beam, package, or jig machine can be utilized for the batching portion of the system.

Vat dyestuffs are used mainly on cellulosic fibers and specifically on cotton. Continuous processes or pad/jig systems generally are used rather than the pad/beck system. Vat dyes exhibit a very high degree of fastness to light, washing, and color destructive chemicals.

Chemical additives to the vat dye process are caustics to keep the dyestuff in the soluble state during dyeing, and oxidation agents such as sodium perborate, acidified sodium bichromate, and hydrogen peroxide. Vat dyestuffs are classified by application method referred to as Methods 1, 2, and 3, corresponding to the hot, warm, and cold dyeing methods in general use. This classification of vat dyes is approved by the Society of Dyers and Colourists. However, individual dye manufacturers have adopted their own specific terminology in referring to these well-known methods of application. The dye bath procedure for the dyes within the following groups is as follows:

| Application type | Reduction temperature °C (°F) | Dyeing temperature °C (°F) | Caustic ozs./gal. (g/L) | Hydro-sulfite ozs./gal. (g/L) | Salt ozs./gal. (g/L) |
|---|---|---|---|---|---|
| Hot | 49-60°C (120-140°F) | 49-60°C (120-140°F) | .25-1.5 (7.1-5.6) | .25-1.5 (7.1-5.6) | None (None) |
| Warm | 49°C (120°F) | 43-49°C (100-120°F) | .16-.75 (4.5-2.8) | .16-1.0 (4.5-3.7) | .5-4.0 (14.2-15.1) |
| Cold | 49°C (120°F) | 21-27°C (70-80°F) | .16-.5 (4.5-1.9) | .16-.75 (4.5-2.8) | 1.0-8.0 (28.3-30.3) |

Application procedures for sulfur dyestuffs are similar to those for vat dyes with the exception that sulfur dyes are reduced with soda ash and sodium sulfide. Sulfur dyes are used mostly for dull shades and are not fast to sodium hydrochlorite (chlorine fastness). The popular application method is padding the dye and then batching on a jig for oxidizing and developing color. Application with low ratio winch becks, jigs, beams, and package machines are used. An example of a typical low ratio winch beck operation is as follows (VPI, 1981):

- Scour, desize, or bleach the fabric (it should exhibit good wetting properties).

- Set the dyebath at 38°C (100°F) with liquid alkaline sulfide; leveling agent; and sequestrant. Run at 38°C (100°F) for 10 minutes.
- Slowly add liquid sulfur dyes (diluted in warm water) to the dyebath. Run for 10 minutes.
- Raise slowly to the recommended dyeing temperature. (This is indicated on the dye manufacturers' shade card.)
- Run 20 minutes at temperature, then add the first salt. (The salt should be added in 3 or 4 portions at 15-20 minute intervals. Always use calcium and magnesium free salt.
- When all the salt is in, run 30-45 minutes at temperature.
- Sample. (The sample must be oxidized and soaped in a pot for determination of the true shade.)
- When on shade, overflow wash until clean.
- Oxidize in a fresh bath. This step contains many variations such as the use of sodium perborate, hydrogen peroxide, and sodium or potassium iodate with acetic acid. The dyer should refer to the shade card for the proper chemicals and instructions.

The goods are run in the oxidation bath for 20 minutes at 43-60°C (110-140°F). Then drop the bath and hot wash 60-71°C (140-160°F.)

- In a fresh bath, soap off the goods with an anionic surfactant and soda ash. Run at 88-93°C (190-200°F) for 15 minutes. Wash until clean.

Sulfur dyes (especially blacks) can cause tendering of cellulose during storage. This can happen due to a gradual oxidation of a portion of the sulfur to sulfuric acid. It can be avoided by padding on a small amount of the buffer, sodium acetate, before drying. On 100% cellulose, another method is to use an alkaline bath in the final rinse. If the goods are to be resin finished then they must be neutralized after the alkali treatment. This method has still been found to be effective in reducing the tendering potential.

Azoic dyes or naphthols consist of two components: the coupling agent and the diazo component. They can provide excellent fastness and very bright shades. Their application method is similar to that for vat dyes but is much more complex. Most naphthol applications are done continuously although low-liquor ratio systems are practical also. The application of naphthol dyestuff on cellulose is a two stage process. First the coupling component (naphthol) is applied to the fiber, then it is reacted with a diazonium compound to form an insoluble dyestuff inside the fabric. Some problems with this process are (VPI 1981):

- Naphthol powders are not soluble in water. They must be dissolved cold with exacting amounts of alcohol, caustic, a protective colloid, and in some cases formaldehyde (they can also be dissolved hot with caustic and boiling water, but when the solution is clear it must be cooled to 38-43°C (100-110°F)).
- The substantivity for cellulose is low and may vary between 10% and 45%. In some cases, salt is added to improve exhaustion.
- In order to determine the amount of diazonium salt or base required to couple with the naphthol, the amount of fixed naphthol on the fiber must be known.

The depth of color is determined by controlling naphthol quantity. An excess of salt (or base) is used and is discarded in the effluent. Dyestuff manufacturers supply this information for each naphthol available. Such information shows graphically the relation between grams per liter of naphthol in the liquor to grams per liter absorbed per kilogram of fiber.

- From the above calculation, the amount of diazo salt or base can be determined. If a base is used, it must first be diazotized with sodium nitrite and hydrochloric acid. At this stage, the base is very sensitive to light. It must also be kept at a temperature of 18.33-21.11°C (65-70°F).

- Finally, the naphtholated fiber is immersed in the cold diazonium liquor and the the dyestuff forms inside the fiber. The dyer must know the coupling rate of the diazonium compound so that the proper pH can be maintained. After coupling, the fiber must be soaped to remove any loose dye pigment, otherwise crocking will be a problem.

7.2.1.5.1 Example effluent calculations for using sulfur dyes with a beck. An example of a typical dyeing operation is a 3.6 meter (12 foot) atmospheric beck operated with approximately 454 kilograms (1,000 pounds) of fabric per batch. The liquor ratio usually operates at 18-20 parts to 1 part fabric. Most becks need 3,846 liters (1,000 gallons) to 5,769 liters (1,500 gallons) or 3,782 kilograms (8,337 pounds) to 5,672 kilograms (12,506 pounds) of water for 454 kilograms (1,000 pounds) of fabric. At 90 percent exhaustion and a sulfur dye formulation of 11.7 percent dye for 454 kilograms (1,000 pounds) of goods, dye losses are calculated to be (assuming a 100% dye concentration):

| Water Usage | | | | | |
|---|---|---|---|---|---|
| Volume in Liters (Gallons) | | Weight in Kilograms (Pounds) | | Liquor Ratio | PPM of Discharge |
| 3,846 | (1,000) | 3,728 | (8,337) | 8-1/3:1 | 148 |
| 5,769 | (1,500) | 5,672 | (12,506) | 12½:1 | 98 |
| 8,307 | (2,160) | 8,168 | (18,008) | 18:1 | 68 |
| 9,234 | (2,401) | 9,080 | (20,017) | 20:1 | 61 |
| 10,619 | (2,761) | 10,441 | (23,018) | 23:1 | 53 |

Actual production data indicate that 5.3 kilograms (11.7 pounds) of sulfur dye is used per 454 kilograms (1,000 pounds) of fabric (Appendix D). Ninety-100% exhaustion rates are typically obtained. The degree of exhaustion achieved depends on the dye used and on the shade, with the darker shades having lower exhaustion rates. The unexhausted (i.e., total amount of dyestuff remaining in the liquor) dyestuff is discharged as effluent with the wastewater. The 3,846 liters (1,000 gallons) - 5,769 liters (1,500 gallons) of effluent water contains from 0-0.5 kilograms (1.2 pounds) of sulfur dye solids per 454 kilograms (1,000 pounds) of fabric processed. A mass balance of the operation is shown in Figure 15.

A typical small plant operates four beck machines processing 2,273 kilograms (5,000 pounds) of fabric per day (Appendix C). If 0.5 kilograms (1.2 pounds) of dye solids result from processing 454 kilograms (1,000 pounds) of fabrics then 2.5 kilograms (6 pounds) of dye solids are generated per day from dyeing 2,273 kilograms (5,000 pounds) of fabric. At this plant, atmospheric becks are not operated full time. However, an average dyeing campaign produces 4,545 kilograms (10,000 pounds) - 6,818 kilograms (15,000 pounds) of fabric. The dyeing campaign averages about 20 hours of machine operation. Therefore, a dyeing campaign will produce 5 kilograms (12 pounds) - 7.5 kilograms (18 pounds) dye solids waste.

Wash water is recycled, however, the volume will vary depending upon the all the fabric and dyes to be used. Therefore, for the purpose of estimating mass balances, it was assumed that the dye solid is discharged with the bath process water and not recycled.

Worker exposure during dye room operations with beck machines is presented here and in Appendix C based on information obtained from the plant visit questionnaire (Appendix C). Three atmospheric beck machines are run by one operator. An operator is required for the "pull-down" procedure during the beck operation. Direct exposure with the dyebath occurs when the operator adjusts or untangles the fabric inside the machine during dyeing operations. This plant utilizes certain industrial hygiene practices during dye room operations to reduce worker exposure. The methods used are (1) gloves worn by workers when handling fabrics, (2) rubber gloves worn by workers at the dye machine, and (3) a washed air ventilation system (wet air scrubber) is utilized.

7.2.1.6 Disperse Dyestuff Procedures. Disperse dyes can be used on acetate, triacetate, polyamide, acrylic, and polyester; their primary use is with polyesters. Since disperse dyes are water insoluble, the

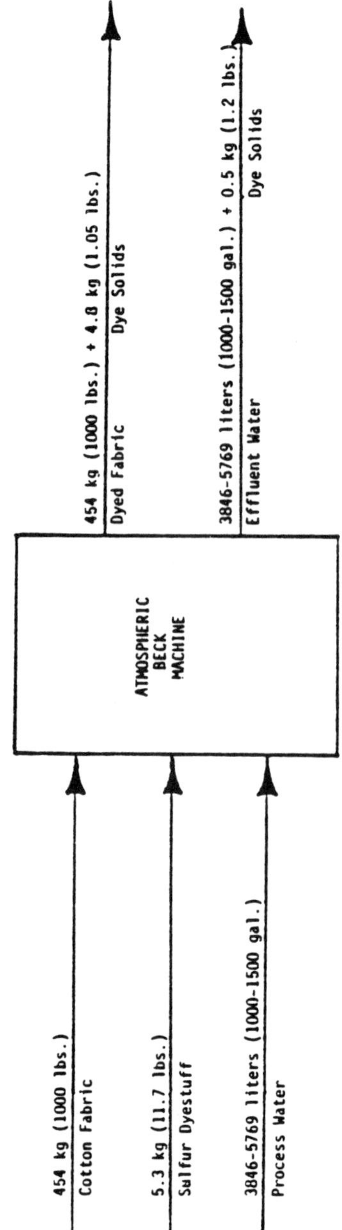


Figure 15. Mass balance of an atmospheric beck operation using sulfur dyes on cotton fabric.

dyeing procedure requires a dispersing agent and filtration steps. The degree of sublimation and leveling of the dye are important selection factors, as well as dye energy level.

Low energy group disperse dyes are dyed at a boil with carriers added. Some typical carriers used are butyl benzoate, biphenyl, and chlorinated benzenes. The low energy dyes are heat fast up to 177°C (350°F). These dyestuffs have extremely poor resistance to sublimation and light when used on texturized polyester. They are normally used to color acetate or nylon at temperatures of 82-100°C (180-212°F).

Medium energy dyes are used mostly between 104-110°C (220-230°F). They provide better sublimation fastness than the low energy group.

High energy dyes are used at temperatures above 129°C (265°F). High energy dyes are suitable for continuous dyeing only because of their high molecular weight and large particle size. These dyes provide all around fastness.

Disperse dyes on triacetate fiber have a slow dyeing rate and require an accelerant or carrier. If dyeing is carried out at temperatures above 121°C (250°F) carriers are not required. An example of a dyeing application cycle (VPI, 1981) for triacetate with disperse dyes is to initially set the dyebath with accelerant or carrier at 7-7.2 pH. The dye is added and the temperature raised to 71°C (160°F) for 30 minutes. Dyebath temperature is then raised to 96-99°C (205-210°F) and dyeing continues for 2-3 hours. The dyeing is followed with a hot rinse at 66°C (150°F) until the lot is clean. After rinsing, the remaining residuals and loose dye are removed from the fiber by scouring wih a dispersant at 49°C (120°F).

Disperse dyes can be applied to acetate fiber on becks, package, skeins, or jigs. The dyebath requires a good dispersing agent and controlled dyeing temperature. Dyebath temperatures from 49-85°C (120°F-185°F) with holds at various temperatures. Dyes are added in portions so as not to cause overuse of dispersing agents and agglomeration of the dyes on the fiber. This dyeing procedure is suggested for light shades and results in a very good fastness.

A general dyebath procedure (VPI, 1981) for disperse dyes on acrylic fibers is to set the dyebath with 1-2% dispersing agent (anionic or non-ionic), maintain the dyebath at slightly alkaline pH (7-7.5) with di-sodium phosphate or tetrasodium phosphate. The dyebath is run for 10-15 minutes, then dyestuffs are added. The temperature is raised quickly to a boil and maintained 30-40 minutes.

Depending on end use, disperse dyes can be used for light to heavy shades on polyamide fibers (nylon). Their wash fastness is low and sublimation fastness is inadequate. A general dye procedure (VPI, 1981) for a nylon dyebath is to set the dyebath at a slightly alkaline pH. An anionic surfactant is added to act as a dispersant. The dye is filtered of lumps and is added, and the temperature is then raised to 96-100°C (205-212°F) for 45-60 minutes.

Three classes of dyes are recommended by fabric suppliers for use on the polyester fibers they produce. The dye classes are disperse, disperse-developed and azoic dyes. A complete range of shades can be obtained with disperse dyes by different methods of application. One application method suggested by the supplier is the carrier dyeing method under pressurized conditions. This procedure results in better fastness properties because dye penetration and the rate of dyeing is greater than with conventional aqueous dye methods. A disadvantage is the adverse effect of some carriers on lightfastness if they are permitted to remain in the fiber after dyeing.

High pressure carrier dyeing methods provide increased dye adsorption and dye transfer over conventional aqueous dyeing. The use of a carrier increases the amount of dye absorbed to about twice that of unassisted dyeing. While dyeing under pressure at 120°C (250°F) with a carrier causes an even greater increase in the rate of dye adsorption, the amount of dye transfer is also increased. This is desirable to facilitate level dyeing. Both the carrier and the high temperatures under pressure increase penetration of the dye into the individual fiber. Complete penetration will result in better fastness to washing, crocking, and sublimation.

The fiber suppliers highly recommend the use of pressure dyeing at 120-130°C (250-260°F) for applying disperse dyes to polyester. The advantages of pressure dyeing over atmospheric dyeing are (1) reduced dye and carrier costs, (2) improved levelness and (3) better colorfastness properties.

The fiber suppliers also suggest paste-type disperse dyes over powder types. The paste-types are more highly dispersed, are of finer particle size, and yield clearer dyeings with better penetration.

The following procedure is recommended by the dye manufacturer for pressure dyeing with disperse dyes on polyester (duPont, 1979):

- Set bath at 71°C (160°F) with
  - 0.5% detergent or surface active agent
  - 1-3% carrier
- Run for 10 minutes, and adjust pH to 4.5-5.5 with acetic acid
- Add disperse dyes
- Run for 10 minutes or until dye is uniformly distributed throughout the load
- Heat bath at 1.5°C (3°F) per minute to 93°C (200°F) and seal machine
- Raise temperature to 130°C (265°F) at 1°C (2°F) per minute
- Run at temperture for one hour
- For dye-additions*, cool to 82°C (180°F); then re-heat to dye temperature at 1°C (2°F) per minute and run 45 minutes
- When shade is reached, cool to 93°C (200°F) and drop dyebath

<u>After-Scour Treatment for Medium-to-Heavy Shades</u>

- Scour at 82°C (180°F) for 20 minutes with:
  - 1.0% sodium hydrosulfite
  - 1.0% caustic soda
  - 1.0% surface active agent

---

* If required to reach shade.

- Rinse hot, and neutralize with acetic acid
- Apply lubricant as needed

After-Scour Treatment for Light Shades

- Scour at 60°C (140°F) for 10 minutes with:
    - 0.5% retarding agent or detergent
    - 1.0% soda ash
- Rinse clear
- Apply lubricant as needed

7.2.1.6.1 Example calculations for using disperse dyes with a jet. An example of a pressure beck is a jet dyeing machine. Jet machines operate on a low liquor ratio with normal fabric to liquor ratio between 1:4 and 1:10. Most jets use 1,650 liters (429 gallons) to 3,300 liters (858 gallons) or 1,622 kilograms (3,577 pounds) to 3,245 kilograms (3,153 pounds) of water for dyeing 200 kilograms (440 pounds) to 400 kilograms (880 pounds) of fabric. Based upon information contained in Appendix C, a range of 0.45-34 kilograms (1-75 pounds) of disperse dye is required for 454 kilograms (1,000 pounds) of fabric. The darker the shade the more dye required. Disperse dyeing requires an estimated 12.4 kilograms (27.2 pounds) of dye per 454 kilograms (1,000 pounds) of fabric (Appendix C), and 90-100% exhaustion rates are attainable. Therefore, the remaining 0-10% is unexhausted and emitted as effluent with the wastewater. The 3,300 liters (858 gallons) or 3,245 kilograms (7,153 pounds) of effluent water will contain from 0 to 1.2 kilograms (2.7 pounds) of disperse dye solids. A mass balance of this operation is shown in Figure 16.

A small plant operation contains 3 jet dyeing machines which process 2,727 kilograms (6,000 pounds) of fabric per day. If 1.2 kilograms (2.7 pounds) of dye solids are produced for 454 kilograms (1,000 pounds) of dyed fabric then 7.2 kilograms (16.2 pounds) will be produced during the dyeing of 2,722 kilograms (6,000 pounds) of fabric per day.

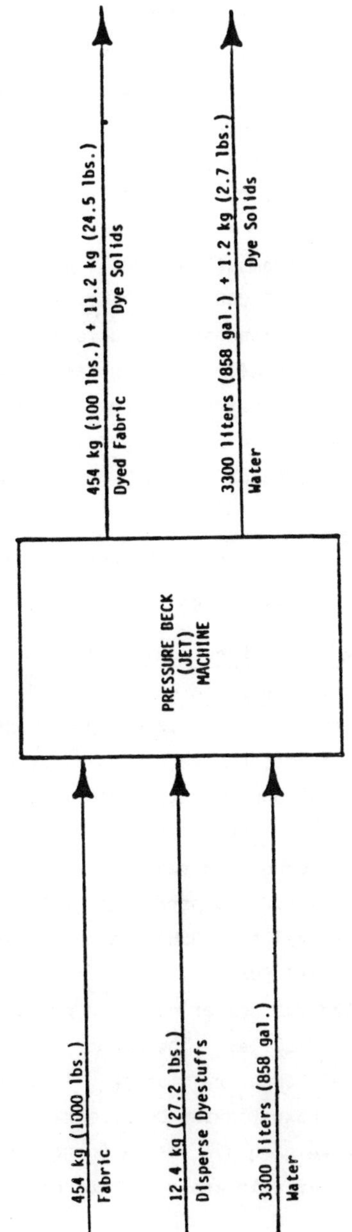


Figure 16. Mass balance of a pressure beck operation using disperse dyes on polyester fabric.

An average dyeing campaign will range from 4,545 kilograms (10,000 pounds) to 6,818 kilograms (15,000 pounds) (Appendix C). Therefore, a dyeing campaign will generate 12 kilograms (27 pounds) to 18 kilograms (40.5 pounds) of dye per campaign.

Water used for washing is recycled in the jet machine. This reduces the amount of water being discharged during dyeing, but it is assumed that all of the dye solids are released with the dyebath.

A large dyeing process uses 60 kilograms (133 pounds) of disperse dyestuffs in processing 5,454 kilograms (12,000 pounds) of fabric. This results in 1.1 kilograms (2.4 pounds) of disperse dyestuffs per 100 kilograms (220 pounds) of fabric. A small dyeing process uses 12.3 kilograms (27 pounds) of disperse dyestuffs for 450 kilograms (991 pounds) of fabric dyed. This results in 2.7 kilograms (6 pounds) of dyestuffs per 100 kilograms (220 pounds) of fabric. Some examples of disperse dye prices are:

Disperse Orange 2RA – $4.00 per kilogram ($1.82 per pound)

Disperse Red F3B – $18.87-$30.00 per kilogram ($8.58-$13.64 per pound)

### 7.2.2 Occupational Exposure to Beck Dyeing Procedures

There are two distinct job functions associated with the dyeing process: (1) dye weighing and handling, and (2) dye equipment operation. Exposure scenarios for each of these functions are discussed separately.

The dye liquor is prepared by drug room operators who weigh and dissolve the required quantities of powder dyestuffs needed in reproducing any given shade of dye. The following drug room scenario was constructed from descriptions in industrial hygiene surveys performed by the National Institute for Occupational Safety and Health (NIOSH) and the Amalgamated Clothing and Textile Workers Union (CTXW) (OSHA, 1980).

The drug room operator scoops the dye powder out of a drum and weighs the required amount on table top scales. The powder is then transferred into a small container for temporary storage. This container is stored near the weighing station. Next, in the color mixing step, the drug room operator pours the pre-weighed dye into a 55-gallon drum where dye, water, and other process chemicals are mixed to formulate a concentrated dye liquor. Agitation is often accomplished manually; but can be accomplished by live steam or mechanical mixers. This dye liquor is then dumped into the dye process equipment (beck machine).

The drug room operator has a high potential for dermal and inhalation exposure. The dermal exposure may occur when scooping the dye out of the receiving drum, during weighing of dyes, and during transfering of the dye in to and out of the temporary storage container. The worker also may be splashed by the concentrated dye liquor while it is being mixed and transferred to the beck dyeing equipment. These dermal exposures can be reduced if workers wear appropriate clothing and gloves and wash after any contact with the dye.

The following dyeing scenario was constructed from descriptions in industrial hygiene surveys performed by NIOSH at several textile mills (NIOSH, A, B, C, D 1978). Beck dye operators load the fabric into the beck dyeing equipment where it is agitated for several hours. Following dyeing to shade, the goods are rinsed and possibly scoured, rerinsed, and aftertreated. These rinse and treatment steps are completed prior to removing the cloth from the dyeing equipment. The dyed fabric is removed manually or with the assistance of a doffing real. Then the fabric is transferred to nipping (or extraction) machines before being dried in an oven.

Dye equipment operators normally do not come in contact with the dry powder dye (NIOSH, A, B, C, D 1978). Therefore, inhalation exposure to the powder dye should be insignificant or minimal for these workers. However, they may inhale the dye carriers as they are emitted in the steam evaporating from the dye bath. This exposure seems likely since it is reported that the operator periodically works under the ventilation hood located over the top of the dye bath (NIOSH, B, 1978).

Monitoring data was obtained from NIOSH industrial hygiene surveys of several textile mills using benzidine dyes. NIOSH monitoring data from three surveys are presented in Appendix E as a representative sample of airborne concentrations of dye particles to which textile mill workers are potentially exposed. In all of the textile mills surveyed, powdered dyes were treated with mineral oil in an attempt to reduce airborne concentrations. One textile mill surveyed in 1977 used powder benzidene dyes to dye cotton disposable work gloves. Only beck dyeing equipment was used in this mill.

Worker exposure during jet process operation is described here and in the plant visit questionnaire in Appendix C. Four jet units require two operators. Since the jet is a closed system, the only exposure occurs when workers are adjusting or untangling the fabric inside the machine during dyeing, sampling for shade (patching), and unloading the machine. This plant utilizes certain industrial hygiene practices to reduce worker exposure during dye room operations. The methods used are: (1) gloves worn by workers when handling dyed fabrics, (2) rubber gloves worn by workers at the dye machines, and (3) a washed air ventilation system is utilized.

### 7.2.3 Beck Dyeing Equipment on the Market

Textile machinery distributors and manufacturers were contacted regarding the types of beck dyeing equipment on the market. One of the machinery distributors provided a technical information brochure on the short liquor ratio dyeing machines (see Figure 17). The distributor presents this new type of becks as the perfected short liquor ratio dyeing machine and the optimum machine for tubular fabrics. The high operation efficiency of this machine is an advantage; it substantially lowers dyeing costs by saving chemical additives and energy, and uses up to 60% less water and effluent in comparison to similar machines. The distributor presents a comparison of the new short liquor dyeing machine to a conventional dyeing winch. For the dyeing of a 400 kilogram (882 pound) lot the dye liquor ratio is 1:6 for the new machines versus a 1:20 for the conventional machines. The new machines have a 6-hour dyeing time compared to an 8-hour dyeing time for the conventional machines. The new machine is offered in models from 250-550 kg/load (Bruckner 1979 and 1980).

The carpet batch-dyeing winch is utilized for final phase dyeing. In the carpet industry, dyeing is included during the final phase of the carpet production. This allows the carpet producer to keep undyed

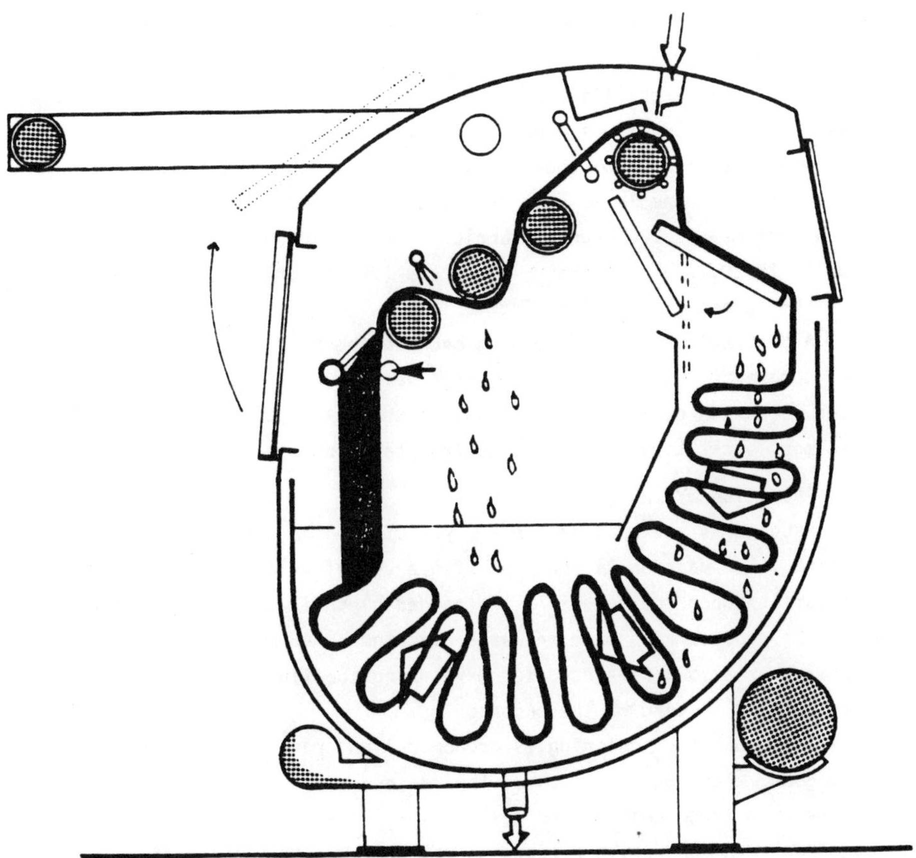

Figure 17. Bruckner's Haspelflow: "A new generation of perfected short liquor ratio dyeing machines."

material in stock to custom dye to the consumer's request. The distributor can customize the system from small batches to 1,200 running meters (1,312 yards) per load.

The general capabilities of the beck machines on the market today were described by a textile machinery producer. The winch or beck type equipment operates at or about 27-40 kilograms (60-90 pounds) fabric per beck foot. An example is a 12 foot beck operating with approximately 373 kilograms) (1,000 pounds) fabric. The liquor ratios are usually 18-20:1. Therefore, 9 kilograms (20 pounds) water are required for 5 kilograms (1 pound) of fabric.

A difficulty with determining beck equipment characteristics was made apparent in a conversation with a machine distributor. Through his experience with carpet dyeing in the northern Atlantic states, he found that most becks today are homemade fabricated open-atmosphere vessels.

## 7.3 PAD/BATCH DYEING

Padding is the application of dyestuff to fabrics by a padding machine. The machine is equipped with a set of wringers that force the dyestuff through the material; the padded cloth is then developed in a batching procedure in an open washer machine or an exhaustion machine. A steam box also can be used for developing the final color or for pad-steaming instead of the padbatching.

This method of coloring is economical and rate of production is very good. Fast colors, such as the vat dyes, are used to a great degree when large columns are desired and large production volumes are required. The pad/batch process can be used for the application of vat, sulfur, azoic, solubilized vat, and diazotized and developed direct dyes.

Pad-batch systems differ in the final step that they use to develop the fabric color. Some systems roll the fabric on a beam after fabric impregnation and squeeze the fabric through the pad mangle. This roll or batch is allowed to stand at room temperature. Another system (see Figure 18) utilizes a steam box for heating the roll of padded fabric. Storing fabric under controlled temperature and humidity provides for

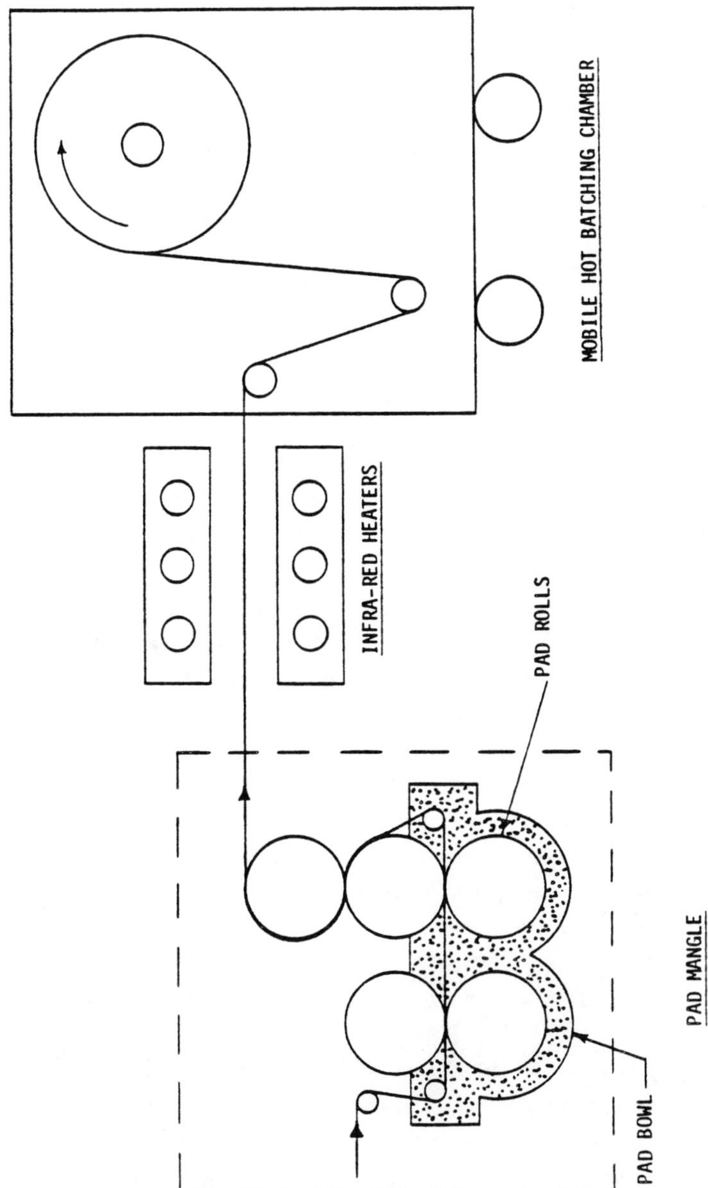


Figure 18. Schematic of pad-roll machine.

controlled shade development. Other versions of the batching process while open washing machines or circulating dye machines for chemically binding the padded dye inside the fabric.

The pad mangle forms the first part of the machine. The entire width fabric is mordanted and dyed by being passed through the pad mangle. There are various configurations of padding systems. In each system the fabric enters a trough and passes through the dye liquor. It is then squeezed between the system of bowls on rollers. The point where the excess dye is squeezed out is referred to as the nip. Constant pressure at the nip allows controlled and uniform retention of the dye liquor into the fabric.

The amount of dye liquor picked up by the fabric is controlled by the pressure on the squeeze rolls at the nip. The wet pick-up can vary from 60-110% of fabric weight. Pressure on the nip rolls is controlled either by a pneumatic or hydraulic cylinder. The pad rolls are constructed of rubber or stainless steel. Pad rolls can be arranged differently as combinations of rubber and stainless steel rolls in a pad bowl. The path of the fabric through the rolls in a system begins with the fabric being immersed in the dye liquor; then being squeezed through the nip of two rolls. Then the fabric is reimmersed in the dye again and the squeezing is repeated through another nip between two rolls.

### 7.3.1 Pad/Batch Dyeing Procedures

During the 1950's and 1960's, jigs were replaced by continuous dyeing ranges for cotton dyeing. This technique was developed prior to 1940, but its use was delayed by World War II. In the 1950's several innovations by chemical, dyestuff and machinery companies led to increased use of the continuous range method and decreased use of dye jigs for dyeing cotton fabrics (Hudak, 1976). Semi-continuous processes of the pad/batch methods of dyeing were part of the change over from exhaustion dyeing.

The pad/batch process is defined as a padding system with a beam machine for semi-continuous dyeing. Other exhausting machines also can be utilized for the batching operation. A jig machine can be used satisfactorily to control shade development from certain dyeings.

Better control over shade development can also be acquired with the pad/batch system by storing the batched beam of fabric under controlled temperature and humidity conditions.

The various versions of the pad/batch process are the pad-roll, pad-batch, and pad-steam systems. These systems are described in Section 7.3.2.

7.3.1.1 Reactive Dyestuff Pad/Batch Procedures. Pad/batch dyeing is the cheapest method for applying reactives; the reproducibility is good, and the dyes can be applied to both small and large batches. Dyestuff selection depends on what batching time is to be used. Short batching times are 2-4 hours, long times range from 12-24 hours. If long runs are anticipated, short batching systems will be advantageous in decreasing the overall length of the dyeing process.

Reactive dyes generally do not have a good affinity for cellulose. While some types may exhaust better than others, pad dyeing can utilize reactive dyes with a low affinity or degree of reactivity. Since no chemical bond spontaneously forms between the dye and the fiber, the addition of alkali in a batch machine is necessary to promote formation of the chemical bond between the fiber and the dyestuff. When the reaction is completed through a pad/batch system, the dye is no longer soluble in water and the wash fastness is very good (VPI, 1981).

The cellulose/nylon blend is usually dyed with a combination of reactive and acid dyestuffs. Reactive dyes have good wash fastness on cotton. A two-step process is required for applying the two dyestuffs. The reactive dye is padded onto the blend while the dyeing of polyamide (nylon) with acid dyes can be accomplished on the jig, in a winch beck, or in a circulating machine.

A dye manufacturer suggests storing some types of padded fabric before batch developing. Storage for 1-2 hours will promote dye diffusion. During storage, the padded fabric should be wrapped in felt and polyethylene to avoid water spotting or migration (ICI, 1971).

One dye manufacturer suggests using a cold pad-batch method for applying all types of reactive dyes (duPont, 1971). This method is presented as the simplest approach for dyeing fast shades on cellulosic piece goods. The procedure is specific for piece goods but the same general principles can be applied to other types of material such as yarn, tow, top or loose fiber where the roll of fabric is rotated. The preferred procedure is the short (2 hour) pad-batch process. However, in special cases a longer batching process (2-4 hours or 24) is used.

The recommended procedure for this pad-batch process is to use an automatic mixer (4:1 mixing ratio). A similar procedure can be used when no mixer is available. The dye and alkali should only be mixed immediately before padding begins. The procedure is outlined as follows (ICI, 1971).

- Dissolve dye and filter dye solution. Add urea where necessary.
- Adjust the temperature to the predetermined value between 20-30°C (75-85°F) and the volume to 4/5 of the final volume required.
- Add the predissolved or diluted wetting agent immediately before the final adjustment to the correct volume.
- Prepare the alkali solution at five times the concentration required in the final pad liquor and adjust the temperature between 20-30°C (75-85°F).
- Mix 4 parts dye solution to 1 part alkali immediately before padding. The dye manufacturer strongly recommends that the dye and alkali be mixed automatically.
- The material is padded. Check that the dye liquor temperature is correct.
- The material is batched.

<u>After Batching</u>

- First cover the material with a wrapper of dry material and then with a sheet of polyethylene film to prevent evaporation.

- o Store the fabric for the appropriate length of time. Storage conditions, although not critical, are important. Storage temperature should be close to the padding temperature; never below 20°C (70°F).
- o Wash the material in any of the conventional ways, on the jig, winch, continuously or using the perforated beam washing system.

Standard additives recommended by the dye manufacturer for pad-batch dyeing vary with the concentration of dye required to achieve a desired shade. If 0-5 parts of dye per 1,000 parts of pad liquor is required, then 5 parts of soda ash is required. When between 5-30 parts of dye per 1,000 parts of pad liquor is used, an equal weight of soda ash to dye is needed. For dye concentrations above 30 parts dye per 1,000 parts of pad liquor, 30 parts of soda ash is required.

A large plant with a batch process pad/batch system will process 1,361 kilogram (3,000 pounds) per day of cotton (Appendix D). The dye usage estimate for this plant is 0.7 kilograms (1.5 pounds) of reactive dye per 45 kilograms (100 pounds) of cloth dyed. The degree of exhaustion from this process ranges from 60-95% (Appendix D, p. 369). The batch is rinsed with water for 4 hours at 26-38 liters (7-10 gallons) per minute. This results in 6,240-9,120 liters (1,648-2,409 gallons) or 6,232-9,110 kilograms (13,739-20,084 pounds) of rinse water containing 5-40% of the dyestuff being discharged. A wet roll of fabric will have a range of 822-4,572 meters (900-5,000 yards) and weigh approximately 3,175 kilograms (7,000 pounds) (Appendix D). Therefore, the dye usage estimate of 0.7 kilograms of dye per 45 kilograms of fabric will result in 48 kilograms (105 pounds) of reactive dyestuffs required to dye the 3,175 kilogram (7,000 pound) roll of fabric, as shown in Figure 19.

The example plant has only the one pad/batch system. This system processes 1,361 kilograms (3,000 pounds) of cotton per day (Appendix D). Therefore, the estimated dye release per day ranges approximately from 1 to 8.1 kilograms (2-18 pounds) per day based on 1,361 kilograms (3,000 pounds) of cotton dyed.

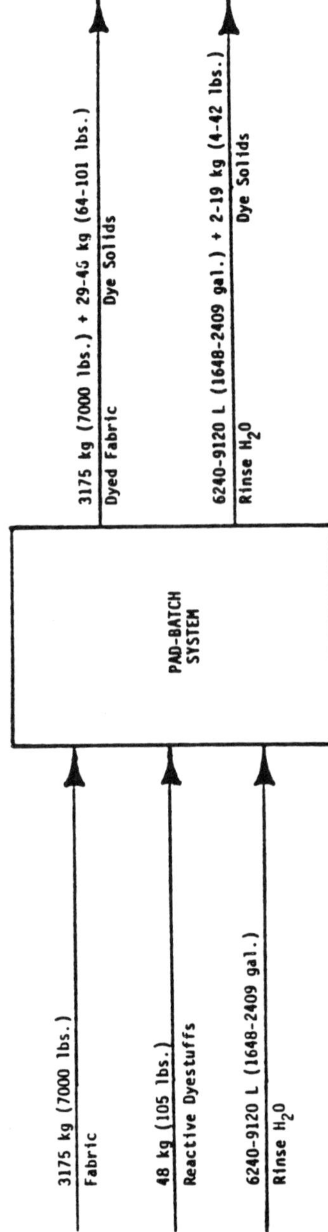


Figure 19. Mass balance of a pad/batch operation for reactive dyeing of cotton.

7.3.1.2 Vat Dyestuff Pad/Batch Procedures. Vat dyes are very popular for pad and continuous processes. The pigment pad-jig system is a form of pad/batch dyeing that can be found in many dye houses. The Williams Unit and the pad-steam process are two very well known systems used by cotton dyers. The units consist of a padder, drier, chemical applicator, wash chamber, oxidation chamber, and a series of wash boxes. These processes are designed for high speeds and high volume production.

Application of the vat dyestuffs is complicated and requires the two-step process of pad/batch systems. Vat dyes are not water soluble and the process of applying them to the fiber requires a number of steps.

The goal is to form the insoluble dye inside the fiber, or alternatively to use the pigment method to apply the dye to the fiber. In the pigmentation or pigment padding process, vat dyes in a very fine state are deposited by padding as the non-substantive, original insoluble dye from an aqueous dispersion on fiber or fabric uniformly. The dye is vatted on the fiber material by batching the dye in a bath with sodium hydrosulphite and sodium hydroxide so that almost instantaneous absorption of the vatted dye takes place in the fiber substance. The reduced vat process is also referred to as the leuco vat process. In the process, the insoluble vat dye is converted into its soluble and substantive form (leuco form) prior to being padded to the textile material. The reduction is carried out with the help of sodium hydroxide and sodium hydrosulphite either in a small amount of water (stock vat) or in bulk (long liquor). After the leuco form of the dye is taken up by the fiber substance, regeneration of the original form of the dye is carried out by oxidation in a batching procedure. Soaping aftertreatments are required to ensure proper fastness properties (Shenai, 1973).

7.3.1.3 Azoic Dyestuff Pad/Batch Procedures. The application of azoic dyes is best suited to lower liquor ratio and pad dyeing machines. The majority of the dyes are applied in a two-stage method such as the pad/batch method.

In the first stage, the fiber or fabric is naphtholated by pad application. The amount of fixed naphtol on the fiber determines the final shade and also the amount of diazonium salt or base required to produce that shade. After the padding the fiber is dried to remove any excess napthol which could cause spotty dyeing.

The next stage in the process involves coupling the naphtholated fiber with an excess of diazonium salt or base; the excess is released in effluent. This batching process can be accomplished in a package or jig machine; most dyers use a jig. If a base is used in the coupling step, it first must be diazotized with sodium nitrite and hydrochloric acid. The temperature must be maintained at a maximum of 65-70°C (149-158°F). The coupling process is simplified by using a diazonium salt because the salt need only be dissolved in water. The pH of the coupling bath is very critical and should be maintained at the level prescribed by the dyestuff manufacturer. The pH levels vary from 4 to 8 for different coupling baths.

Soaping off after dyeing is important to maintain the dye's fastness properties and help develop the true shade. Some dyeing combinations may require soaping with a synthetic dispersing agent and soda ash at the boil; others require neutral soaping at 140-150°C (284-302°F) (VPI, 1981).

7.3.2 Pad/Batch Equipment

All pad/batch systems are essentially the same for the first step of the two-step procedure. Most machines consist of a jacketed padder with a temperature controlled feed tank and sometimes infrared heating equipment for raising the temperature of the cloth after padding. The second step is accomplished in different ways by different systems.

7.3.2.1 Pad-Roll Systems. The pad-roll machine is a version of the pad/batch system. The pad-roll machine is used extensively for woven fabrics, and is suitable for applying dyes to warp-knitted goods. The machine contains a pad mangle, a pre-heating unit, and a batching chamber. Dye diffuses into the fibers while the fabric rotates on the roll at the prescribed temperature and humidity for the required time.

The pad and mangle can be arranged vertically or horizontally, with the vertical tangenital take-off preferred to avoid leaving the guide rollers.

General operational procedures for pad-roll systems were presented in Haigh's Dyeing Machinery Survey. The process begins with the prepared fabric being padded with dye and auxiliary products, then passed between the infrared heater to raise the temperature quickly to the desired dyeing temperature without causing evaporation of liquor (at 50-95°C (122-203°F)). Next, the fabric is batched on a large diameter roller (holds up to 5,000 meters (5,468 yards)) in the hot chamber. The padding trough should be thermo-regulated, and the mangle pressure adjusted to give about 1:1 pick-up, with uniform squeezing. Infrared heating is adjusted to maintain the wet-bulb temperature constant, approximately 5°C (41°F) below the dry-bulb temperature, in order to avoid evaporation or condensation. Batching is achieved by maintaining straight fabric edges, and keeping the fabric free from wrinkles, and under low tension. An electrical heating device and a steam inlet valve are regulated to provide a wet-bulb temperature of 5°C (41°F) below the dry-bulb temperature, as during the pre-heating. These conditions must be maintained during the winding-on of the fabric, and during the rotation of the beam.

Dyeing time is determined by the depth of the dyeing, the type of dye and the type and structure of the fabric. For example, direct dyes applied to cotton goods are dyed for the following amount of time at 85°C (185°F) dry-bulb, 80°C (176°F) wet-bulb temperature.

| | |
|---|---|
| Light shades, light-weight fabrics | - 3 hours |
| Heavier depths | - 4-5 hours |
| Navy blue and black shades | - 8 hours |

7.3.2.2 Pad-Steam Systems. A version of the pad/batch method is the pad-steam process. The pad-steam process can be used to apply vat, sulfur, azoic, solubilized vat, and diazotized and developed direct dyes to cotton. The process is used to dye polyester-cellulose blends with vat dyes following the thermofixation of the vat dye on the cotton component. The units of pad-steam machines are pad-mangles, hot-flue driers, steamers, wash-boxes, and final drying units. The units can be arranged in the appropriate order for the type of dye being employed. For the most part, the pad-steam process is considered a continuous dyeing range (Haigh, 1971).

The pad-thermosol system is a type of dye range similar to the pad-steam. The primary purpose of thermo dyeing is to dye polyester fibers. Although other fibers can be dyed with thermo energy, for example cotton with reactive dyes, the technology primarily apples to polyesters. Thermosol treatment occurs after the fabric has been padded with dye and dryed. The temperature range for thermosol treatment ranges from 200-220°C (392-428°F). The exposure time of the treatment varies from 50-120 seconds, depending on the dyestuff selection.

Variations in pad-thermol dye units are numerous. Some of the possible routings of semi-continuous thermosol dyeing units are as follows (VPI, 1981).

pad→pre-dry→dry→thermosol→pad/batch→wash
pad→pre-dry→dry→thermosol→jig
pad→pre-dry→dry→thermosol→pad/batch→jig
pad→pre-dry→dry→thermosol→beck

7.3.2.3 Pad-Batch System. A popular semi-continuous dyeing process is the use of the jig in a two-stage pad/batch system. The jig units can be used to batch the fabric after padding and then to treat the fabric with other dyes, chemical coupling agents, or temperature controlled washes. An example is the use of reactive and naphtol dyes with the pad-jig system. The fabric is padded with the napthol or reactive dyes, batched by being rolled up on the jig, and subsequently coupled or washed on the jig machine (VPI, 1981).

Other machines can be used for the batching portion, such as becks or package machines (for yarns), but they are not used as much as the jig machine. This may be due to the fact that the other machines require handling after the padding step for loading the fabric into the machines; the jig machines load (batch) the fabric straight onto the shafts used for winding the fabric back and forth through the machine.

### 7.3.3 Advantages and Disadvantages of Pad/Batch Dyeing

Continuous processes are economically feasible if the following conditions are met: (a) long lengths of fabric must be dyed the same shade; (b) sufficient annual production requires that the expensive machinery be in constant use; and (c) shade matching tolerance of a greater degree than exhaustion processes (of the order of 1/16 7.5%) is required. It is also necessary to ensure that the unit be readily cleaned to effect efficient change-over from one shade to another.

Some of the process problems that occur with these methods, are different from those associated with normal dyeing problems. A measured quantity of dye liquor must be evenly applied across the width of the fabric in such a way that there is no difference between the shade obtained at the beginning of a batch and that obtained at the end. The affinity effects of dyes or auxiliary chemicals must be prevented if fabric impregnation by the dye is to be unhindered.

A comparison of the cost efficiency of the pad/batch dyeing system vs. an exhaust dyeing process was presented in a seminar at North Carolina State University's Department of Textile Colouring. The results are presented in Table 39. The exhaust system used is an atmospheric dye beck. The total cost per pound of dyed 100% cotton fabric was $0.022 for the pad/batch and $.109 for the beck unit. The large cost difference results from pad/batch system energy and water savings.

One dyestuff manufacturer disputed the economic advantage of pad-batch dyeing used in the industry today. He reasoned that the amount of labor involved in the pad/batch system escalates the cost over the benefits of the dyeing advantages because the fabric requires handling at the two separate processes.

## 7.4 TRANSFER PRINTING

Transfer printing technology is a two-step process. The first step is the printing of the desired design onto the transfer paper by using inks containing sublimable dyestuffs. The paper can be printed by a gravure, flexographic, lithographic or rotary screen brochure. Secondly, the paper is placed in contact with the fabric and the print is transferred to the dye receptive fabric under controlled conditions of

TABLE 39. COMPARISON OF PAD/BATCH VS. EXHAUST DYEING
100% COTTON FABRIC (NCSU, 1982)

| Item | Pad/batch metric (English) | Beck metric (English) |
|---|---|---|
| Energy | 1750 Btu/lb. (794 Btu/kg) | 9100 Btu/lb. (4128 Btu/kg) |
| Water | 1.5 gal/lb. (12.5 L/kg) | 17 gal/lb. (141 L/kg) |
| Labor | \$.008/lb. (\$.018/kg) | \$.027/lb. (0.06/kg) |
| Fuel cost | \$.011/lb. (includes drying) (\$.024/kg) | \$.028/lb. (\$0.06/kg) |
| Water cost | \$.001/lb. (\$.0022/kg) | \$0.01/lb. (\$.0022/kg) |
| Dry cost | Approximately equal both systems | |
| Chemical cost | | |
| Salt | \$.000/lb. (\$.000/kg) | \$0.35/lb. (\$0.77/kg) |
| Alkali | \$.002/lb. (\$0.0044/kg) | \$0.009/lb. (\$0.0088/kg) |
| Total | \$.022/lb. (\$.048/kg) | \$.109/lb. (\$.239/kg) |
| Annual cost (9,652,500 lb/yr.) | \$212,355 | \$1,052,122 |

Savings with pad/batch - \$0.191/kg (\$.087/lb.) or \$839,767/year.

Pad/batch system - pad entry, guiders, pad, batcher, two beam wash-off stands, metering pump, ten perforated beams, rotating A-frames, cradle let-off, spray.

Exhaust dye system - Nineteen 1,000 lb (454 kg) atmospheric dye becks.

time, temperature, and pressure. The process is accomplished either through a flat bed press for cut-parts or a continuous rotary calendar for yardgoods printing.

There are three methods of transfer printing: dry, melt and wet. These three methods will be discussed further in Section 7.4.1. The dry transfer is known as vapor phase transfer or sublimation transfer. The basis of the dry method is the sublimation of the dye molecules on the paper, followed by condensation of the dye on the fabric surface and diffusion of the dye into the fiber molecule.

Melt or decal transfer consists of printing dyes/pigments and chemicals with a thermoplastic binder on paper. This decal then is transferred by heat and pressure to the fabric.

Wet transfer is similar to the dry transfer except that with the former, the fabric is heated beforehand. Wet transfer consists of padding the substrate with a carrier to increase its affinity for the dye compound printed on the paper. The wet system was designed because the dry system can only be used with certain fiber types. Wet systems such as DewPrint claim to permit transfer printing of natural fibers, blends, nylon and acrylics.

Printing of the transfer paper is generally done on a standard gravure printing press. Some textile dyeing machinery such as rotary screens, can be used for printing transfer paper. However, the gravure printing process can produce designs that the rotary screen cannot match. Flexography and litography (offset) are other methods of printing transfer paper (Reichman, 1976).

The printing vehicles are generally disperse dyes with sublimation points of approximately 200°C (392°F) and companion inks. Some basic dyes also are being used but these do not produce as clear results as the disperse dyes. The basic dye class is usually confined to transfer printing knitted fabrics made of acrylic.

Considering the structure of world textile production, one forecast is for about 3,000 million square meters (3588 million square yards) of fabric to be transfer printed in 1980 compared to a world production of about 450 million square meters (538 million square yards) in 1974.

In the United States transfer printing was expected to have captured 20% of the 4 billion meter (4.4 billion yard) print fabric market in the Unites States with about 60% being screen printed and 20% roller printed by 1980 (Hudak, 1976).

7.4.1 Transfer Printing Method

7.4.1.1 Sublimation Transfer Process. The key element in transfer printing is sublimation, the chemical process whereby a solid is converted into a vapor (by heat) and back again into a solid when cooled. It is for this reason that the process is sometimes referred to as sublimation, gaseous, or vapor phase transfer printing. The process also is called dry heat pressure printing (Reichman, 1976).

The transfer printing process was pioneered by the Swiss-based firm Sublistatic S.A. It became commercially important after an exhibition in Atlantic City in 1969 and was first described as dry dyeing.

Many firms print paper suitable for sublimation transfer printing and it is common to hear the phrase "Sublistatic printing." However, this is incorrect unless the paper was produced by the Sublistatic Corporation and sold under their trademark. Sublimation transfer printing requires dyes, invariably disperse dyes, which will sublime at temperatures below those which will damage the fabric. The dye (in gaseous form) is able to penetrate rapidly into the fiber. Such penetrated dye exhibits the same level of fastness as if it had been fixed by conventional methods. Nothing else sublimes from this type of transfer paper so the operation avoids both a subsequent fixing and a washing-off process. Given a supply of suitably printed sublimation transfer paper all that is needed for transfer printing is a supply of fabric and a heat transfer press (Clarke, 1977).

7.4.1.2 Melt Transfer Process. A relatively small number of firms specialize in the melt transfer process. Little data have been published on the ink compositions used, but PVC is employed in some instances. The most successful areas in which heat-melt transfers are used are labels, motifs for T-shirts and similar outlets. The transfers are supplied either on paper or transparent plastic film. The common features of this type of transfer with other methods of transfer printing are that coloring is by pigments and the printed ink is thermoplastic (heat pressing causes the pattern to adhere to the fabric). The paper or plastic sheet in the non-printed areas does not adhere and can be peeled off, leaving the pattern. No further treatment is necessary to fix the transferred pigments and no washing-off process is required (Clarke, 1977).

7.4.1.3 Wet Transfer Process. The Star and Fastran processes are two wet transfer printing processes. Both use conventional paper-printing machinery to print a variety of textile dyes on paper. The paper, which may be stored until it is convenient to process it further, is then used to effect a transfer onto fabric. Some form of dye fixation and washing off is required.

The Star process was named after the pioneering Italian firm, Stampa Tessuti Artistici of Milan, and is the older of the two processes. The Star system uses inks and papers so that when cloth and transfer paper are passed through the nip formed by a heated metal calender bowl and a cotton-covered one, a large proportion of the dye is physically transferred to the fabric. Both dye fixation and washing-off operations are needed to complete the process.

The Fastran process was originally developed for printing woollen garments such as sweaters. It requires a flat-bed non-continuous press. The garment is first padded in a special fixer. Next, a sheet of transfer paper is then placed on each side of the garment, printed side to the fiber surface, and a sandwich is formed by placing the composite between two sheets of silicone rubber. Depending on the press size, a number of such sandwiches may be loaded. When the press head is lowered, the garments and transfer are securely held. The Intertherm press, which generates heat by radio-frequency heating, is recommended for this type of transfer printing. The term wet-transfer is often applied to these processes, but they are different than other wet processes. With Fastran the transfer and fixation takes place in an aqueous medium. In the others heat and pressure cause the dye to transfer to the fabric and fixation is a separate treatment. In all cases a washing-off treatment (aqueous or solvent) is needed to remove surplus dye, resin binder, and other unwanted materials from the fabric (Clarke, 1977).

### 7.4.2 Transfer Printing Procedures

Wet transfer printing utilizes the migration properties of soluble dyes under hot aqueous conditions, to enable a dye to transfer from an ink layer on paper into water filled interstices of an adjacent fabric. The water contained in the interstices of the fabric acts as a miniature dye bath and causes localized dyeing to take place. To assist the dyeing process and to maintain pattern definition, textile auxiliary products are introduced into the water phase. Consequently, a thickener acts as a catalyst or fixation agent for the dyes during transfer. The pick up of the solution or thickener varies from fiber to fiber and also with fabric construction.

It is essential to this wet process that a film of moisture be kept at all times against the ink film of the paper. The pressure rollers play an important part in maintaining this moisture film. The latter allows the design to be transferred from paper to fabric with fixation being almost simultaneous due to the rapid dyeing conditions associated with an extremely low liquor ratio. Fixation is complete after one time around the cylinder and further fixation is not necessary.

The rollers may be adjusted in increasing scale of pressure creating a situation where dyes are not released faster than the fabric can absorb them. As the fabric begins its journey around the cylinder it slowly heats up and thus is more receptive to the dye. Increased roller pressure through this journey allows slow and even transfer with strong fixation due to increased pressure. The operating controls of the padder and pressure rolls are interlocked to prevent pattern smudging; the pressure on the rolls must not exceed that of the padder.

The DewPrint machine marketed by the Gesner Company uses the wet transfer printing method. The machine utilizes the wet process because fabric is "wet-out" in a solution containing a thickener of the normal textile type dissolved in water. There is also a pH buffer system for maintaining the correct pH during the fixation stage. A description of the operational procedure of the wet transfer machine is as follows:

Fabric is unrolled into a padder equipped with a wet-out tank containing the thickening solution. Accurate guiding equipment insures that the fabric is matched precisely with the padder prior to entering the machine. The calender must have a moisture proof blanket similar to the kind used on rotary screen printing machines. Later it will become apparent why a moisture proof blanket is essential to this wet transfer system.

After leaving the padder, the fabric is fed into the machine on the blanket. Where the fabric begins its journey around the heat cylinder it is joined by the special transfer paper. There are nine individual pressure rolls around the cylinder. These rolls are controlled separately and generally are increased in pressure as the fabric passes around the cylinder or bowl.

The cylinder is steam heated at a temperature of approximately 107°C (225°F). Once the fabric passes around the circumference of the cylinder it exits and separates from the paper. The fabric then passes through a standard J-box washer. This is necessary to remove the residue of the wetting solution. The fabric then passes through an extractor and is folded in a mill truck. Next it is dried and framed to the desired width on standard auxiliary equipment (Reichman, 1976).

Some recommended times and temperatures for the use of a transfer press with various fibers are as follows:

| Fibers | Temperature | Time |
|---|---|---|
| Polyester | 200-230°C (392-446°F) | 20-45s |
| Nylon 66 | 190-210°C (374-410°F) | 20-40s |
| Nylon 6 | 190-200°C (374-392°F) | 20-30s |
| Secondary acetate | 190-200°C (374-392°F) | 15-30s |
| Cellulose triacetate | 190-210°C (374-410°F) | 20-40s |
| Acrylics | | |
| Courtelle | 190°C (374°F) | 20-40s |
| Acrilan, Orlon, etc. | 200-210°C (392-410°F) | 15-30s |

The recommended time and temperature conditions for various fibers given above are average values. The temperature is that of the press head; the temperature achieved on the fabric will be influenced by the press pressure and the thickness of paper between the press and the fabric.

The thickness of the fabric itself is also an important factor since a thick fabric requires more heat to reach a high enough temperature for transfer than a thin fabric. It is recommended that experiments with transfer printing first be conducted at the lowest temperature and shortest time. If this is not satisfactory, the time should be extended before the temperature is raised (Clarke, 1977).

The typical plant described in Appendix C has two transfer printing machines. The two machines have a production rate of 13,716 meters (15,000 yards) of polyester fabric per day. The given fabric weights for 227-340 grams (8-12 ounces) fabric is 454 kilograms (1,000 pounds) for 1,463 meters (1,600 yards). Based on this data, the 13,716 meter production per day would weigh approximately 4,252 kilograms (9,375 pounds). Estimated disperse dyestuffs used for this plant are 0.5 kilograms (1.1 pounds) per 45 kilograms (100 pounds) of fabric. Therefore, 47 kilograms (103 pounds) of disperse dyestuff would be required to process the 13,716 meters of fabric or 0.5 kilograms (1.1 pounds) per 45 kilograms (100 pounds) of fabric.

The transfer printing method will exhaust almost 100% of the disperse dyestuffs from the transfer paper onto the fabric. Disposal of the transfer paper after printing produces a paper waste stream; dye wastes are produced during the printing of the transfer paper.

### 7.4.3 Transfer Printing Machines

Sublimation transfer printing onto synthetic fabrics is based on the use of disperse or other sublimable dyestuffs. A variety of machines are suitable for printing onto piece goods. The basic operational procedures are as follows. A particular variety of prepared paper is printed in a design embodying one or more colors with specially formulated printing inks, actually dyes. The paper is then placed on the surface of the knitted fabric or textile. At elevated heat (390°F) plus pressure, the dye is sublimed and absorbed into the fabric.

Most machines have oil heated cylinders and are belt driven. Processing temperatures vary among the different machines, but roughly fall within a range of 150°-250°C (302-482°F). Production rates range up to 14 meters per minute (15 yards per minute). Appreciable differences exist among the transfer papers of different makers.

Temperatures around 180°C (356°F) were appropriate for acrylic fibers, 200°C (392°F) for nylon, and 210°C (410°F) for polyesters and triacetate (Textile Month, 1972).

Two distinct pieces of equipment have been developed for the transfer printing of yardgoods and assembled garment forms. The flat bed press is used on assembled garments and continuous calenders have been developed for knitted fabrics.

The flat bed press is used for transferring a design from printed paper to the front, back, or both sides of a sweater or knitted blouse or a pair of stockings. This type of equipment is generally no different from a standard buck used for pressing knitted and woven garments. Some companies have engineered specially designed presses for transfer printing. These are either the twinheaded type or use a conveyor or similar arrangement. Generally, such presses are capable of reaching temperatures as high as 220°C (428°F) and pressure up to .14 kilograms per square cubic meter (2 pounds per square inch).

The continuous calenders have been developed with special fabric feeding devices. Heating of the fabric usually is accomplished with oil bath-heated cylinders. There has been some use of a unit which is heated by infrared means (Reichman, 1976).

The paper and fabric should be in contact for approximately 30 seconds with the drum at the recommended temperatures. This varies with dye color, weight of fabric, yarn content and finish of fabric and type and weight of paper.

Machines used for heat transfer printing continuous lengths of knitted cloths are referred to in the trade as heat transfer printing calenders. These machines are used on warp knit fabric such as single or double knit tricot or tubular fabric. There are three types of printing machines, each based on the system used in heating the cylinder. These three types are: (1) calenders that rely on an indirect method of heating the cylinder, which utilizes circulating hot oil; (2) calenders in which the cylinder is directly heated by electricity with contact coils or some similar element; (3) calenders whose cylinders are directly heated by an open gas flame (Reichman, 1976).

### 7.4.4 Heat Transfer Printing Calenders on the Market

7.4.4.1 Stork-Brabant (Holland) Vacuum Transfer Machine. This machine uses high vacuum in a continuous transfer machine. Both paper and fabric are easily fed in and discharged yet the process is fully controlled by the operator. The transfer process takes place in a perfectly sealed area with an accurately adjustable vacuum.

In 1975 this machine had a drum diameter of 1.4 meters (4½ feet) and ran at a speed of 41 meters per minute (45 yards per minute) with a drum temperature of 210°C (410°F). Very good dyestuff penetration is evident in the cloth at a dwell time of 4½ seconds while other printers normally have a dwell time of 12 seconds (Reichman, 1976).

7.4.4.2 Singer Machine Model 8000. This machine can utilize all types of transfer printing paper. The cylinder is 122 centimeter (48 inches) in diameter by 203 centimeters (80 inches) face with an internal spiral between its double shell design to insure uniform surface temperature. An electric oil heater yields automatically controlled temperatures up to 232.2°C (450°F) and is completely contained within the machine frame.

The machine's main drive motor has variable speed control of up to 18 meters (20 yards) per minute. The machine comes with a driven scroll roll for fabrics that require edges to be uncurled plus a doctor blade to keep the heated drum clean of foreign matter (Reichman, 1976).

7.4.4.3 Lemaire Heat Transfer Printing Machine. In 1976, Lemaire claimed to have more than 50 percent of the transfer printing machines on the world market. They build machines with three cylinder diameters. The models with 51 centimeter (20 inch) diameter cylinders operate at speeds of 2-5 meters (3-6 yards) per minute. The 102 centimeter (40 inch) model operates at speeds of 5-10 meters (6-12 yards) per minute and the 152 centimeter (60 inch) model operates at speeds of 12-20 meters (14-22 yards) per minute.

The Lemaire machines have internal electric heating systems with the heating elements submerged in oil in the drum. Lemaire uses a temperature controller instead of a thermostat on the machine. This provides precise temperature attainability (Reichman, 1976).

7.4.4.4 Morrison's Transmorr 960. This machine was introduced by Morrison Machine Co., Patterson, NJ and is said to double or triple the output of dry printing equipment on the market. The increased capacity is attributed mainly to the machine's 244 centimeter (96 inch) diameter drum which can increase plant output to the 23 meter (25 yard) per minute range (Knitting Times, 1974). The oil can be heated with a choice of gas, propane, oil, or electricity and is designed to require short heat-up times. The oil temperature during printing is maintained at 280°C (536°F) with temperature control within 2°C (35°F) (Morrison, 1982).

7.4.4.5 Perkins Printech Model 400. This machine has a claimed production capability of up to 27 meters (30 yards) per minute; in 1976 this was the fastest commercially proven transfer printer built in the U.S. The machine has a 183 centimeter (72 inch) diameter oil-heated cylinder that utilizes a unique inner spiral design to provide a highly efficient turbulent flow of heating oil. The heat transfer is electrically heated by means of a 160 K.W. high flow system (Reichman, 1976).

7.4.4.6 Gessner Transcolorizer. Gessner was the first American company to produce a heat transfer printing machine in the United States. The Gessner models have four prime characteristics: (1) precise processing time and temperature control; (2) uniform heat across the transfer surface; (3) even pressure; and (4) accurate feeding and proper handling of the fabric and the processing paper to ensure perfect transfer of the design, and to prevent dimensional distortion.

The Gessner 152 centimeter (60 inch) machine operates at speeds up to 32 meters (35 yards) per minute. The 122 centimeter (48 inch) machine operates at speeds up to 27 meters (30 yards) per minute and the

91 centimeter (36 inch) machine operates up to 23 meters (25 yards) per minute (Reichman, 1976). Gessner also produces smaller machines of 51 and 61 centimeters (20 and 24 inches) for economical shorter runs.

Gessner machines have a central oil heating system for heating the main cylinders with thermostatically controlled temperature ranges up to 260°C (500°F). The oil is heated electrically in a continuous circulating system. Gessner has developed an exclusive feature called a sublimation impeller. This device utilizes infra-red heat to continuously burn off errant dyestuffs and oils that reach the blanket; thereby eliminating the possibility of color being offset onto the reverse side of the fabric (Gessner, 1982).

7.4.4.7 Bates' Transfer Printing Machine. The Bates machines are for small scale production ranges, the machines are 91 and 168 centimeters (36 and 66 inches) in width. The general printing speeds are up to 61 centimeters (2 feet) per minute. The machines are completely electric and operate at temperatures from 100-230°C (212-446°F). The machines can use all types of transfer paper and feature simple operation with low maintenance and low costs (Bates, 1982).

7.4.5 Advantages and Disadvantages of Transfer Printing.

The economics of the machinery involved has placed transfer printing within the reach of a broad spectrum of textile plants. The process is unique and uncomplicated, and the skill requirements are considerably reduced. Therefore, it is easy to produce a high-quality printed fabric with rather limited skills compared to other methods of textile printing. The cost of the printing paper is expensive for short runs but is more economical at runs above the 9,144 meter (10,000 yard) mark. Also, competition in the transfer paper supply business has increased which has resulted in a gradual lowering of transfer paper costs. Advantages of transfer printing include a rapid turnaround without the need for any after-processing. When paper and machinery are available, garments can be printed in as little as two hours, and even with fabrics, the process time can be measured in hours (Textile Month, 1972). A drawback is the waiting time for custom designs if the design has to be printed. For commonly used designs, it is cheaper to hold the transfer paper in inventory than to do the same with printed fabrics.

Transfer printing is ecologically favorable because is does not require enormous expenditures of energy and does not generate much gaseous and liquid wastes. However, enormous amounts of waste paper are being generated, and no economical reuse has yet been identified.

One of the main advantages of transfer printing is that it is best applied to polyester. Polyester has been one of the most difficult fibers to prepare and print by conventional means. However, transfer printing circumvents these problems since it makes the sublimation property of disperse dyes an advantage rather than a disadvantage. Also, certain fabrics notable for barré are successfully covered by transfer printing (Reichman, 1976).

Generally, the best results for transfer printing with disperse dyes are obtained with 100 percent polyester fabric. A problem occurs when acetate, triacetate, and nylon are exposed to the extreme temperatures used for transfer printing. Another problem is the fact that temperature uniformity across the face of the drum must be monitored carefully to eliminate side-to-side shading of the fabric. Differences of a few percentage points in temperature can cause unacceptable shading and, therefore, inferior quality printing.

Recent improvements in disperse dyes and the development of faster transfer papers allow for color matching at greater speeds. Therefore, greater transfer running speeds can be achieved at conventional, nondestructive temperatures. The resulting designs are sharp, the color gradations are pleasingly subtle and the colors have good clarity and bloom (Reichman, 1976).

## 7.5 DIRECT TEXTILE PRINTING

Textile printing is the production, through a combination of various mechancial and chemical means, of colored designs or patterns on textile substrates. The term "direct textile printing" here describes the direct printing methods that do not utilize transfer paper as a temporary substrate. The two primary direct printing methods are roller and screen printing (Hudak, 1976).

Since a localized dyeing process takes place when printing directly on textiles, the general chemical and physical parameters of dyeing apply. The general textile printing method can be divided into three steps. First, the colorant is applied as pigment dispersion, dye dispersion, or dye solution from a vehicle called print paste or printing ink. In addition to the colorant, such solutions (as required by the colorant or textile substrate) contain additives to improve and assist in dye solubility, dispersion stability, pH, lubricity, hygroscopicity, rate of dye fixation to the substrate, and colorant-fiber bonding. The required viscosity characteristics of a print paste are produced by adding natural or synthetic thickening agents, or by using emulsions. In most cases, after the print paste is deposited on the textile, the prints are dried and stored until further processing in dye fixation. However, for printing of carpeting materials, the drying step is generally omitted and the textile is exposed to the dye fixation step directly after printing. As a rule, a dried print is not fast to washing or crocking, or may have inferior light-fastness and, with the exception of pigments, does not show the correct and final shade.

The second step in processing printed textiles is the fixation process. During the fixation process the printed textile material is exposed to heat, heat and steam, or chemical solutions at temperatures and lengths of time governed by the type of fiber processed and by the dye class itself. During this treatment, the dyes diffuse from the fiber surface into the fiber structure and undergo physical or chemical bonding to the fiber. In the case of pigment prints, latexes (resins) applied simultaneously with the pigment bond the pigments during a heat treatment and impart to the print the final desired fastness.

During after-scouring, the third step in the textile printing process, the prints are rinsed and scoured in a detergent solution to remove auxiliary chemicals, thickening agents, and portions of unfixed dyes remaining on the surface of the printed fibers. After the scouring operation, only the dye adhering firmly to the textile remains.

Frequently, the scouring operation includes the use of chemicals to assist in removal of dye or dye fragments and/or chemicals reacting with textile fibers or with removed dye in order to prevent redeposition of dye during scouring. Pigment prints, in general, do not undergo a scouring operation.

The basic printing steps can be accomplished on the roller machines and the two versions of the screen printing machines. Screen printing can be accomplished with a flat bed screen machine and a rotary screen machine. Flat bed screen printing uses a screen on which print paste is applied. The screen then is lowered onto a section of fabric and a squeegee is moved across the screen, forcing the paste into a design onto the fabric. Rotary screen printing uses a tubular screen that rotates at the same velocity as the fabric. The print paste distributed inside the tubular screen is forced into the fabric as it is pressed between the screen and a continuous rubber belt used for a printing blanket. The complete screen process and a machine description is presented in Section 7.5.2.

The roller printing process begins with the print paste applied to an engraved roller. The fabric is then guided between the roller and the fabric cylinder. The pressure of the roller and the cylinder at a "nip" forces the print paste into the fabric. The complete roller printing process is presented in Section 7.5.1 along with the machinery utilized for the process.

The American Textile Manufacturers Institute (ATMI) conducted a survey of 35 printing companies using roller and screen printing operations. This represented over 50 percent of the 1979 woven fabric production for both types of machines. The industry data showed 1,743,006,000 yards were printed in 1979. There were 169 roller machines and 178 screen print machines reported in a 1980 ATMI survey. From the 50 percent of the industry that responded to the 1979 survey, 55 percent of the yards printed were on screen machines and 45 percent were on roller machines (ATMI, 1980).

Colors for the printing machines or screen machines are prepared in the color shop which is supervised by the colorist. He matches the shades and supervises the preparation of the print colors. The colorist has one or more assistants who explain the detailed work assignments to the workmen who weigh, mix, and strain the print pastes.

### 7.5.1 Roller Printing

Roller printing is the use of rollers to direct the print patterns onto material. The rollers are usually made of copper and engraved to form the pattern on the goods when applied. This method is also referenced as calender, roller, or cylinder printing. The roller printing machines may produce from 914.4-3,657.6 meters (1,000 to 4,000 yards) per hour.

Roller printing involves an engraved dye-carrying roller revolving against a padded cylinder. The entire roller is first covered with dye and the unengraved portion is then scraped by a steel blade. The dye remaining in the engraving is deposited on the cloth as it passes the point of contact. The cycle is repeated continuously as the roller revolves. Each color in the pattern is engraved on a separate roller.

Roller printing can best be compared to the way print is applied to newspaper or magazine paper. The design applied to the fabric is etched or milled into the roller. A separate engraved cylinder is usually required for each color in the print although fall-ons of one or more colors on one another also can be used. Once prepared, rollers may be used almost indefinitely. However, the cost of changing patterns is high.

Once the roller printed fabric has passed through the printing machine and the color is registered on the cloth, further treatment is necessary to set the color. This part of the process is similar to the dyeing process where the dye must be made to combine with the fiber.

7.5.1.1 Roller Printing Procedure. The operation of printing machines can be seen in Figure 20. P is a color box containing the paste that is to be printed on the fabric passing around the pressure bowl, D. M is a roller or "furnisher" which transfers the paste to the engraved printing roller, E, which is positively driven and serves to rotate D by frictional contact and M through an intermediate spur wheel.

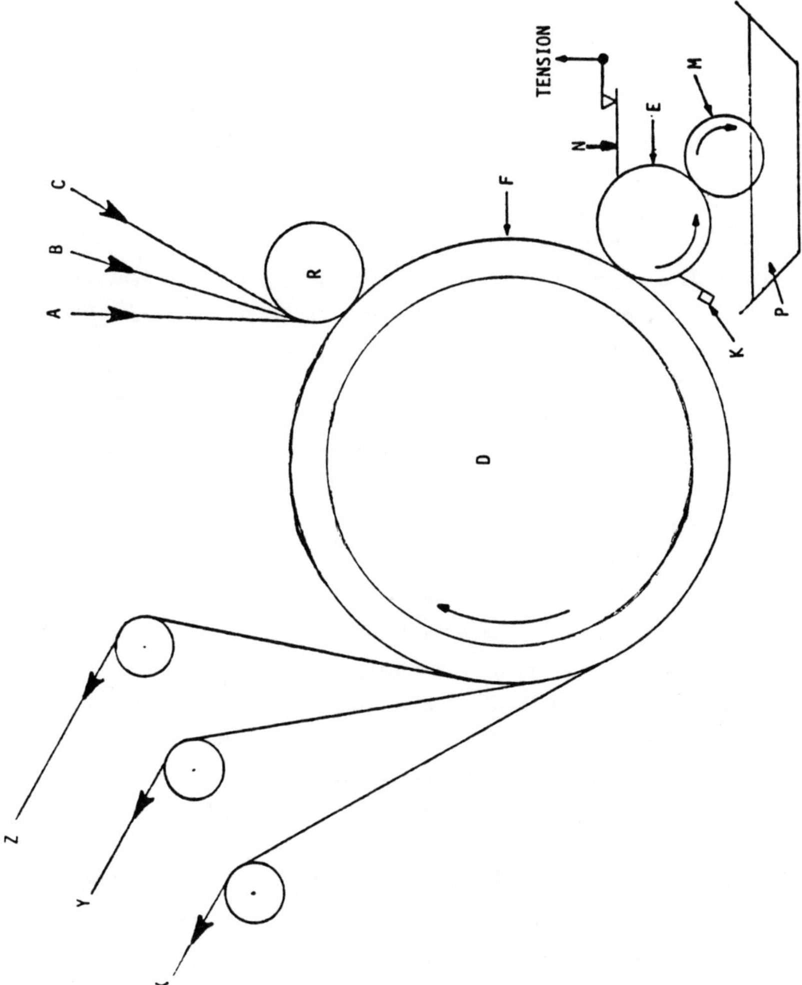


Figure 20. Construction of a single-color printing machine.

In order to remove excess color paste from the surface of E, the printing roller has a color doctor, N, which is a sharp steel blade. Another doctor, K, the lint doctor, is also provided for the purpose of removing loose fibers picked up by the printing roller during contact with the fabric. The cleaning doctor is the more important, since the clarity of the printed fabric is entirely dependent on the efficiency with which this doctor removes color from the smooth parts of the printing roller and leaves color within the engraved design.

The cleaning doctor is usually 5-8 centimeters (2-3 inches) wide and up to .16 centimeter (1/16 inch) thick; its length is dependent on the length of the printing roller. The edge bearing on the printing roller is angled sharply, and its pressure on this roller is adjusted by means of levers carrying adjustable weights. A cleaning doctor is also given a small traversing motion so that it wears evenly. This motion is achieved through a small eccentric drive. The lint doctor has no traverse motion and is usually made of brass.

The pressure bowl, D, is usually made of cast iron and is lapped with not more than a dozen thicknesses of a linen-wool union fabric, F. Further, the fabric, C, being printed is always supported by a blanket, A. Staining of the blanket is largely avoided by means of the back-grey, B. Printed fabric C, back-grey B and blanket A pass through the printing machine together, directed to the pressure bowl by the freely-rotating drag roller, R. The other fabrics present in addition to the printed fabric give the printing surface elasticity. X, Y and Z are freely-rotating guide rollers (Hall, 1926).

The printing machine is operated by the "Printer" and his assistants the "Back Tender," "Grey Tender," and "Color Boy" where required. The printer installs lapping, blankets, prepares the doctors, and adjusts and operates the machine with the help of this crew.

Compared to other types of textile printing, the printing machine is the most precise in pattern reproduction and the most productive in yardage. Refinements in engraving allow the reproduction of designs as fine as the structure of the fabric permits. The size of the design is, however, limited by the circumference of the rollers usually at the maximum 61 centimeters (24 inches). Large rollers or oversize machines may be used for special procedure but these become cumbersome and productivity is apt to decline sharply.

Normally, speeds up to 82 meters (90 yards) per minute may be reached; some special high-speed machines are adapted to double this rate. The time spent in setting up the pattern reduces the average production speed to a much lower figure. The length of the run to be made is consequently of major importance in determining the rate of production.

7.5.1.2 Emissions From Roller Printing Process. In the roller printing process, all atmospheric emissions are fugitives. A schematic diagram is presented in Figure 21 with the sources of fugitive volatile organic compound (VOC) emissions. The back grey absorbs excess colorant paste and generates fugitive VOC emissions since it is dried before being washed. In some processes where the back grey is washed before drying, most of the fugitive VOC emissions from the back grey are discharged into the wastewater. The roller printing processes have enclosed steam cans for drying the printed fabric and the subsequent drying process emissions are vented directly to the atmosphere (Research Triangle Institute, 1981).

### 7.5.2 Screen Printing

Screen printing is a relatively simple method of printing which can be carried out without the use of complicated and expensive equipment. This method of printing is a specialized form of stenching and is sometimes performed by hand at long tables on which the cloth is fastened by pins or adhesive. Two versions of the screen printing method are flat bed screen printing and rotary screen printing. The flat bed method can either be used with manually or automatically operated screens.

7.5.2.1 Flat Bed Screen Printing. This printing process consists of the transfer of print paste through a stencil to the substrate to be printed. Manufacture of the stencil (or screen) is described as follows. The stencil is made of polyamide or polyester (also metal in some cases) bolting cloth stretched tightly over a metal frame. The pattern or design is produced in the stencil or screen by coating those parts that

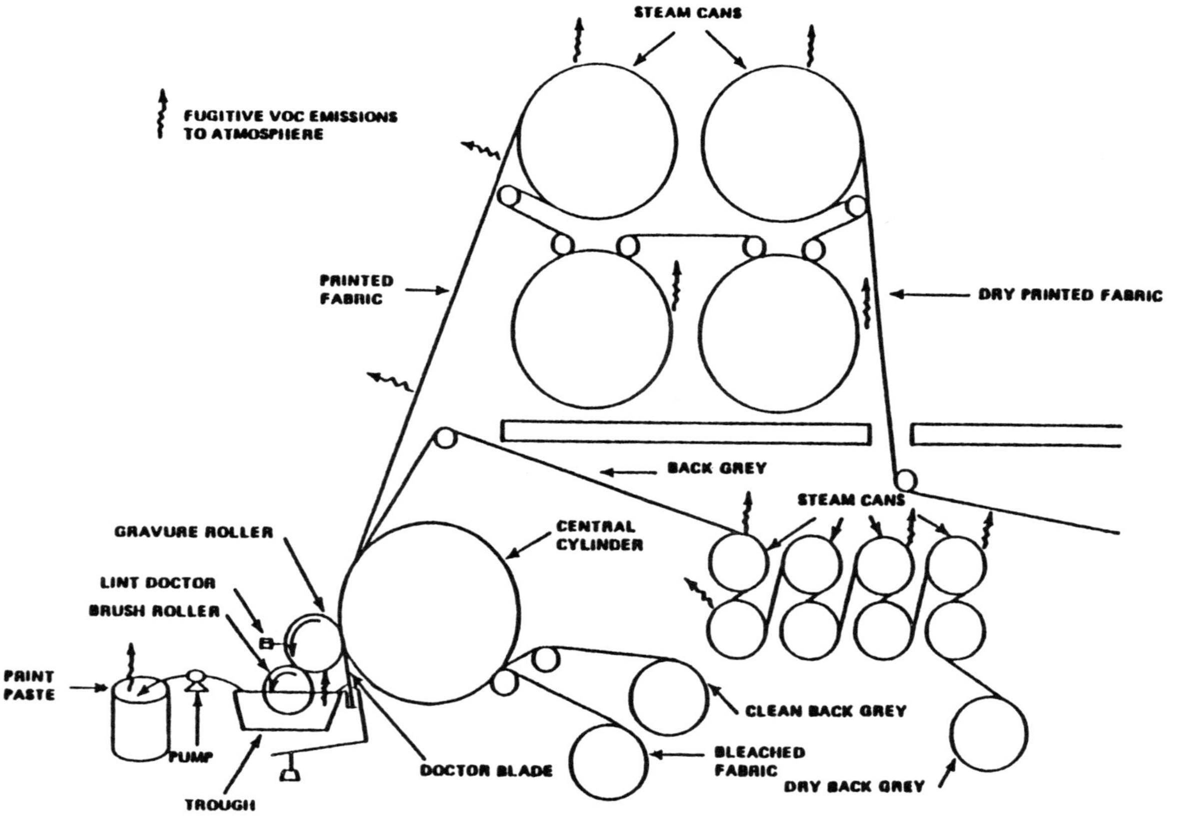


Figure 21. Schematic diagram of the roller printing process with VOC emission sources.

should not transfer the print paste with an impervious material. The design is transferred to a film and the film placed on the bolting cloth, which is coated with light-sensitive material. After light exposure, the unexposed parts, having been protected by the light-impervious areas of the film, are removed by rinsing thus creating the pattern on the screen. To withstand the mechanical stress of prolonged printing, the light-sensitive coating must be very strong or reinforced with suitable screen lacquer.

The general flat bed screen printing procedure begins with spreading the roll of fabric to be printed smoothly onto the table. The surface of the table is coated with a light adhesive to prevent the material from shifting. The design is applied to the fabric from a series of either manually manipulated or automatically operated framed screens. The design for the fabric is etched on the screen. The screen frames are moved successively along the whole table, printing one frame at a time, until the entire fabric is printed. Each frame contains one color of the print. A three color print, for example, generally requires three frames and three applications to the fabric (Hudak, 1976), although fall-ons of two colors or more can be used to produce a desired color.

Manual or hand screen printing is commonly referred to as silk screen. The fabric is stretched over tables that are usually 73.1-91 meters (80-100 yards) long. The screen is placed on the textile material and the print paste is scraped across the screen with a squeegee. This causes the paste to penetrate through the open areas in the screen onto the textile. Then the screen is lifted and moved along the table by hand or in a carriage to the next print position.

Mechanized screen printing is done on flat bed screen printing machines. On these machines the screens remain stationary while the textile material is moved underneath the screens in intermittent steps. The textile material is glued to an endless blanket which serves as support for the textile material and which is cleaned with water once during each revolution. When the screens are in a lifted position, the blanket, and the textile material with it, move forward. When they are in a lower position the squeegees perform the printing. The movement of the squeegees can be controlled mechanically or electromagnetically (Kirk-Othmer, 1978). Automatic mechanized screen printing has a production rate of from 229-411 meters (250-450 yards) per hour (Hudak, 1976).

7.5.2.2 Rotary Screen Printing. Rotary screen printing machines were developed in 1965 to make screen printing more continuous. The screens were configured from being flat to being round or rotary cylinders. The printing color is passed through a series of seamless rotary perforated screens made of metal foil. A squeegee inside each rotary screen forces the printing paste onto the fabric. The fabric is anchored to a continuously moving printing blanket. The rotary screen printing is the fastest method of screen printing; production ranges from 2,286 3,200 meters (2,500 to 3,500 yards) per hour.

7.5.2.3 Screen Printing Procedures. Although used for small yardages of extremely fine fabrics, hand screening is not a major factor in the textile printing industry today. Screen printing begins with pouring the paste into the well of the screen frame and then transferring the paste onto the cloth underneath, by drawing it across the screen with the squeegee. Two to four passages of the squeegee are generally required. Before beginning to print with a screen it is advisable to wet out the screen first, by printing on to a piece of spare fabric or absorbent paper. A properly wet-out screen ensures a good transfer of dyestuff paste to the fabric being printed in bulk. To avoid color overlaps, the screen printer does not continuously print, but prints in alternate positions. That is, he prints position 1, then misses position 2 and prints on position 3, and then on to position 5 and so on until the whole table length has been completed. The drying of the printed material is assisted by hot air blowing over the table or by heated tables. If the printing pastes are not too hygroscopic and the material is not too light in weight (and consequently limited in absorbency), the material should then be dry. Otherwise it is necessary to wait until the print is dry enough to avoid picking-up and marking-off. Printing is then continued in positions 2, 4, 6, etc., until the whole table is printed with the first color. The same procedure is followed for the second and subsequent colours in the pattern.

It is important that each screen be washed as soon as possible after use. A screen that is left to dry with print paste on it is difficult to clean; in extreme cases this may lead to blocking of the screen mesh, which renders it useless for future printing. Screens are usually cleaned by using a jet of water, and drying is carried out by wiping them with an absorbent cloth and keeping them in a warm place. Too much heat will warp a screen frame. After printing, the table should be washed if the fabric has been affixed. The printed fabric is either allowed to dry on the table or is dried by hanging in a drying chamber before further processing, which depends on the type of fabric and the dyestuffs used (Clarke, 1977).

Dye manufacturers recommend selected acid dyes because of their capability for reacting with nylon to give prints with very good wet fastness (ICI, 1965). These acid dyes are suitable for producing a wide range of shades with good all-around fastness.

A recommended recipe for applying acid and reactive dyes or a mixture of both is suggested by the dye manufacturer.

<u>Printing Recipe</u>

- Dissolve:
  - 30-60 parts dye
  - 50 parts thiodiglycol
  - 320-350 parts water

Add the solution to:

- 450 parts thickening solution:
  - 70 parts thiourea
  - 30 parts ammonium sulphate
  - 20 parts perminal KB

<u>Processing After Printing</u>

- Steam the printed and dried fabric for 30 minutes at atmospheric pressure

- Rinse the goods well in cold water
- Treat for 5 minutes at 50°C (120°F) in a solution containing 2 parts of Lissapol ND per 1,000 parts of water
- Rinse again in cold water

The procedure described above is recommended for the production of a wide range of printed shades on the most produced nylon fabrics, nylon 66 and nylon 6 polyamide fabrics, using acid dyes.

The direct printing process can be used on roller printing and rotary screen printing machines. The plant in Appendix D uses seven rotary screen machines for processing 26,989 kilograms (59,500 pounds) per day of nylon, cotton, and polyester fabrics. The dye usage estimate for acid dyes is 1.2 kilograms (2.6 pounds) of dye per 45 kilograms (100 pounds) of fabric. Therefore, 720 kilograms (1,587 pounds) of acid dye would be required in processing the 26,989 kilograms of fabric. The Carlisle printing operations (p. 360) estimate that 100% exhaustion of the dye onto the fabric is achieved. However, this value may be too ideal, since some dye may subsequently be washed off in the rinsing steps.

7.5.2.4 Equipment For Screen Printing. The equipment necessary for the screen printing process is a printing table, printing screen with a frame, and squeegees. Following is a discussion of the construction and use of each piece of equipment.

A large operating area is required for the printing process because printing table lengths can exceed 101 meters (110 yards). The table is usually 76 centimeters (30 inches) high and approximately 122-157 centimeters (48-62 inches) in width, although the width can be smaller. The table is made of well seasoned wood, reinforced concrete or a combination of iron frames and iron stands with wooden tops. It is usually covered with a woolen felt and/or heavy oil cloth and then a layer of back grey. A waterproof cover is required if the goods are to be stuck down with adhesive. A guide rail made of angle iron with one leg pointing up runs along the side. Tables are usually arranged in pairs with the guide rails on adjoining sides so that two table lengths of the same pattern can be printed continuously.

The printing screens are made of fine meshed cloth such as that used for screening flour. The frames for the screens are usually made of either wood or metal. Screen frames vary in size and may be as large as 9 feet x 6 feet. They are usually prepared from wood approximately 5 centimeters (2 inches) in depth and 5-13 centimeters (2-5 inches) in width. The screen mesh varies from a coarse #8 mesh to a fine #14 mesh; the mesh selected depends on the fabric and the design being printed. For example, a finer mesh is used for a fine smooth fabric, where an excess of paste sould be avoided. A coarser mesh is preferred for linens, where a good print paste coverage is required (Clarke, 1977).

Various types of squeegees are available. Some are made entirely of wood while others have wooden handles with rubber or metal plates inserted. The length of the squeegee is approximately 2.5-13 centimeters (1-5 inches) shorter than the internal dimensions of the screen.

7.5.2.5 Waste Streams From the Screen Printing Process. The rotary and screen printing processes have both atmospheric emissions and wastewater effluents. The atmospheric emissions come from both process and fugitive sources. The schematic diagram in Figure 22 shows the rotary screen printing process which has the same process steps as the flat screen printing process. As seen in the figure, fugitive emissions originate from the step in which the print paste is applied to the fabric. Process emissions consist of the solvents driven off during the drying step.

There are two sources of wastewater effluents containing print paste, those resulting from: 1) washing of the printing blanket, and 2) scouring of the printed fabric. Other emissions are produced by the washing of screens, print paste containers, and sublimation in the drier for some disperse dyes.

### 7.5.3 Advantages and Disadvantages of Roller and Screen Printing Methods

Screen printing offers several advantages over roller printing. Designs with large repeat patterns can be readily produced in as many

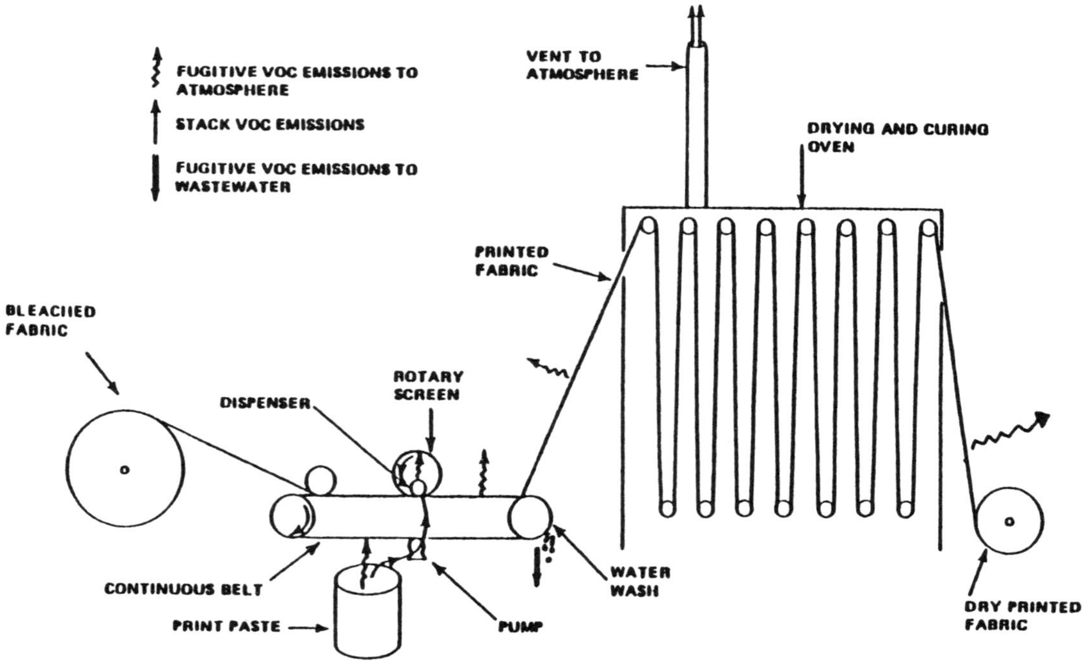

Figure 22. Schematic diagram of the rotary screen printing process with VOC emission sources.

colors as possible. Short runs on patterns of many colors can be produced economically. Screens represent a much smaller investment than copper rollers and designs cost less to reproduce with screens than with copper rollers. Due to the nature of the process, heavy surface prints of high bloom are obtained with screen printing. These are very difficult to duplicate on the roller printing machine where each color is crushed by the succeeding rollers. Contamination-free shades can be obtained with screen printing since the colors do not run into each other as in the roller machine; pleasing effects are obtained by allowing colors to fall on each other. Screen printing is, however, slow and expensive and the precision and fine details of the roller process cannot be achieved (Greene, 1958).

Roller printing methods produce designs of high quality. This makes roller printing the most appealing method for printing designer and fashion apparel fabrics (Research Triangle Institute, 1981).

Most knit fabric is printed by the rotary screen method, because it does not stress the fabric during the printing process (Research Triangle Institute, 1981). The limitations and disadvantages of the roller and screen printing methods are listed in Table 36.

## 7.6 PACKAGE DYEING

Modern dye machinery designs are based on one of three basic principles: (1) circulation of the dye through the fiber, (2) circulation of the fiber through the dye, and (3) padding of the dye onto the fiber. Package machines circulate the dye through the fiber. Figure 23 presents a package machine and demonstrates how the dye solution is forced through the package of fiber in alternating inside-out and outside-in directions by a suitable pumping system.

The type of machinery and dyeing method used by the textile producer is determined by the form in which the fiber is to be dyed. Package machinery is utilized to dye fiber in various forms because it is adaptable and is the most controllable dyeing system in use. Raw stock or staple fiber can be dyed on many package machines by adapting the machines with a suitable basket or cage for holding the loose stock. The dye liquor is then pumped through the stock.

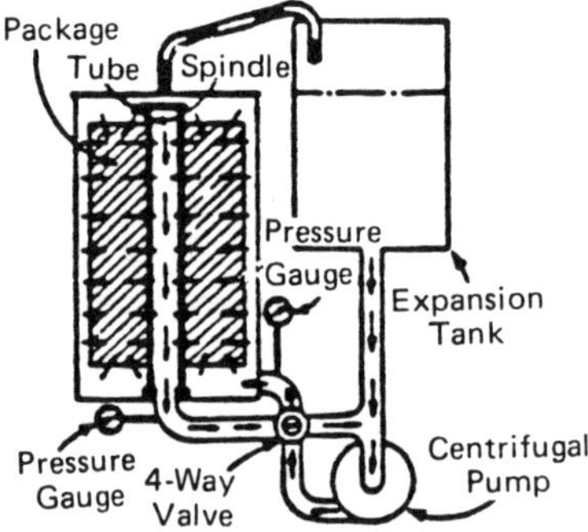


OUTSIDE-IN FLOW CYCLE

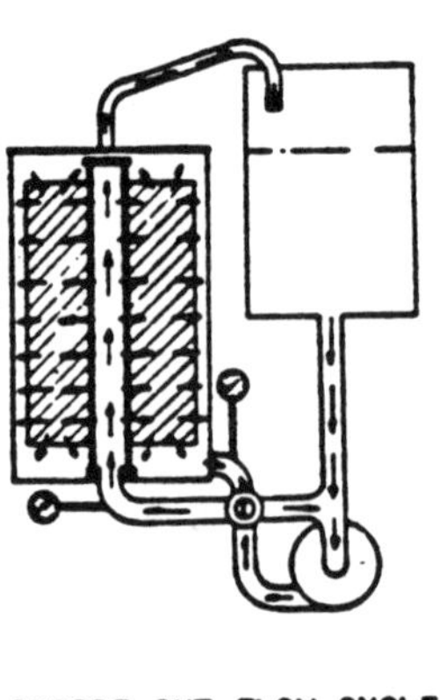

INSIDE-OUT FLOW CYCLE

Figure 23. Schematic of a package machine (for yarns) with two flow cycles.

A "top" is the fiber formed when a sliver is wound into a ball of 30 centimeters (12 inches) or more in diameter. Tops are generally dyed in package machines. The fiber is loaded over a perforated spindle into perforated cans, then fastened to a seating in the bottom of the package machine. The dye cycles can be used in both directions of flow. Some dyeing procedures require steaming and washing to develop the true shade of the fiber. The dyeings also will require drying on an apron or over a suction drum drier.

Continuous filament fiber is the form in which synthetic fibers leave the last manufacturing operation. The fiber may be wound individually as a continuous filament or gathered together, 1,000 to 1,000,000 individual filament yarns in bundles to form a tow. The individual continuous filament yarn can be dyed in package machines by winding the yarn on springs or bobbings, or by dyeing it in the form of cakes or muffs. Tow bundles of yarn can be packed into baskets and dyed on package machines.

Most spun yarns are either package dyed or skein dyed. Package machines can be adapted for dyeing the yarns that are rolled onto beams as they are spun (VPI, 1981).

Pressurized dyeing at temperatures above 100°C (212°F) became increasingly important with the growth of synthetic fibers because of their hydrophobic nature. Package machines were adapted with a secondary pump for pressure dyeing. The secondary pump created a static high pressure in the dye vessel for obtaining dyeing temperatures above 100°C (212°F). A constant elevated pressure could not be maintained satisfactorily by the main pump alone because it would vary according to the density of the package windings and other factors such as the motor speed. The secondary pump will extract extra dye liquor from the expansion tank and introduces it into the pressure vessel in such a manner that a static pressure is maintained (Trotman, 1968).

### 7.6.1 Package Dyeing Procedures

Package dyeing is an exhaustion process similar to beck dyeing. Dyeing procedures for package and beam dyeing are interchangeable and are discussed in detail in Section 7.7. However, beck dyeing moves the material through the dye liquor while package dyeing machines move the dye liquor through the material. Package dyeing is utilized for all forms of fiber except for those that have already been spun. Most of the same dyes used with beck machines can be utilized on package machines. Package dyeing circulates the dyebath through the package until all the dye has been exhausted. This not only requires a good pump, but the packages must be properly wound - neither too tight nor too loose. An example of the procedure used for controlling shrinkage is that used on terylene yarn. The yarn is wound onto a 6.3 centimeter (2½ inch) parallel sided paper tube at a rate of approximately 193 meters (200 yards) per minute and under low tension. This paper package is steamed for 20 minutes at 136°C (57°F) to promote the full contraction of the yarn which takes place as the paper tubes collapse. The fully relaxed yarn can then be wound onto the machine cones or cheeses for dyeing (Haigh, 1971).

The complicated application of Azoic and Vat dyestuffs can be accomplished with a package machine. The general application properties and uses of these dyestuffs are described in Section 7.2.1.5.

An example dyeing procedure for 15 one-pound packages of bleached cotton yarn using naphthol (azoic) dyes in a 35 pound package dye machine at a 8:1 liquor ratio is as follows (Horning, 1978):

- Prepare machine at 29°C (85°F) with:
  - 5.0% caustic soda
- Run at 110°C (230°F) for 10 minutes, add:
  - 2.0% Naphthol AS-SW solution
  - ½ solution inside out
  - ½ solution outside in
- Run 30 minutes at 54°C (130°F), then add:
  - 10.0% salt
- Run 15 minutes
- Drop bath - drain machine
- Make up salt rinse solution of:
  - 59 grams/liter (8 ounces/gallon) salt

- Add to machine and run 10 minutes at 60°F
- Drop bath - drain machine completely
- Make up coupling bath solution of:
  - 8.0% Fast Scarlet R salt
  - 1.0% acetic acid (56%)
- Add solution to machine and run cold in machine for 30 minutes
- Drop bath
- Raise temperature to 77°C (170°F) over 20 minutes
- Drop bath
- Set soaping bath with:
  - 2.0% Product BCO (surfactant)
  - 2.0% soda ash
  - 0.5% oz/gal Calgon
- Raise temperature to 93°C (200°F) and run 20 minutes then cool to 82°C (180°F)
- Drop bath
- Rinse three times at 24°C (75°F) each rinse, 5 minutes each rinse

Hydroextraction and oven drying is required to complete dyeing.

### 7.6.2 Package Dyeing Machinery

Figure 24 presents a schematic of the package machine and how it operates. The essential features common to all package machines are (VPI, 1981):

a. a kier to hold the packages
b. an expansion tank to feed the dyes and chemicals
c. piping to allow inside-out, or outside-in circulation
d. a pump to force the dye liquor through the packages
e. a heat exchanger for heating and cooling
f. a filter to protect the pump from lint etc.

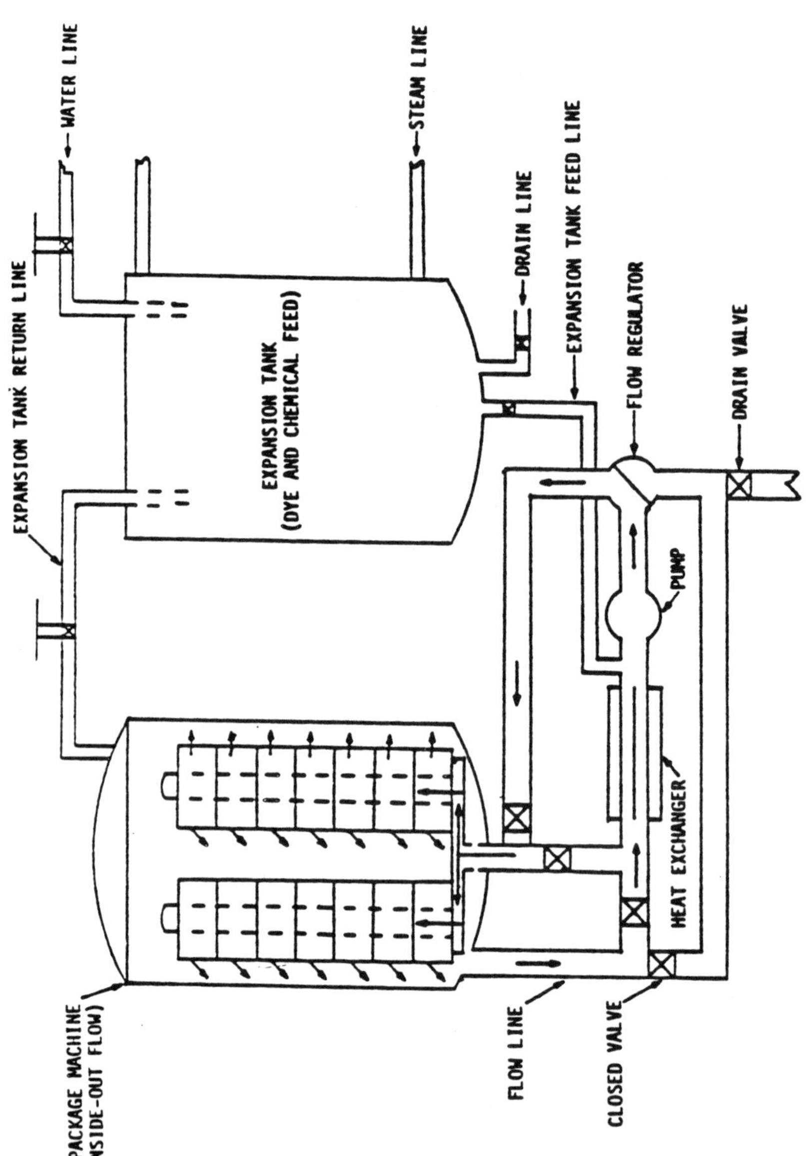


Figure 24. Schematic of the package machinery with operational flows during an inside-out cycle for yarn dyeing.

g. a sample pot or similar device

h. pressure and temperature gauges (or controllers)

Modern package machines are controlled from an instrument panel; the full cycle runs automatically on a cam or programmed tape. Flow direction is controlled by a timer and it may for instance, be set to run for 10 minutes on an outside-in flow, then run 5 minutes on an inside-out flow. The setting will depend on the fiber and dyeing system being used. Some dyeings are entirely outside-in cycles - but seldom will an inside-out cycle be used exclusively because the outside of the package is so much larger than the inside and therefore requires more exposure time to the dye liquor (VPI, 1981).

Different kinds of packages are dyed in package machinery; particular type of package depends on the fiber in the yarn. Cops, cakes, cheeses, cones, rockets, muffs, and beams can all be dyed with package machines. Packages such as cones and cheeses are for general use on most fibers, while others are for specific fibers. For example, cakes are used for viscose rayon and muffs for textured nylon (Haigh, 1971).

Most package machines are designed to operate under two conditions: at the atmospheric boil and at high temperatures of 130°-140°C (266-284°F). A standard feature of modern package dyeing machines are pressure covers which are raised and lowered by pneumatic power controlled by a programmed automation control unit. Package machine circulatory systems vary widely. Various flow pumps designs used in the machine include: centrifugal, axial, semi-axial and mixed. The pump systems can be set up in different configurations such as a double, in parallel, or in series.

7.6.3 Package Dyeing Machinery on the Market

7.6.3.1 Pegg's High Temperature Pressure Dyeing Machines. The Pegg package machines come in 45 kilogram (100 pound), 277 kilogram (500 pound), and 363 kilogram (800 pound) sizes. The machines are also capable of being coupled. They contain mixed flow pumps to allow variable flow control in each liquor flow direction (Haigh, 1971).

7.6.3.2 Platt-Longclose's High Temperature Pressure Dyeing Machines. Platt dyeing machines come in a variety of sizes. The machine incorporates a high output centrifugal pump with a swan-neck reversal device. Coupled pairs or sets of four large machines can be used for large batches. A special mixer unit is used to obtain a high flow rate throughout the various coupled machines with centralized temperature control. The machines each have a single pressurized main dyeing vessel. The top section acts as the compensating chamber to allow for expansion of the dye liquor when it is heated. It is claimed that this feature offers a unique advantage in that shallower (or even half-depth) package holders can be used in deep machines with just enough liquor to cover the material adequately. This feature favors the attainment of constant liquor/goods ratios of batches of different size in a given machine.

7.6.3.3 Henriksen's GRU-Intermix Package Dyeing Machines. The Henriksen's GRU-Intermix is available in various versions. Different models are designed to deliver temperatures of 100°C, 140°C (212°F, 284°F), or 110°/140°C (230°/284°F). The 100°C model works without static pressure and the 140°C (284°C) or 110/140°C (230/284°F) models work under static pressures at a range of -0.5 – -4 atmospheres. The static pressure is created by means of compressed air with the expansion taking place in the lid of the machine. All the models come in 35, 75, 150, and 300 kilogram (77.2, 165.3, 330.7 and 661.4 pound) sizes.

The circulation of the liquor is provided by a two-rim propeller motor. The maximum bath turnover of 6½ per minute means the liquor makes a complete cycle every nine seconds.

Various carriers can be used and can be adapted to control the quantity of liquor required for each carrier. The different carriers with adaptions available for use on the Henrikson machine are: (1) normal or hard package, (2) soft packages, (3) yarn in hanks, (4) tops, and (5) loose material (Henriksen, 1982).

### 7.6.4 Advantages and Disadvantages of Package Dyeing

The versatility of the package machine is illustrated by the fact that it can be used to dye fiber in the following forms: (1) raw stock or staple fiber, (2) tops and sliver, (3) tow bundles or continuous filament fiber, and (4) spun yarn. Most package machines can even be adapted to dye beams. Package machines are a simple and very controllable piece of equipment.

Success in package dyeing is a direct result of the winding of the packages; they cannot be wound too tight or too loose. Shrinkage of the fiber is very important and must be taken into account by checking shrinkages of different fibers with a sample machine. The proper temperature control of the systems is essential for insuring uniformly dyed packages.

## 7.7 BEAM DYEING

Dyeing with beam machines is similar to package dyeing previously described in Section 7.6. Beam dyeing is an exhaustion method in which the dye liquor is forced through the textile fiber. The dye liquor is pumped through the beams in a similar manner to package dyeing. The preparation of the beam is extremely critical if a good dyeing is to be expected. The winding and shrinkage of the fabric must be carefully considered as they are with package dyeing.

Beams can be dyed in a vertical position as in the case of package machines which have a flange adaptor. However, most beam dyeing machines are built in a horizontal position. The beam is loaded into a cylindrical chamber and the door is shut and sealed. The dye liquor is pumped through the beam usually on a two-way cycle (inside-out/outside-in), in the same manner as package dyeing. Controls are used to regulate pump pressure, temperature control, cycle timers, etc. The information on package dyeing procedures and machinery also apply to beam dyeing with a few exceptions. In fact, most package machines can be adapted to dye beams. Figure 25 illustrates the operation of the beam machine (VPI, 1981).

Warp beam is a form of yarn dyeing used in package dyeing machinery. Some consider warp beam dyeing to be the most economical way of dyeing cotton (Haigh, 1971). Warp beam dyeing was developed because of the rapid growth of warp knitting. The main fibers used in producing warp-knitted fabric suitable for beam dyeing are the polyamide, polyester and triacetate types.

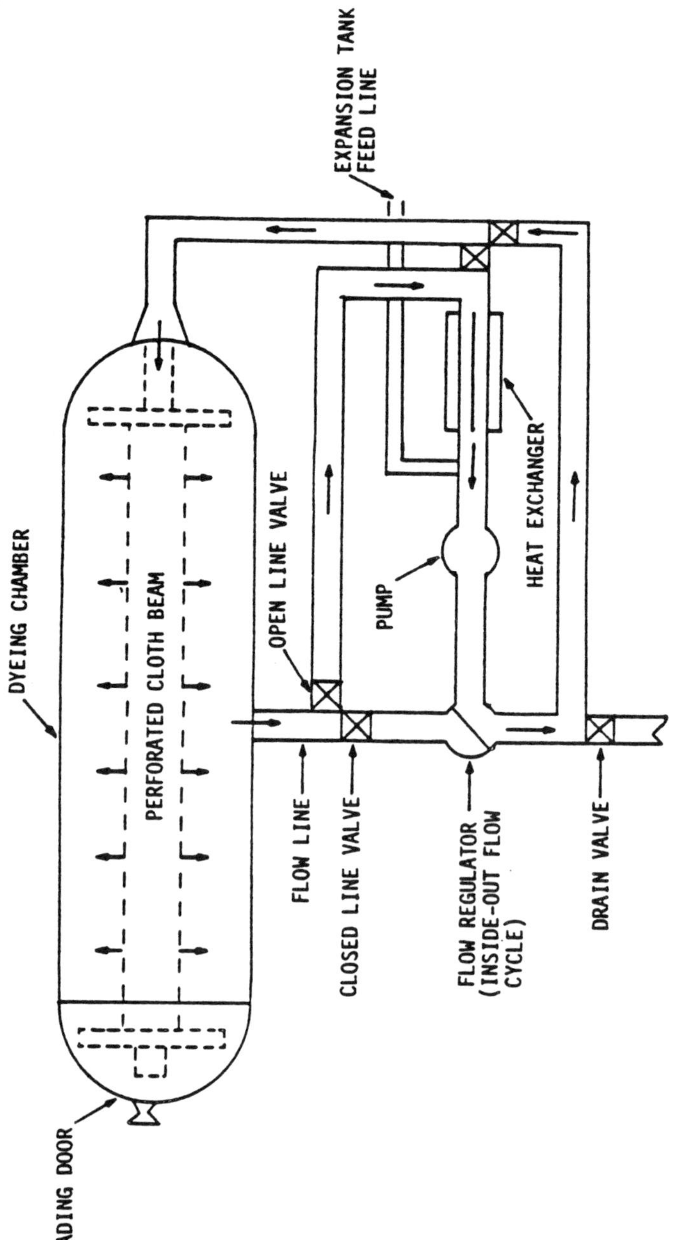


Figure 25. Schematic of beam dyeing machinery with operational flows during inside-out cycle.

Pressurized beam dyeing gained importance with the increase in fabrics made from polyester yarns and the demand for a much wider range of shades than could be obtained without the aid of carriers at an atmospheric boil. Beam dyeing uses pressurized dyeing equipment for processing fabric in open-widths. Therefore, a wider range of shades are obtainable under pressurized conditions and polyester yarns can be easily dyed at open-width.

Pressurized dyeing techniques increased the number of beam and package machines used for dyeing synthetic yarns. A study performed for the U.S. Department of the Treasury (Hudak, 1976) showed that of the total amount of yarn dyed in 1963, 42 percent was on non-pressure package/beam machines, 12 percent on package/beam pressure machines and 46 percent on other yarn dyeing machines. But, in 1973 the trend changed with 8 percent on non-pressure package/beam machines, 80 percent on package/beam pressure machines and 12 percent on other yarn dye machines.

With the trend towards producing synthetic yarns, many yarn dyeing firms that were producing only cotton dyed yarns began processing synthetic yarns as well. The growth in dyeing of filament yarns created the demand for the new package dye capacity of pressurized dyeing. Therefore, new yarn dyeing machines purchased during the 1963-1974 period were, in almost all cases, pressure machines for high temperature dyeing. Most of these machines were combination package and beam dyeing machine (Hudak, 1976).

Another use for the beam is in semi-continuous pad/batch dyeing. For example, a fabric is padded with dyes such as naphtol or reactive dyes, then rolled up or batched on a beam, and subsequently coupled, steamed and/or washed on the beam.

7.7.1 Beam Dyeing Procedures

The principle of beam dyeing is the same as the package dyeing procedures given in Section 7.6.1 with one exception: fewer forms are dyed on a beam in comparison with package machinery.

Beam dyeing of yarn requires that several hundred parallel ends be wound on a large spool or beam with flanged ends. The beam is then processed much as if it were a single large package in a package dyeing machine. Some types of fabric may also be dyed by winding open width on a perforated beam and then circulating the dye bath through it. The ratio of liquor to goods on package and beam dyeing machines may be seven or eight to one (Horning, 1978).

In most cases, beam dyeing is used for dyeing wide width filament fabrics or any fabric type which could not be dyed in rope form because of creasing, excessive pull or tension, and possible abrasion damage. It offers a much better and more compact system for dyeing polyester fabrics (and blends) than would be the case with a pressure jig.

The loading of the beam must be carefully controlled to obtain the best results. The perforated beam is first covered with 10-20 layers of cotton fabric (American padding cotton) before loading the fabric to be dyed. The fabric is then run on under controlled tension and at full width, ensuring that the selvedges are even and slightly overlap the end of the beam perforations. For filament fabrics this overlap should equal half the batch thickness, or one inch whichever is the greater; and for spun fabrics it should be equal to the thickness of the batch, or one inch, whichever is the greater. If the overlap is too small the liquor will tend to flow more rapidly at the selvedges, resulting in a slower rate of dyeing at the center of the batch owing to the consequent reduction in back pressure. If the overlap is excessive there will be reduced flow at the selvedges which will dye paler as a result of this.

When the fabric has been batched, several more thicknesses of cotton are wound to completely surround the batch, and clipped, thus forming a protective filter to the material being dyed.

Entrapped air gradually moves to the top of the beam during dyeing, causing undyed areas to be formed. It should be avoided as far as possible during batching, and care should be taken to expel air through an open bleed-valve in the top of the vessel prior to commencing the dyeing, by filling the vessel with maximum load on the pump using inside-out flow. When the air has been expressed, the system is sealed and pressurized to enable the high temperature to be obtained.

Side loading beam dyeing machines have to be de-pressurized and the vessel emptied before the hinged door can be opened to unload the batch. This door is secured for safety by a pneumatically activated quick action lock which prevents premature opening taking place. To avoid the formation of air or vapor locks at the top of the beam, there is usually provision made to lead off some of the dye liquor by a small bore tube through a valve and condenser to a side tank, from which it is pumped back into the main circulation system. Any vapor formed escapes by this route and does not cause unlevelness as would be the case if allowed to accumulate at the top of the beam. This side tank is used to prepare the dye liquor before transfer to the beam dyeing machine, or to accommodate the exhausted dye liquor at the conclusion of dyeing (Haigh, 1971).

A yarn manufacturer suggested dyeing blends of their polyester and cotton in package or beam form; however, a high shrink or bulky yarn will require skein dyeing for maximum bulking.

Certain precautions are necessary for successful dyeing of polyester/cotton blends. Factors which influence dye levelness in package dyeing are package density, variation of package size, yarn twist and count, type of polyester, type of cotton fiber, and the dye technique. Uniform package density is the most important factor in obtaining package to package levelness.

Factors that influence the dyeing technique are the flow rate, cycle time, dye selection, dyeing temperature, rate of rise, and dyeing auxiliaries.

A problem that occurs when dyeing an ethylene terephthalate polyester is the cyclic trimer of the polyester forming a fine white deposit on package dyeing and winding equipment. This problem can be reduced by using at least 2 grams/liter of a 1,2,4-trichlorobenzene carrier and by dropping the dyebath hot at 93°C (200°F) or above when dyeing is completed. But, the fabric manufacturer warns that these carriers are toxic. Also, some existing and new dyeing machines flash-off or blow down under pressure as a means of controlling the trimer problem.

The following procedure is recommended by the dye manufacturer as a typical pressure package-dyeing procedure for a polyester/cotton blend with disperse and vat dyes (duPont, 1979):

- Pre-scour with:
  - 1% detergent
  - 1% TSPP
- Run for 10 minutes at 71°C (160°F) and wash well
- Set bath at 60°C (140°F) with:
  - 1% sodium hydrocarbon sulfonate
  - 0.5% detergent (for light shades)
  - 1 to 3 grams/liter carrier (for optimum leveling)
  - acetic acid to pH 5.5 to 6.0
- Run 10 minutes and add on "outside-inside" cycle:
  - 1% disperse dye
- Run 10 minutes then set cycle on "automatic" (generally 3 minutes of "outside-inside" and 3 minutes of "inside-outside")
- Heat to 93°C (200°F) at 1-3°F/minute
- Circulate for 20 minutes then pressurize the dye machine and heat to 121°C (250°F) at 1-3°F/minute
- Dye at 121°C (250°F) for 1-3 hours depending on shade
- If dye additions are made, cool to 77°C (170°F). Add the disperse dye, run 10 minutes, reheat to 121°C (250°F) at 1-3 °F/minute and then dye for a minimum of 30 minutes.
- When shade is acceptable, cool to 71°C (160°F). Add vat dyes, continue cooling to 54°C (130°F). Run 20 minutes and add:
  - 8 grams/liter caustic soda
  - 10 grams/liter hydrosulfite concentration
  - 0.5 grams/liter surface active agent
- Dye 30 minutes then wash well

- Set bath at 38°C (100°F) and add:
  - 3 grams/liter sodium perborate
- Heat to 60°C (140°F) and run 30 minutes
- Add:
  - 1% sodium ether-alcohol sulfate
  - 1% soda ash
- Heat to 88-93°C (190-200°F) and run for 20 minutes
- Wash well and apply antistatic and lubricating finish as desired

A typical beam process uses 3,407-4,731 liters (900-1,250 gallons) or 3,403-4,727 kilograms (7,503-10,421 pounds) of water and dyes 227-272 kilograms (500-600 pounds) of cloth per cycle. The maximum dye amount is 36 kilograms (80 pounds) of dye for 454 kilograms (1,000 pounds) of cloth dyed black, 18 kilograms for a 227 kilogram (40 pounds for a 500 pound) cloth cycle. Production estimates of acid dyeing indicate approximately 3 kilograms (6.7 pounds) of dye per 227 kilograms (500 pounds) of fabric (Appendix C), with 90-100% exhaustion rates being attainable (Alamance Knit, p. 350). Therefore, the dyestuff remaining is not exhausted into the fabric but is discharged as effluent with the wastewater. The water effluent will contain from 0 to 0.4 kilograms (0.97 pounds) of acid dye solids. About 1,136 liters (300 gallons) of this effluent is discharged, the remainder is recycled as process water (see Figure 26).

A typical small plant has five beam machines which can process 4,536 kilograms (10,000 pounds) per day of polyester, nylon, and blends. If 0.4 kilograms (0.97 pounds) of dye solids is produced for 227-272 kilograms (500-600 pounds) of fabric, then 1.8-1.5 kilograms (3.9-3.2 pounds) of dye solids per day are produced by each beam machine. Since the plant has five beam machines operating at 4,536 kilograms (10,000 pounds) of fabric per day, the resulting emission is approximately 8.8-7.3 kilograms (19.4-16.2 pounds) of dye solids per day.

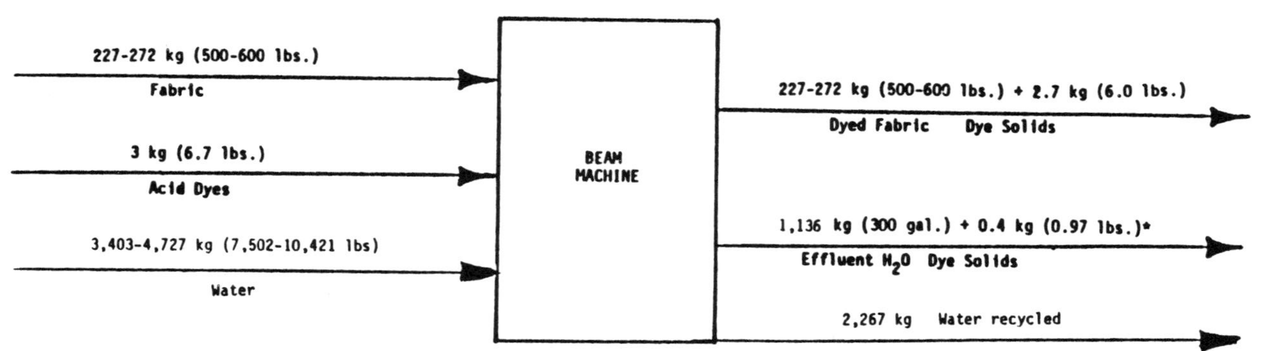


Figure 26. Mass balance of a beam operation using disperse dyes on polyester/cotton blend fabric.

Operation of five beam machines requires two operators per shift (see Appendix C). One batch operator and one drugroom operator. The operators are directly exposed during the 10 minute loading and unloading periods and when making additions of dye to the dyebath.

7.7.2 Batching Procedure With Beam Equipment

There are several methods of batching the fabric on to a beam, much depending upon the characteristics of the fabric to be dyed as to which is most suitable. It may be necessary to set the material previously to dyeing, and it may then be advantageous to batch from the tenter. Care must be taken to take out creases and curling at the selvedges before wrapping the fabric around the beam. When the selvedge is likely to be appreciably thicker than the body of the fabric, a slight traversing motion would be introduced during wind-on. Nylon fabrics, for example, may be passed in open width through a wetting-out solution and batched directly for a wet setting with water, or scouring solution, at a temperature sufficiently above the maximum dyeing temperature to be used.

Contact batching is carried out with the tension being maintained constant by the constant speed of wind which is obtained by a driven roller being in direct contact with the outer surface of the batch. If the beam is driven by means of a central spindle there has to be an infinitely variable speed gear between the driving motor and the spindle, and the cloth must first pass over a tension bar to detect any variation in tension and to actuate the speed gear to reduce the rotational speed to the correct rate as the batch grows in diameter (Haigh, 1971).

7.7.2.1 Beam Dying and Batching Equipment. The size of beam dyeing machines on the market varies. One manufacturer of non-pressurized beam machines that operate at atmospheric conditions builds beam machine in 680-1,134 kilogram (1,500-2,500 pound) sizes (Burlington Textile Machinery Brochure, 1982).

The pressureized beam dyeing machines are almost invariably cylindrical with the dimensions depending upon the maximum length of beam and the diameter of the batch. A 1966 survey of beam-dyeing machines indicated that an average sized machine had an internal diameter of 51" and will accomodate a beam of 61 centimeter (24 inch) diameter batched with fabric to a 112 centimeter (44 inch) external diameter. Side-loading beam machines require bogies and tracks so that the beam can be run into position on its carriage into the autoclave. The development of top-loading beam dyeing machines avoids the use of bogies and tracks (Haigh, 1971).

Beams are used on straightening and stretching machine as a built-on centre contact batcher. The machine is used for the wet winding of knitted goods on to dye beams for further treatment in high temperature or non-pressurized beam dyeing equipment (Bruckner, 1982).

The equipment used for batching varies with the size of the batch. Dyeing beams are used for large batches while cardboard tubes are used for small batches.

7.7.2.2 Bruckner's Suprafex High Temperature Beam Dyeing Machine. This machine is suitable for open-width piece dyeing or processing of woven, knitted, and hoisery goods in a horizontal dye vessel. The fabric carriers for dyeing can be cheeses, cones, muffs, or springs. The differential pressure for the machine is by means of a pump by-pass that allows for adjusting the pressure in the machine. A multi-stage axial pump provides the liquor circulation. The vessel diameter is available in sizes of 1,000, 1,200, 1,550, and 1,800 millimeters (40, 48, 62, and 72 inches) (Bruckner, 1982).

#### 7.7.3 Advantages and Disadvantages of Beam Dyeing

Problems with beam dyeing related to the circulation of the dye liquor as rapidly as possible without disturbing the package, and of effecting smooth and reliable change-in-direction of flow. It is also important in pressured beam dyeing to shape the autoclave for enabling the dye liquor to flow smoothly when dealing with a single large package such as a beam (Haigh, 1971).

### 7.8 JET DYEING MACHINES

The demand for synthetic fibers and yarns created the demand for pressure dyeing equipment, thus affecting the demand for atmospheric machinery. However, the economics of dyeing played an equally important role. Of the three main factors that had to be controlled in dyeing time, temperature, and amount of carrier; time proved to be the most costly of the three and could be accomplished or better met through high temperature dyeing (Hudak, 1976). The commercialization of high temperature dyeing was first carried out in yarn dyeing because much of the existing machinery in place in the United States could be converted at a minimum of cost in the early 1960s. This resulted in the use of pressure dyeing equipment such as pressure beck and jet dyeing machines.

Jet dyeing machines were devised to surmount the disadvantages of the winch beck machines. The jet machines utilize the same principle as a dye beck in that an endless loop of roped fabric is continuously conveyed in and out of the dye liquor. However, in place of a rotating reel a powerful stream of the treating liquor producing a Venturi effect in guiding tubes is responsible for moving the fabric through the dyebath. The powerful jet of dye solution also provides excellent penetration and intimate contact of dye and fiber, improving efficiency and level dyeing. Figure 27 illustrates the basic principal of the jet machine (VPI, 1981).

In the figure, the fabric is pulled out of the dye liquor by a lifter roll; then passes down the venturi tube where the "jet" flow of the dye liquor on the fabric forces it back down into the main chamber; the fabric piles on itself and forces or pushes the mass back to the front of the kettle. The jet supply is provided by drawing the dyebath through a pipe, up through the pump to the heat exchanger (also a cooling chamber) and then back through a pipe to the venturi. The speed of the fabric may vary from 41 to 411 meters (45 to 450 yards) per minute. Each tube (or jet) can hold between 45 to 181 kilograms (100 to 400 pounds) of material depending on the machine and also the type of material. The jet machine not only allows for very good temperature control but also the dyeing takes place in very low liquor ratios of 10:1 to 5:1 (VPI, 1981).

The earliest example of the jet dyeing machine was the Gaston County Jet Dyeing Machine which was first introduced in 1961. The Superjets in 1970 were four-tube machines with capacities of 400-600 kilos.

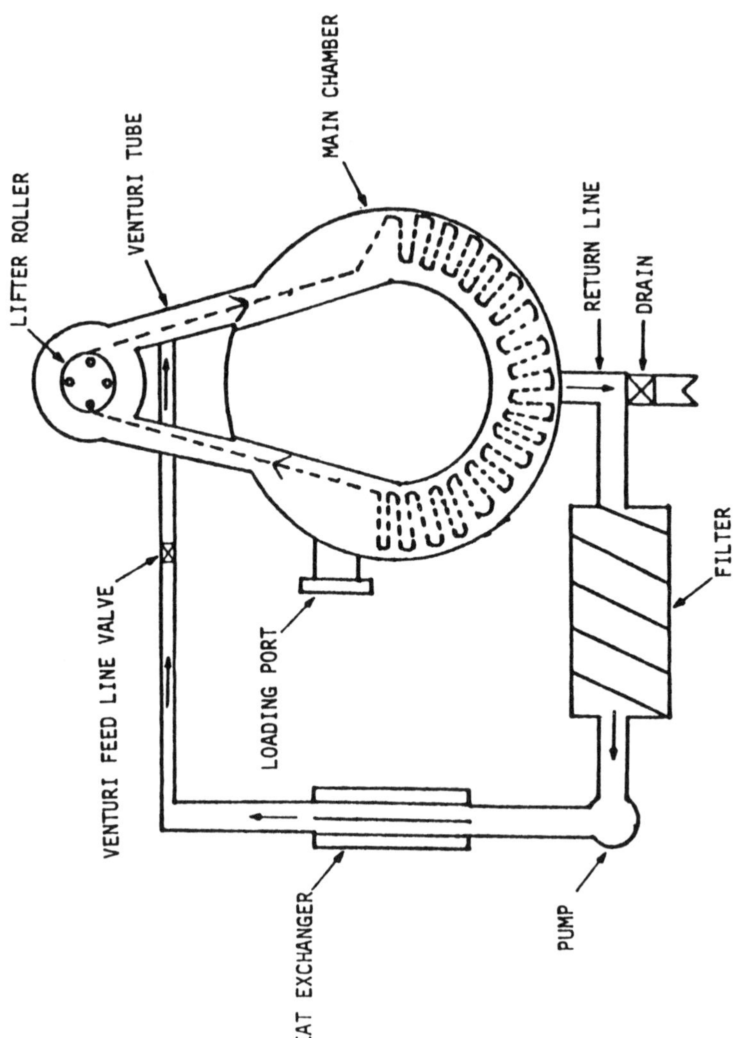


Figure 27. Schematic of jet dyeing machinery with operational flow directions.

Several jet machines were developed by different machine manufacturers. Table 40 represents the jet machines at a 1967 exhibition with some of their characteristics (Haigh, 1971).

The circuit of the fabric and the action of the venturi jet has been determined by investigations using a transparent unit in which the movement of fabric and liquor can be observed. The fabric was never stationary during dyeing. An unusual path of fabric and liquid follows the tube which is considered to be responsible for the absence of creasing. The fluid travels to the outside of the elbows and the fabric stays at the inside forcing the liquor that was at the inside to penetrate the fabric in passing to the outside. Leaving the first elbow, the cloth and liquor travel through the horizontal tube with the liquor very largely at the top of the tube, though there is some conveying fluid under the fabric. The liquor at the outside of the tube now descends in a long swoop and dives under the fabric just before it enters the second elbow, repeating the penetration of the fabric (Haigh, 1971).

The circulation in jet machines is circumferential or longitudinal (i.e., from end to end). The circumferential arrangement allows several ropes of fabric to be processed side by side in the same pressure vessel, while some machines with longitudinal circulation process two ropes side by side.

All machines have a section in the circulating path in which the fabric accumulates between successive passage through the jet system through which it moves forward relatively slowly. Linear speeds through the jet system are commonly up to 150 meters per minute.

### 7.8.1 Jet Dyeing Procedures

Jet dyeing is an exhaustion process similar to the beck dyeing. The principle of dyeing varies with the beck dyeing machines having the movement of the material through the dye liquor while the jet dyeing machines have the movement of both the material and the dye liquor. The principle of pressure jet dyeing is used for cloth dyed in rope form. The necessary movement of the cloth is brought about by the movement of the dye liquor.

TABLE 40. CHARACTERISTICS OF JET DYEING MACHINES (Neal, 1982)

| Manufacturer | Name | Capacity (kilos) | Tubes | Shape | Dyeing temp. | Liquor ratio | General remarks |
|---|---|---|---|---|---|---|---|
| Bene & Cie., France | Unibak | 17<br>20<br>50 | 1<br>1<br>1 | Square U Tubed | | About 10:1 | The small unit has a single winch reel. The others have two. Units can be connected together for larger loads. COMPLETELY FILLED WITH LIQUOR, therefore jet below liquor. |
| Callebaut de Blicquy, Belgium | Aspiromat | 30 - 50<br>80 - 100 | 1<br>1 | Vertical | 140°C. | Not less than 20:1 | The fabric passes over the surface of a submerged perforated winch reel, then descends spirally around the central tube, directed by two jets positioned near the reel. It is taken up to the reel through this central tube COMPLETELY FILLED WITH LIQUOR. Speed 30-150 metres per min. |
| Frauchiger, Switzerland | Fastral 69 | 10 to 130 | 1 | Vertical | | | The jet works with a static air cushion which expands the liquor during its circulation. Vertical stabilization plates enclose the material mass during its passage through the dyeing chamber. Single rope machine, but several machines can be coupled. |
| Gaston County, U.S.A. | Jet and Superjet | 100 - 150 per jet tube | 1<br>3<br>4 | Cylindrical | | 8:1 to 10:1 | A multi-tube machine (Superjet) of large capacity. The fabric is transferred through the tube by dye liquor which is introduced at the bottom of the entry leg of each tube by a venturi jet. Anti-foaming precautions necessary. Speed 100-130 metres per minute. |
| Krantz, Germany | Jet<br>Twin Jet | | 1<br>2 | Almost Circular U Tubed | | 10:1 | Goods circulated in annular, COMPLETELY FILLED pressure vessel by means of a jet system. Speed 100 metres per min. |
| Mezzera/hisaka, Italy/Japan | Circular | 100<br>200<br>300 | 1<br>2<br>3 | Horizontal U Tubed | 130°C. | Not less than 20:1 | The machine comprises a header tank which is cylindrical with a driven ground and polished fabric guider roller. The fabric is circulated with the dye liquor by a pump through the internally polished U-shaped tubes. Speed 50-150 metres per minute. |

(continued)

TABLE 40. CHARACTERISTICS OF JET DYEING MACHINES (Neal, 1982) (continued)

| Manufacturer | Name | Capacity (kilos) | Tubes | Shape | Dyeing temp. | Liquor ratio | General remarks |
|---|---|---|---|---|---|---|---|
| Masuda, Japan | Masflow | 50<br>100<br>200 | 1<br>1<br>1 | Vertical | 130°C | Approx. 20:1 | The fabric in rope form travels with the flow of dye liquor at very low pressure (0.05 kilos $cm^2$) in the carrier pipe. Floating of fabric controlled by "Resume" system. Speed 30-120 m/min. |
| Platt-Longclose, England | Ventura | 110 per tube | 2 | Inclined horizontal | 140C°. | | Flow tube and circulation system moves fabric and liquor at different relative speeds. FABRIC TOTALLY IMMERSED. |
| Rudolf Then, Germany | Thenjet | 100<br>140<br>250 | 1<br>1<br>2 | Horizontal | 140°C | 10:1 to 12:1 | The fabric is circulated by a two-step injector fitted to the exit side of store tube, which sucks it off and feeds it through the transport tube tensionless. Alternating suction propels piled fabric through store tube. COMPLETELY FILLED. |
| Thies, Germany | Jet-Stream | 40 - 100 per tube | Up to eight may be combined | Vertical U Tubed | | | The fabric is sucked up the upward tube by lowering its pressure and creating a pressure difference. A jet stream is generated to transport the fabric rope through the unit. COMPLETELY FILLED. |

An example dyeing procedure from American Hoechst for dyeing 100% polyester fabric in a jet machines are as follows (Neal, 1982):

- Prescour for 30 minutes at 88°C (190°F) with:
  - 1% Remol NFE
  - 2% Soda Ash
- Rinse, neutralize any residual alkali - rinse and check pH of cloth with Indicator OBS
- Set dyebath at 49-60°C (120-140°F) with:
  - 0.5-1% Remol LE
  - 1-1.5% Leomin HNF
  - pH 4.0-5.0 Acetic Acid 56%
- Run 10 minutes
- Add pre-dispersed dyes which have been prepared in the drugroom as follows:
  - add ½-1% Solegal P Liq. to water between 38-49°C (100-120°F) NO HOTTER THAN 120°F
  - add 0.25% owg EDTA Sequestrant to Solegal P Liq. solution
  - add enough acetic acid to give a pH of 5.0 or less
  - sprinkle in disperse dye powder or pour in disperse dye paste while stirring with a low rpm mixer (200-400 rpm). DO NOT USE SHEAR FLOW MIXERS. If no low rpm mixer is available, use a hand paddle
  - mix approximately five minutes, strain, and add to the machine
- Circulate five to ten minutes after dye is added
- Heat 2-3°F/minute to 129°C (265°F)
- Run 30 minutes at 129°C (265°F)
- Cut steam off, cool to 82°C (180°F), depressurize and sample
- If cool additions are necessary - cool to 71-77°C (160-170°F). The dye addition is pre-dispersed as outlined above when Step 5, except the amount of Solegal P Liq/acetic acid/EDTA

tetra sodium salt is based on the size of the add. The addition is then made, ran 10 minutes, and reheated to 129°C (265°F) for 20 minutes.

- After the shade is correct, cool to 71-77°C (160-170°F), running rinse until clear
- On light to medium shades, no afterscour is necessary - on heavy shades, an afterscour is often given as follows:
  - fill machine with 60°C (140°F) water
  - add 2% alkali (usually soda ash or caustic) and 1% Remol NFE
  - heat to 82°C (180°F), sprinkle in 3-4% hydro, run 15 minutes
- Cool, rinse well. If the dyes used are non-pH sensitive and non-metal sensitive, go to Step 15
- On all shades contain metallic sensitive colors, add 1.0-1.5% Oxalic Acid or 1.5% acetic acid and 0.5% EDTA Sequestrant. Heat to 100-110°F, run five minutes
- Drop bath

### 7.8.2 Advantages and Disadvantages of Jet Dyeing

The advantages of jet machines are evident in the dyeing of woven as well as knitted fabrics. Some of the jet dyeing advantages are: (1) minimizing or avoiding completely the need for carriers; (2) the complete or virtual elimination of rope marking; (3) more rapid dyeing than is possible by other methods; (4) good coverage of barre' tendencies in the fabric; and (5) the capacity dyeing with modest liquor/goods ratio (Textile Month, 1972).

Some disadvantages of jet machine are the obtaining of samples during pressurized dyeing and the possibility of troublesome foaming on machines which have an air space above the liquor bath. The monitoring of the dyeing cycle requires bath sampling from the dye machine. The newer jet machines have designed systems for sampling without interrupting dyeing.

The problem with the jet machine developing foam can cause tangles and "jamming." Careful selection of dyes and chemicals is very critical. Some of the newer designs in jets utilize a total fabric immersion in the dye liquor which offsets the foam problem (VPI, 1981).

Foaming will cause cavitation in the pump and the flow of dye liquor may become very weak or even stop. It is essential to reduce the possibility of foaming by the use of an effective antifoaming agent. Some machines have attempted filling the vessels completely with dye liquor so as to avoid any possibility of foaming. The pegg-jet machine is an example of a fully flooded machine in which there is no air in the chamber containing the circulating liquor. The interchangeable venturi jet can be selected to suit the fabric weight and can be changed in a few seconds. The machine can be erected either horizontally or vertically (Trotman, 1970).

A study on the operational costs of a low liquor jet vs. an atmospheric beck is presented in Table 41. The cost savings from the jet on a per weight of fabric dyed results from less water and steam required because of the pressurized vessel vs. the atmospheric vessel and the shorter dyeing cycle. Costly chemical additives are reduced when the fabric and dye are in more contact which aids in the jet's exhaustion rate, while the beck requires chemical additions to aid in the exhaustion rate (NCSU, 1982).

### 7.8.3 Jet Dyeing Equipment on the Market

Jet dyeing machines come in various shapes and sizes. Shapes include the tube type and the cylindrical or compact type. Other models may also have a vertical, horizontal, or angled dyeing vessel.

Two examples of presently used jet dyeing machines are the Henriksens' VH-Jet 80 and VH-Jet SLA. Both models are a low liquor ratio dyeing machine, suitable for dyeing of knitted and woven fabrics.

An example of a jet with a vertical dye vessel (the Henriksen VH-Jet 80) is shown in Figure 28. The machine is designed for low liquor ratio dyeing and is suitable for the dyeing of knitted and woven fabrics. The charge size of the machine is 150-200 kilogram/chamber. The machines can be designed with 2, 4, or 6 chambers. It is also

TABLE 41. OPERATIONAL COSTS OF A
LOW LIQUOR JET VS. ATMOSPHERIC BECK (NCSU, 1982)

| Machine type (lb) | Jet | Beck |
|---|---|---|
| Cycle load (lb) | 1,600 | 1,100 |
| (kg) | 725.7 | 498.9 |
| Cycle time (hr) | 7 | 14 |
| Lb/week | 21,920 | 7,590 |
| Kg/week | 9,943 | 3,606 |
| Costs/lb ($) | | |
| Direct labor | $0.0136 | $0.0395 |
| Water | .0105 | .0453 |
| Steam | .0100 | .0408 |
| Electricity | .0042 | .0021 |
| Chemicals | .0200 | .0950 |
| | $0.0584 | $0.2227 |

Fabric used was 50/50 polyester-cotton T-shirt material.

Jet used was a Gaston County Aqualuft machine with four separate chambers, each with an individual jet and port.

Beck used was 12 ft.

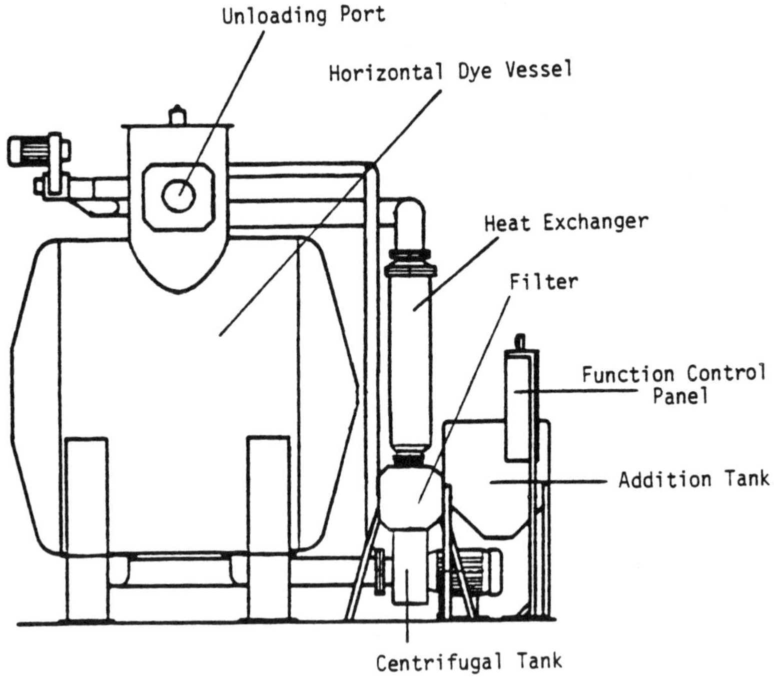


Figure 28. Henriksen VH-Jet 80.

possible to couple two machines. The normal operating parameters of the machine has a material to liquor ratio between 1:4 and 1:10. The parameters of operating a 2, 4, or 6 chamber machine is advertised as follows:

| | 2 Chamber | 4 Chamber | 6 Chamber |
|---|---|---|---|
| Capacity depending on fabric type (kg) | 300-400 | 600-800 | 900-1200 |
| (lbs) | (661.4-882) | (1,323-1,764) | (1,984-2,645) |
| Operating pressure of machine @110°C (230°F) (bar) | 0.5 | 0.5 | 0.5 |
| Operating pressure of machine @140°C (284°F) (Bar) | 3 | 3 | 3 |

An example of a jet with a horizontal dye vessel is the Henriksen VH-Jet SLA (see Figure 29). The machine is designed for fully flooded high temperature piece dyeing. High fabric speed during dyeing in this jet ensures best levelness and short processing times. The machine is supplied in one ring or can be modified for executing in dual rings with one ring above the other. The operating parameters of the horizontal dye machine is as follows:

| | 1 Ring | 2 Ring |
|---|---|---|
| Maximum capacity (depending on fabric type) (kg) | 200 | 400 |
| (lbs) | 441 | 882 |
| Cloth velocity (m/min) | 50-350 | 50-350 |
| (yds/min) | 59.8-418.6 | 49.8-418.6 |
| Dye liquor capacity in ring (L) | 1650 | 3300 |
| (U.S. gallons) | 435.8 | 871.7 |
| Maximum dye liquor of expansion tank (L) | 300 | 600 |
| (U.S. gallons) | 79.2 | 158.5 |
| Heating 10-100°C (50-212°F) (min) | 18 | 18 |
| Heating 100-130°C (212-265°F) (min) | 10 | 10 |
| Cooling down 130-90°C (265-194°F) (min) | 9 | 9 |
| Cooling down 90-60°C (194-140°F) (min) | 12 | 12 |

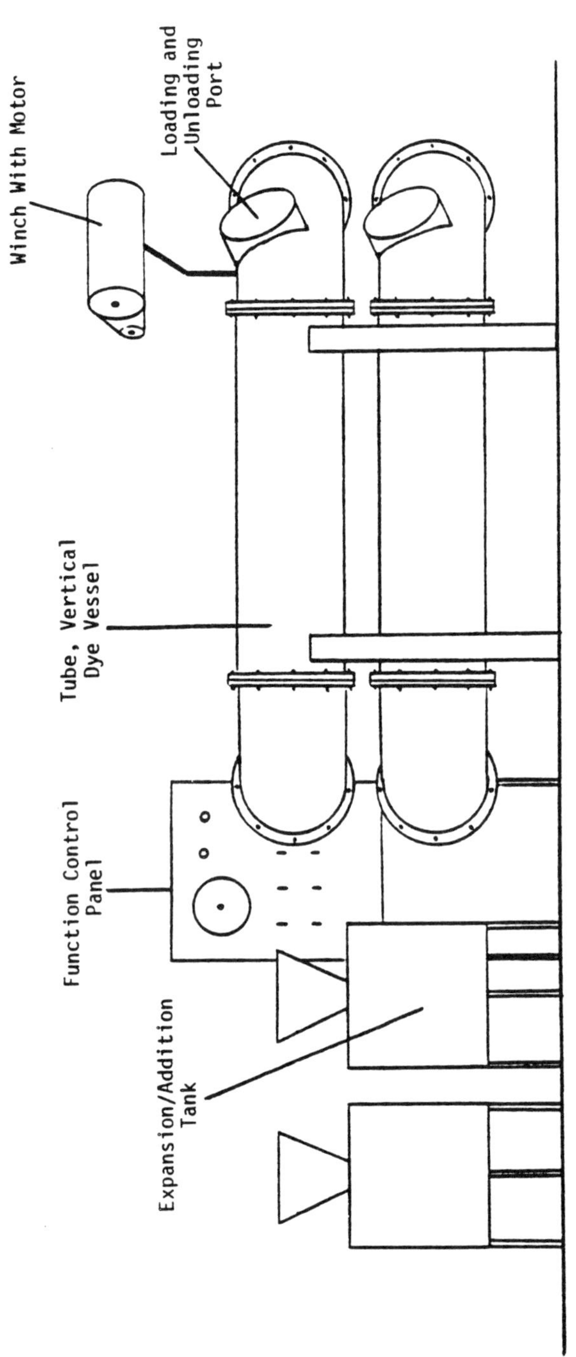


**Figure 29. Henriksen VH-Jet SLA.**

## 7.9 JIG DYEING

Jig dyeing machines are utilized for dyeing of fabric in open width. The jig's primary uses are for woven fabrics made from cotton, the rayons and certain synthetic fibers. Only a few yards of the fabric being dyed is immersed in the dyebath at a time, therefore making it possible to work with short liquor ratios.

The jig dyeing process is an exhaustion process. The operating principle of jig dyeing is to move the fabric through the dye for aiding the exhaustion process. The machine consists of two draw rollers for pulling the fabric back and forth through the dye liquor. A basic schematic of the fundamental parts are illustrated in Figure 30 (Horning, 1978). Each pass through the dye liquor is called an end and the number of ends run for dyeing is always even.

One practice for using jigs as a high-pressure machine is to enclose a jig in a pressure-withstanding chamber such as an autoclave. End-opening pressure vessels are made, into which jigs can be run in and out on rails. This arrangement allows the possibility of loading up a second jig while the first is dyeing.

Another use for the jig today is in semi-continuous pad/batch dyeing procedure. The jig is used for the batching step such as the beam machines. The batching procedure is described in Section 7.7.2.

### 7.9.1 Jig Dyeing Procedures

The principle of dyeing with jig machines is based on a very low liquor ratio. In jig dyeing systems, the dyeing takes place in the roll and it is important that the dye is distributed uniformly in order to avoid shade variations from side to side and end to end. These various jig dyeing procedures can utilize exhaustion agents, high temperatures and/or pressures (VPI, 1981).

There is only a short length of fabric immersed in the dye liquor at any given time during dyeing. The diffusion of dye into the fiber takes place from the interstitial liquor which is taken up during the rotation of the roll. A suitable length of end cloth is attached to each end of the fabric being dyed so that it can be dyed throughout its length.

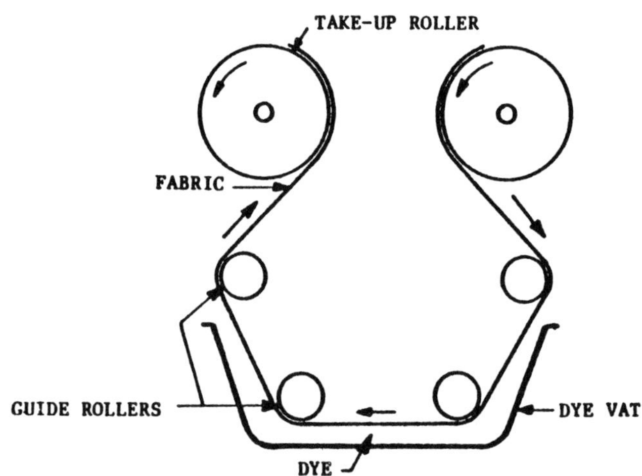


Figure 30. Schematic of a jig machine.

Ending and listing are major defects that can occur during jig-dyeing and must be considered during dyeing. Ending is the variation in shade depth or hue from one end of the fabric to the other. Listing is the variation in shade from side-to-side. Ending is largely associated with the dyes used and listing is caused by temperature difference from the selvedges to the center of the batched-up cloth on the jig roller or by uneven batching-up of the cloth on the rollers.

The operational procedure of the jig dyeing is in cycles with a cycle being the fabric rolling onto one roller then reversing directions and rolling back to the original roller. The rollers rotate in clockwise and anti-clockwise directions alternatively, pulling the fabric backward and forward through the dye liquor with guide rollers placed at the bottom of the dyeliquor trough.

The rotation of the rollers is accomplished with a line-shaft type system or a constant speed type system. The line-shaft type drives the rollers at a constant speed, but the speed of the fabric varies from 20-120 meters (23.9-143.5 yards) per minute over one end. The constant speed type applies a variable-speed drive to each roller, therefore, a constant speed of the fabric is obtained through the dyeliquor. The development of constant speed jigs aided in solving the problem with ending. Pressurized jig dyeing is extremely beneficial for minimizing the ending problem with higher temperatures than open atmospheric dyeing.

### 7.9.2 Jig Dyeing Machines on the Market

7.9.2.1 Henriksen's Jig Machine. The Henriksen's Super Jig has a constant cloth tension obtained by a single spiral spring that is adjusted by a lever to the required tension. The tension can be varied from 0-100 kilos. The cloth speed can be varied from 10-20 and 60-120-meters (12-24 and 72-144 yards) per minute.

Today's Henriksen jig machines come in sizes of 800 millimeter, 1000 millimeter, and 1200 millimeter cloth roll diameter. The length of material on one batch is determined by the thickness of the cloth being dyed. The approximate batch length or material can be calculated by the equations:

$$\text{Metres on 800 millimeter machine} = \frac{450}{t}$$

$$\text{Metres on 1000 millimeter machine} = \frac{700}{t}$$

$$\text{Metres on 1200 millimeter machine} = \frac{1000}{t}$$

In the equations t is the cloth thickness in mm.

A dye-liquor ratio of approximately 1:3 is used when the jig is fully loaded and the dye vat is filled. Heating of the dye vat can be accomplished with direct and indirect steam heating. The maximum liquor for each model will vary for the different cloth thickness: Super 800 = 609-821 liters (161-217 gallons), Super 1000 = 900-1,200 liters (238-317 gallons), Super 1200 = 1,359-1,802 liters (359-476 gallons) (Henriksen, 1982).

7.9.3 Advantages and Disadvantages of Jig Dyeing

The use of beam dyeing for open-width fabric has become a more common practice than dyeing in pressure jigs. The beam is simpler to use than jigs enclosed in pressure vessels for dyeing at temperatures above 100°C (212°F) especially for open-width warp-knitted materials. This is one reason why jig dyeing has declined (Table 34).

Problems encountered during jig dyeing are (VPI, 1981)

- temperature control from side to side and end to end of the roll is hard to achieve
- tension control from end to end is hard to achieve (causing excessive stretch)
- constant speed control from one end to the other is hard to achieve
- prevention of creases is not possible

Although these problems have been overcome by many machine manufacturers, expert monitoring is required to obtain quality dyeing with this low liquor dyeing method. Worker exposure in open jigs can be relatively high since dyebaths are concentrated and misting may be prevalent.

## 7.10 PADDLE DYEING

The term "vat dyeing" is not found in many sources of technical literature on dyeing processes, however, the term is used in discussions of the dyeing procedures for garment dyeing. The garment dyeing machinery that resembles a vat type machine is the paddle machine. Side-paddle and the overhead-paddle machines are used for many types of delicate garments including ladies' hose, cardigans, pullovers, and sweaters. Figure 31 is a schematic of a side paddle machine and Figure 32 is a schematic of an overhead paddle machine (VPI, 1981). Dyeing is discussed in Section 7.10.2.

The paddle dyeing process is an exhaustion process. The process of applying the dye involves constantly moving the substrate through the dye liquor.

### 7.10.1 Paddle Dyeing Procedures

Paddle machines are especially good for delicate fabrics since the fabric is not under stress, therefore the full bulk and dimensional stability is maintained.

The pieces or garments are generally placed in bags to avoid entanglement during dyeing. The paddle rotates in the machine at a speed of 13-15 rounds per minute. Paddle rotation is reversed during the dyeing process every 5-6 minutes. This prevents bags called "floaters" in the back of the machine from not circulating through the vat. If the garments or fabric pieces are allowed to get loose, excessive tangling, uneven dyeing, and possible abrasive damage may occur.

Two example procedures of paddle dyeing garments and socks of 100 percent polyester are presented below. One procedure uses disperse dyes while the other uses basic dyes. With both procedures, garments are prepared by being turned inside out and washed, then loosely bagged in the paddle-dyeing machine. The washing scours and relieve knitting tensions. The disperse procedure is as follows:

- Set bath at 140°F with:
  - 0.5% to 1% Merpol HCS
  - 1% Avitone T

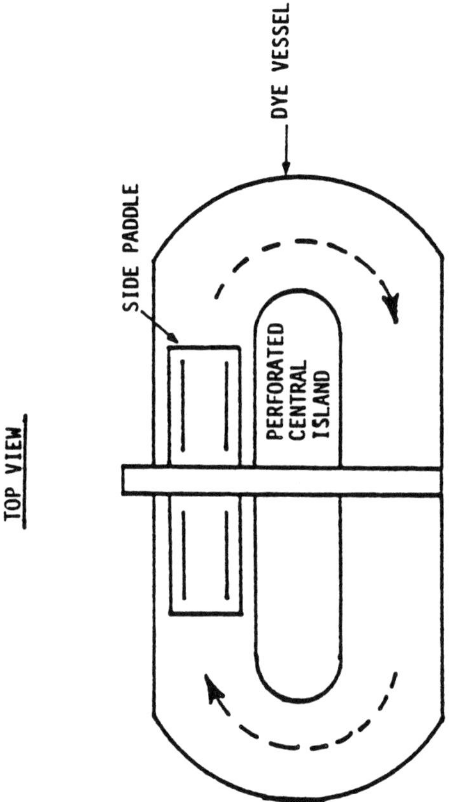


Figure 31. Schematic of a side paddle machine with direction of goods and dye liquor movement.

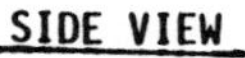


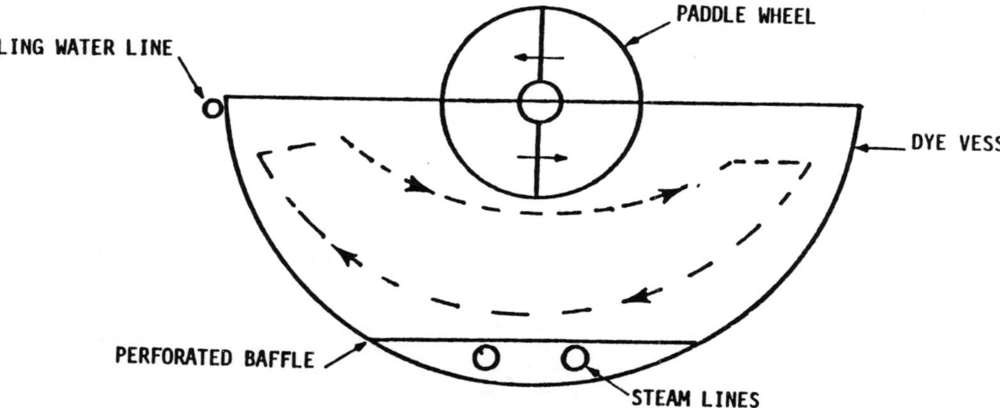


Figure 32. Schematic of an overhead paddle machine with direction of goods and dye liquor movement.

- Acetic acid to pH 6.0
- 6 g/l anhydrous sodium sulfate.

- Run for 10 minutes and add:
  - X% disperse dye.
- Run for 15 minutes and then, over a 15 minute period add:
  - 3 to 5 g/l carrier.
- Heat to a boil at 1 to 3°F/minute.
- Dye at the boil for 1 to 3 hours.
- Cool bath by radiation to 170°F for dye additions. If dye additions are not necessary, add cold water slowly after 170°F is reached.
- Wash garments or socks well.
- If necessary, afterscour at 160°F for 15 minutes with:
  - 1% Merpol HCS
  - 1% soda ash.
- Wash garments or socks well.

A graphical representation of the temperature profile for the dyeing steps is presented in Figure 33.

The procedure for paddle dyeing of 100% polyester garments and/or socks is as follows:

- Set bath at 140°F with:
  - 0.5% Merpol HCS
  - 6 g/l anhydrous sodium sulfate
  - acetic acid to pH 5.0.
- Run for 10 minutes and add:
  - X% cationic dye.
- Run for 15 minutes and then, over a 15 minute period add:
  - 3 to 5 g/l nonionic carrier.
- Heat to a boil at 6°C (1°F) per minute.

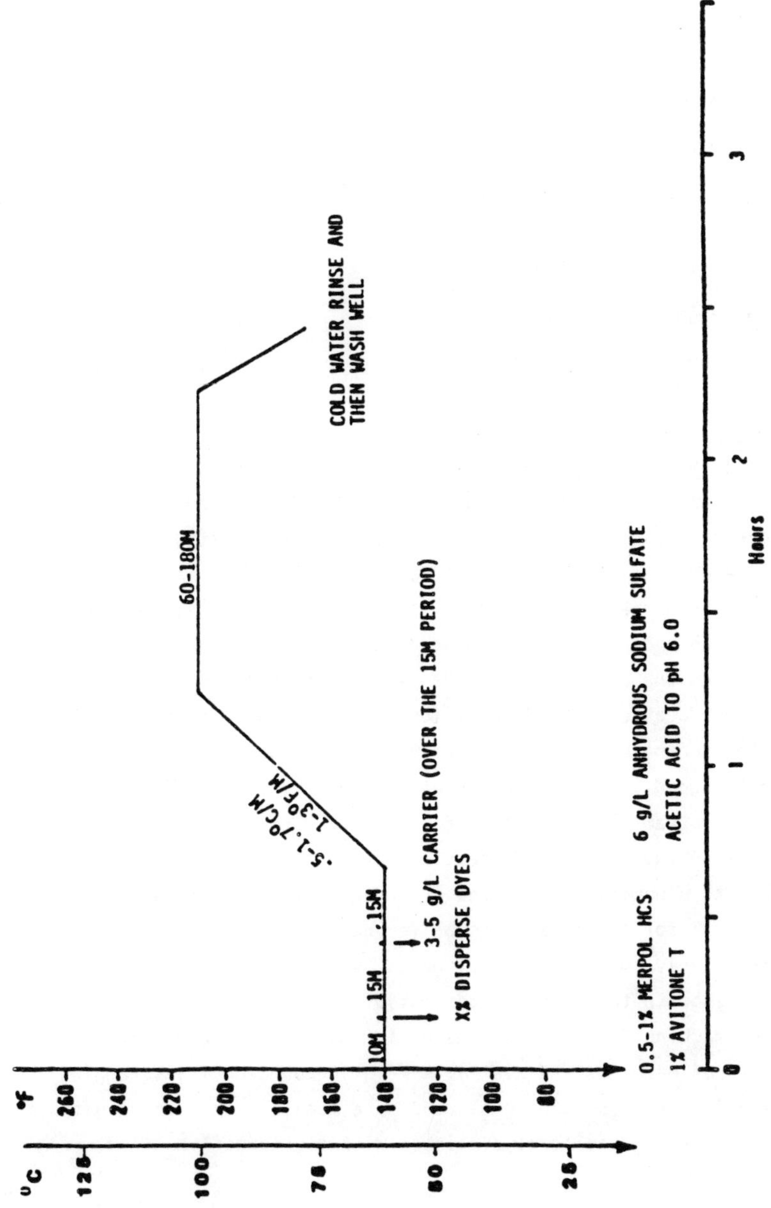


Figure 33. Dyeing 100% polyester with disperse dyes: exhaust dyeing with a paddle machine.

- Dye at the boil for 1 to 2 hours.
- Cool bath by radiation to 77°C (170°F), then slowly add cold water.
- Wash garments and socks well.
- If necessary, afterscour at 71°C (160°F) for 15 minutes with:
  - 1% Merpol HCS
  - 1% acetic acid.
- Wash garments or socks well.

A graphical representation of the temperature profile of dyeing steps is presented in Figure 34.

7.10.2 Paddle Dyeing Machines

7.10.2.1 Side-Paddle Dyeing Machines. The side-paddle dying machine, originally known as the Gorrie side-paddle machine, is widely used for dyeing ladies' hose and half-hose, and other knitted garments. Figure 31 presents a schematic representation of a paddle machine. The oval shaped machine is constructed of stainless steel and is enclosed. A central "island" contains the outlet plug. The side paddle propels the goods around the vessel in the dye liquor, assisted by steam injection through the perforated steam pipes which are situated below the projected baffle plates in the bottom of the vessel. The blades of the side paddle are designed to direct the goods towards the outer wall of the vessel and the steam injectors tend to lift the garments from the bottom. The effect is to cause more satisfactory movement of garments around the machine, and to minimize the chances of entanglement. A vessel of this kind is suitable for loose garments or for bagged goods, and it can be used for relatively small batches of goods, with the liquor level reduced in height to shorten the liquor:goods ratio.

Various machine manufacturers make side-paddle dyeing machines. Various sizes of machines are available with liquor capacities ranging from 189-4,542 liters (50-1200 gallons). The models come with or without enclosing lids; some models are available with closed coil heating.

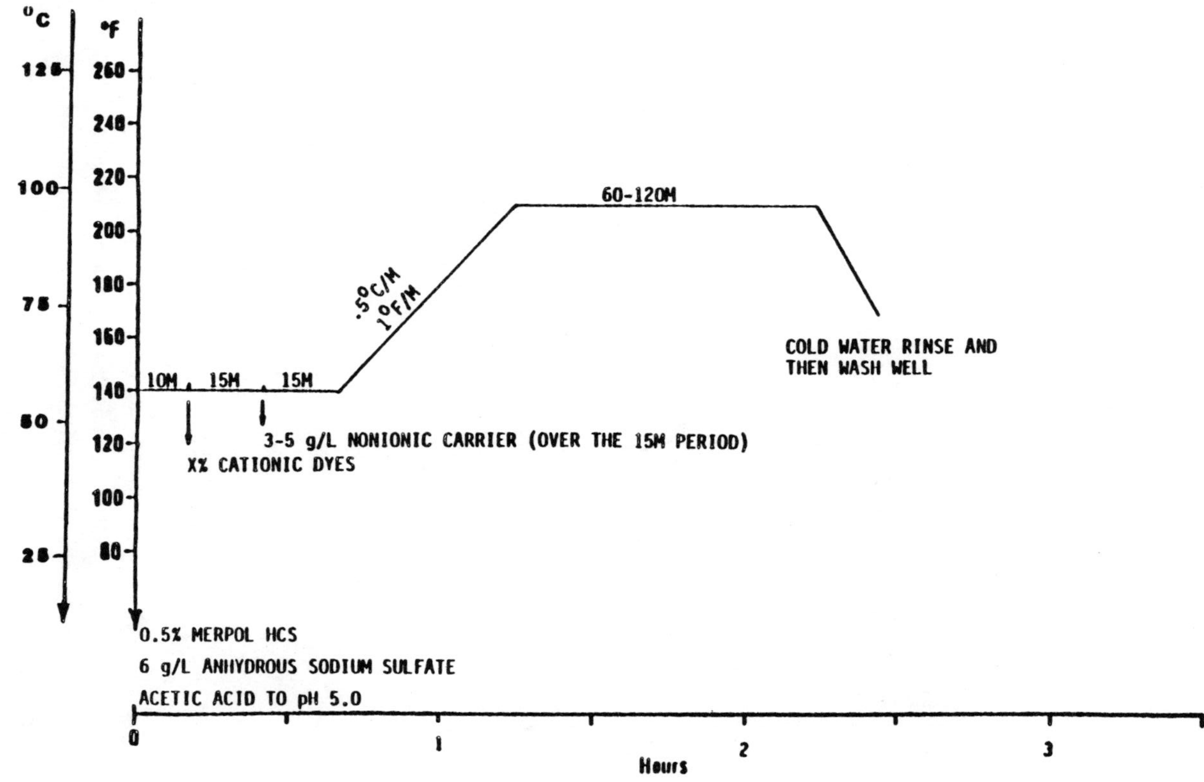


Figure 34. Dyeing 100% polyester with cationic dyes: exhaust dyeing with a paddle machine.

7.10.2.2 Overhead Paddle Dyeing Machines. The overhead paddle dyeing machine (Figure 32) consists of a specially shaped dye tank, designed to permit movement of liquor and garments without any development of stagnant pockets where individual garments can aggregate and remain static for any undue length of time. Dipping into the dye liquor is a wide paddle, of the same overall width as that of the machine, which contains four short blades. Each blade dips only a few inches into the liquor. The action of this type of paddle is much milder than the side paddle, and there is less likelihood of fraying. Care must be taken with this machine to maintain the liquor level constant to obtain repeatable results. The temperature throughout the dyebath in an overhead paddle machine is more easily maintained than the side paddle machine.

Multi-compartment overhead paddle dyeing machines are available for garment sample dyeing. The system consists of small units mounted side-by-side on a common shaft driven by an electric motor. This system is convenient for dyeing garments simultaneously to different shades (Haigh, 1971).

## 7.11 LEATHER DYEING

Dyeing of leather presents difficulties not encountered in the dyeing of textiles. Leather is derived from protein collagen and is treated for use with one or more tanning agents. Unlike textiles, leather is not a homogeneous product of definite composition with accurately defined chemical properties. Collagen is derived from skin or hide substance with known chemical characteristics, but the variety of materials that convert collagen into leather leave the chemical composition of leather indeterminant (Kirk-Othmer, 1978).

Three main types of dyes are used to color leather: acid, direct, and basic. Generally, leather dyeing requires two or more dyes or dye types to produce a given shade. The acid dyes used are usually azo, triarylmethane, or anthraquinone dyes with acid substituents such as nitro-, carboxy-, or sulfonic acid. Basic dyes contain free amino groups. Direct dyes are principally water-soluble salts of sulfonic acids of azo dyes (EPA, 1978).

Leather dyeing systems utilize drum, wheel, paddle, brush or spray dyeing equipment. The procedure is usually a simple batch mode process of retanning, coloring, and fat liquoring. These operations are usually performed in sequence with the same equipment without intermediate steps of washing and drying. Most leather dyeing takes place in drums (Kirk-Othmer, 1978).

The leather is dyed in the blue or chrome stage of the hide. The procedure for drum dyeing is to place the blue hides in drums and add the retanning formulations. The dye formulations are added at the appropriate time after the retanning cycle. The amount of dye solution ranges from 1-2 times the weight of wet leather or from 4-8 times the weight of dry leather. Dyeing temperatures range from 46-52°C (115-126°F). The dye formulation is usually mixed by rotation. Then the fat liquoring chemicals are added at the prescribed time in the cycle. Cycle times for this sequence range from 4-8 hours.

Drum dyeing procedures take place in revolving cylinders ranging from approximately 1-1.5 millimeters (3-5 feet) in width and 2.4-3.7 millimeters (8-12 feet) in diameter (Kirk-Othmer, 1978). Leather dyeing formulations are either trade secrets or handed down in family-owned businesses (EPA, 1978).

## 7.12 NON-WOVEN DYEING

The first non-woven or disposable fabrics were cellulosic fibers. The original non-wovens were generally made from cottons (AII, 1963). But due to the need for water repellancy, many new non-wovens have been developed from polypropylene and polymer fabrics (INDA, 1978).

Non-wovens are generally dyed in top forms in batch type equipment such as a package machine. Direct dyes are usually used for cellulosic non-wovens because of their affinity for cotton. Disperse dyes are utilized to dye synthetic non-woven fabric because of their bonding characteristics. Non-wovens are pigment printed because color additions can occur at the fabric bonding agent (AII, 1963).

# 8. Wastewaters and Wastewater Treatment

## 8.1 INTRODUCTION

This section identifies the wastewater sources and treatment technologies in use at textile operations. It also characterizes textile dyeing operations with respect to wastewater treatment plant size, plant production volumes, and volume of redyed fabric. As with the other aspects of textile dyeing described in this study, the majority of the available information in the area of wastewater treatment for textile dyeing is closely associated with the more general subject of textile finishing operations. Consequently, very little data are available specifically for textile dyeing. The end result is that it is often difficult to distinguish between these two areas while attempting to focus upon textile dyeing operations.

## 8.2 TEXTILE MILL WASTEWATER FROM DYE OPERATIONS

Dyeing is without question the most complex of all the textile mills with wet finishing operations. The dye process contributes from 10-30% of total plant BOD (biological oxygen demand). Soap, acetic acid, sodium acetate, sodium sulfide, sodium hydrosulfite, sodium sulfite, glucose, and emulsifying oils are major contributors to the dye wastes.

In a study in North Carolina, dyeing operations with such dyes as sulfur, direct, vat, acid, developed, naphthol, and disperse dyes were observed. The main pollution characteristics of their wastes were noted as intense color (which is obtained even at low levels of contamination), high pH and alkalinity, high COD (chemical oxygen demand), high chlorine content, high temperature, and extreme toxicity of sulfur dye wastes. Suggestions for treatment of these wastes were: equalization of the strong and weak wastes, neutralization of acid and alkaline wastes, proportioning the flow into sewage flow, removal of color, and removal of oxygen and chlorine demands via aeration, chemical precipitation and biological oxidation (Horning, 1978).

Acetic acid (along with starch from desizing) has a big biological oxygen demand (BOD) impact in dye operations since it is used by many mills as the acidifying agent in the dye house. Its use may result in as much as 50-90 percent of the dye house waste BOD, which may cause to 15-30 percent of the total plant BOD.

A study of textile mills was performed for the EPA's Development Document for Effluent Limitations Guidelines and Standards for the Textile Mills. The textile mills were grouped into subcategories according to the types of process. The dyeing portions of the text from the subcategories with wet-finishing operations follows.

### 8.2.1 Woven Fabric Finishing Mills

Woven fabric is usually dyed as piece goods with batch or continuous dye equipment, depending on the type of fabric, the type of dyes used, the type of equipment employed, and the efficiency of the process. The waste stream from the dyeing of woven fabric may contain any combination of the dyes and auxiliary chemicals. It can contribute substantially to the total waste load and is responsible for most of the waste volume. Color is an obvious adverse pollutant and high levels of dissolved solids are present. Suspended solids are relatively low.

For various Woven Fabric Finishing mills that process 100 percent cotton, the BOD contribution resulting from the dyeing process was found to vary from 1.5 to 30 percent of the total. Carriers, which are essential for dyeing polyester, can result in an even greater BOD contribution when cotton/polyester blends and pure polyesters are being processed.

### 8.2.2 Knit Fabric Finishing Mills

The dyeing operation is a major source of wastewater in knit fabric finishing. Beck, beam, and jet dyeing are all commonly employed using either atmospheric or pressure operating modes. Paddle, rotary, or tub dyeing may also be employed, especially for hosiery. Jig dyeing and continuous dyeing are less common. The types of dyestuff, auxiliary chemicals, and conditions employed for dyeing knit goods are essentially the same as for woven goods of comparable fiber composition. The discussion previously concerning waste characteristics associated with dyeing woven fabrics is also relevant to knit fabric dyeing. In knit fabric finishing, rinse liquors are often mechanically extracted. In this step a centrifugal extractor is used to draw water out of the fabric.

### 8.2.3 Carpet Finishing Mills

Nearly all Carpet Finishing mills perform piece dyeing, and the wastewaters are greatly influenced by the dyes used and dye machines employed. Nylon is the major fiber type in the manufacture of carpet, although the use of polyester fiber is also substantial. Dyeing is typically accomplished using atmospheric dye becks, or, to a lesser extent, continuous dye ranges. Only four dye classifications were identified as being used by carpet finishing mills. Acid dyes, disperse dyes, and cationic dyes are most frequently employed, and small quantities of direct dyes are sometimes used. In addition to these dyestuffs themselves, numerous auxiliary chemicals, such as leveling agents, inorganic compounds, acids, sequestering agents, organic compounds, dispersing agents, and various carriers may also be employed. Since most of these auxiliary chemicals perform a function during the dyeing operation, they do not remain with the carpet. As a result they are found in the waste stream along with excess dyes and contribute substantially to BOD, COD, dissolved solids, and color.

### 8.2.4 Stock and Yarn Finishing Mills

Stock dyeing is usually performed in a vat or pressure kettle. Yarn dyeing is usually performed by skein or package dyeing methods. A specialty yarn dyeing process, similar to and sometimes referred to as printing, is known as space dyeing. Virtually all dye classes are used in stock and yarn dyeing, and the waste generated will be similar to those generated in dyeing fabric or carpet of the same fiber type.

### 8.2.5 Wool Finishing Mills

Some of the dyes and dye chemicals used for wool goods are specific to the wool fiber. The acid and metalized dyes are commonly used, while mordant and fiber reactive dyes are used to a small extent. Because of the recognized hazards of chromium entering the waste stream, the use of mordant dyes has greatly diminished and they presently are used only if exceptional fastness is mandatory.

In sensitive dyeing, a pre-scour step is often used. Detergents and wetting agents are added, the scouring performed, and the fabric thoroughly rinsed. The waste generated contributes to the hydraulic load but adds little to the strength.

For acid dyes, the main consideration is to create a pH value suitable to the type of dye in use. The ingredients, in addition to the dyes, include Glauber's salt crystals ($Na_2SO_4$ - $10H_2O$, sulfuric acid, and formic acid).

The metalized dyes, which are very fast and have a very high affinity for wool even under mildly acidic conditions and at low temperatures (below 110°C (230°F)), are often used on 100 percent wool fabric. These dyes are almost completely exhausted so only a small quantity of metallic ions (chromium) enters the waste stream.

Blends of wool and synthetic fibers are sometimes dyed in a single bath and sometimes dyed in two separate baths. When two baths are used, dyes specific to each fabric type are used and the hydraulic load can increase by 50 percent. In each type of dyeing the fabric is cooled with clear water and thoroughly rinsed; both steps add significantly to the hydraulic load.

## 8.3 TREATMENT TECHNOLOGY

A recent study (EPA, 1980) identified the current treatment technologies in use by textile operations and described the availability of treatability data for these technologies. A summary of this information is shown below; however, no distinction was made between data from direct and indirect discharges.

| | Number of data sets | | |
|---|---|---|---|
| | Data sets with both influent and effluent data | | |
| | Full scale | Pilot scale | Bench scale |
| Activated sludge | 43 | | |
| Filtration | 1 | 15 | |
| Gas flotation with chemical addition | 1 | | |
| Granular activated carbon adsorption | | 12 | |
| Lagoon, aerated | 7 | | |
| Lagoon, effluent polishing | 2 | | |
| Ozonation | | 3 | |
| Powdered activated carbon adsorption | 1 | | 10 |
| Reverse osmosis | | 12 | |
| Sedimentation | | 1 | |
| Sedimentation with chemical addition | 1 | 5 | 2 |
| Total | 56 | 48 | 12 |

The above information indicates that the most prevalent treatment technology currently in use by textile operations is activated sludge. Second is the aerated lagoon. However, as indicated by the pilot scale data, filtration, granular activated carbon adsorption, and reverse osmosis technologies are being intensively investigated for possible use by the industry. The candidate treatment and control technologies for the textile industry are: chemical coagulation, multimedia filtration, and coagulation plus filtration (EPA 1980). These three technologies are believed to show immediate promise for use in the textile industry for additional wastewater treatment.

## 8.4 CHARACTERIZATION OF TEXTILE DYEING OPERATIONS

As indicated previously in Section 6.1 much of the information available on textile dyeing is merged with other general textile information, and is often indistinguishable as being directly applicable to textile dyeing. In an effort to more clearly characterize information on textile dyeing, copies of the summary data on textile plants were obtained from EPA (Jordon 1983). This information was used by EPA as background information for development of the Effluent Guidelines for textile plants. Although the information was originally compiled in 1977, it is still the most current data available on textile operations.

In order to focus upon textile dyeing operations, only plant data for standard, industrial classification codes 223 and 226 were obtained. These codes represent wool weaving and finishing mills, and textile finishing (excluding wool), respectively. These data were summarized in order to further characterize textile dyeing operations.

Plant data were separated into two categories based on the method of wastewater discharge: indirect (i.e., to a municipal treatment plant) or direct to their receiving waters. Plants then were classified as large, medium, or small based on their total daily production rate. An average of all production data was determined for direct and indirect discharging plants. Medium sized plants are those whose daily production volume is between 1.25 and 0.75 of the previously determined production average. Plants with production rates above this range are considered large operations, and plants below the range are considered small operations.

Although the data base used is extensive, there are gaps in the data available for each plant. The following statistical characterization is based on the data available, albeit not totally complete, as shown by the varying number of data points used. The results of this data analysis are presented in Tables 42 and 43.

TABLE 42. CHARACTERIZATION OF DIRECT DISCHARGING DYEING OPERATIONS (Jordan 1983)

| | Plant size | | | | | |
|---|---|---|---|---|---|---|
| | Small | | Medium | | Large | |
| Data points | 84 | | 25 | | 38 | |
| Fabric production range in 1,000 Kg/day (2,200 lbs/day) | <35 | (<78) | 35 to 59 | (78 to 130) | >59 | (130) |
| Average fabric production rate in 1,000 Kg/day (2,200 lbs/day) | 14 | (31) | 44 | (97) | 107 | (236) |
| Average wastewater treatment plant flow in $m^3/S$ (MGD) | 0.02 | (0.40) | 0.04 | (0.90) | 0.08 | (1.90) |
| Average daily redyes[a] in Kg (lbs) | 968 | (2,134) | 862 | (1,900) | 1,211 | (2,670) |

[a]Redyes are those items, fabrics, etc. that have already passed through the dyeing process, but which were dyed off-specification and were dyed again to meet the dyeing specifications.

TABLE 43. CHARACTERIZATION OF INDIRECT DISCHARGING TEXTILE DYEING OPERATIONS (Jordan 1983)

| | Plant size | | | | | |
|---|---|---|---|---|---|---|
| | Small | | Medium | | Large | |
| Data points | 206 | | 55 | | 86 | |
| Fabric production range in 1,000 Kg/day (2,200 lbs/day) | 18 | (<40) | 18 to 30 | (40 to 67) | >30 | (>67) |
| Average fabric production rate in 1,000 Kg/day (2,200 lbs/day) | 6 | (14) | 23 | (50) | 86 | (189) |
| Average plant wastewater pretreatment system flow in $m^3/S$ (MGD) | 0.01 | (0.16) | 0.02 | (0.52) | 0.05 | (1.1) |
| Average municipal wastewater treatment plant flow in $m^3/S$ (MGD) | 0.73 | (16.70) | 0.83 | (18.90) | 1.20 | (28.40) |
| Average daily redyes[a] in Kg (lbs) | 759 | (1,674) | 2,231 | (4,918) | 453 | (999) |

[a]Redyes are those items, fabrics, etc. that have already passed through the dyeing process, but which were dyed off-specification and were dyed again to meet the dyeing specifications.

# 9. Air Emissions from Textile Dyeing and Printing Processes

## 9.1 INTRODUCTION

This section presents data on air emissions from various textile dyeing and printing processes. It is primarily based upon air emissions tests from several test reports and, therefore, contains only sparse information on the release of textile dyestuffs to the atmosphere. Both library searches and telephone contacts with those involved in this aspect of the textile industry resulted in very little information about dyestuff emissions to the atmosphere.

However, some information concerning hydrocarbon and organic emissions from textile dyeing operations were found in plant emission test reports. The remainder of this section describes that data.

## 9.2 AIR EMISSIONS

By far the most significant type of air emissions from textile dyeing and printing are in the form of hydrocarbon carrier vapor emissions with some particulate emissions noted in the case of thermosol dyeing. These data are presented in the following tables for textile plants A, B, C, and D as identified by the source test reports.

Plant A is a cotton and synthetic woven fabric finishing plant. Two thermosol dyeing ovens were tested at this plant for emissions of particulates, total hydrocarbons, nonmethane hydrocarbons, and organics in the $C_1$-$C_6$ range. Particulate matter was emitted from the #4 thermosol oven at a rate of 68 milligrams per actual cubic meter which resulted in a 144 milligram per kilogram of fabric emission factor. The emissions of $C_1$-$C_6$ hydrocarbons (other than $CH_4$) from the #4 thermosol oven averaged 2,049 ppm as $CH_2$ (McCurley, 1980). Tables 44 and 45 show total hydrocarbon and organic compounds emitted.

TABLE 44. TOTAL HYDROCARBON EMISSIONS DATA AND NONMETHANE TOTAL HYDROCARBON EMISSION FACTORS - PLANT A (McCurley, 1980)

| Process sampled | Total hydrocarbon concentration, ppm as $CH_4$ | | | Average concentration of methane, ppm[a] | Nonmethane total hydrocarbon emission factors, mg/kg of fabric |
|---|---|---|---|---|---|
| | Peak 1 | Peak 2 | Total | | |
| No. 1 Thermosol oven | 8 | 0 | 8 | 0 | 0.062 |
| No. 1 Thermosol oven | 6 | 16 | 22 | 7 | 0.15 |
| No. 4 Thermosol oven | 8 | 17 | 25 | 3 | 0.057 |

[a]Conversion factor for ppm ($mL/m^3$) to $g/m^3$ is (16 g/mole) (mole/22,400 ml).

TABLE 45. EMISSION FACTORS FOR ORGANIC COMPOUND - DYEING ON NO. 4 THERMOSOL OVEN - PLANT A (McCurley, 1980)

| Organic species | Concentration in effluent gas stream mg/m$^3$ (actual) | Emission factor mg/kg of fabric |
|---|---|---|
| Diethyl phthalate | <0.014 | <0.051 |
| Dipropyl phthalate | 0.015 | 0.050 |
| Dibutyl phthalate | 0.014 | 0.047 |
| Di-$C_8$ alkyl phthalate | 0.039 | 0.15 |
| Methyl palmitate | 4.9 | 18 |
| Methyl stearate | 5.6 | 20 |
| Palmitic acid | 0.43 | 1.6 |
| Bromodinitrobenzene | 0.83 | 3.0 |
| Dichloronitroaniline | 0.17 | 0.60 |
| Bromodinitroaniline | 0.34 | 1.2 |
| Methyl-$C_{11}$-ester | 0.11 | 0.40 |
| Methyl-$C_{12}$-ester | 0.18 | 0.65 |
| Methyl-$C_{13}$-ester | 0.15 | 0.53 |
| Methyl-$C_{14}$-ester | 0.99 | 3.6 |
| Methyl-$C_{15}$-ester | 0.49 | 1.8 |
| Methyl-$C_{17}$-ester | 1.1 | 4.0 |
| Methyl-$C_{19}$-ester | 0.24 | 0.88 |
| Methyl-$C_{20}$-ester | 0.13 | 0.48 |
| Paraffins/olefins ($C_{12}$-$C_{20}$) | 0.73 | 2.6 |
| Paraffins ($C_{16}$-$C_{34}$) | 1.7 | 6.1 |

Plant B is a cotton and synthetic woven fabric finishing plant. The gas effluent from the thermosol oven was sampled for particulates, total hydrocarbons, nonmethane total hydrocarbons, and organics in the $C_1$-$C_6$ range. Table 46 gives the characteristics of the gas effluent sampled. The concentration of particulates in the effluent gas was 59 milligrams per actual cubic meter which resulted in a daily mass emission rate of 15.5 kilogram and an emission factor of 410 milligrams per kilogram of fabric (McCurley, 1980). Tables 47 and 48 show the results of the tests for $C_1$-$C_6$ organics and hydrocarbons, respectively.

Plant C is a cotton and synthetic woven fabric finishing plant. The thermosol dye range was tested for particulates, organics, $C_1$-$C_6$ hydrocarbons, and nonmethane total hydrocarbons. Particulates were emitted from the second zone of the #11 oven at a concentration of 5.9 milligrams per actual cubic meter which results in a mass emission rate of 61 kilograms per day and an emission factor of 53 milligrams per kilogram of fabric (McCurley, 1980). The stack conditions for the particulate tests are listed in Table 49. The emissions of organics are listed in Table 50. Table 51 lists the conditions of the thermosol stack effluent during the hydrocarbon testing and Tables 52 and 53 list the nonmethane hydrocarbons and $C_1$-$C_6$ hydrocarbons, respectively. In addition to the thermosol dye range, an atmosphere beck and a wash box were sampled for hydrocarbons. The results of these tests are also listed in Tables 51, 52, and 53.

Plant D was tested in order to find the quantity of hydrocarbon carrier emissions from an atmospheric dye beck. The carrier used in the dyeing process during the testing period was biphenyl. The beck was sampled twice with the biphenyl emissions being 30.1 kilograms in test 1 and 45.2 kilograms in test 2. This represents emission rates of 39.0 percent and 58.6 percent of total biphenyl charged, respectively. The emission rates were 18.4 grams of biphenyl per kilogram of cloth for test 1 and 277 grams of biphenyl per kilogram of cloth for test 2 (Hawks, 1977). The factor with the greatest effect on the emission rate was the duration of the boiling phase of the dyeing process.

TABLE 46. CHARACTERISTICS OF THE EFFLUENT GAS STREAMS - PLANT B (McCurley, 1980)

| Effluent parameter | Units | Run 1: Dyeing on a thermosol dye range |
|---|---|---|
| Oxygen ($O_2$) content | Volume % | –[a] |
| Carbon dioxide ($CO_2$) content | Volume % | –[a] |
| Nitrogen ($N_2$) content | Volume % | –[a] |
| Moisture ($H_2O$) content | Volume % | 4.24 |
| Dry molecular weight of stack gas | g/mole | 29.14 |
| Molecular weight of stack gas | g/mole | 28.67[b] |
| Stack gas temperature (average) | °C | 192 |
| Stack gas temperature (range) | °C | 185 to 197 |
| Average stack gas velocity | m/s | 9.58 |
| Average stack gas flow rate (actual) | $m^3/s$ | 3.035 |
| Average stack gas flow rate (standard conditions) | $m^3/s$ | 1.862 |

[a]Not measured.

[b]Based on the assumed dry molecular weight of 29.14 g/mole.

TABLE 47. EMISSIONS DATA FOR ORGANIC COMPOUNDS - DYEING ON THERMOSOL DYE RANGE - PLANT B (McCurley, 1980)

| Organic species | Concentration in the effluent gas stream, $mg/m^3$ | Percentage of compound collected in the particulate phase, weight % | Emission rate kg/day | Emission factor, mg/kg of fabric |
|---|---|---|---|---|
| $C_4$-$C_5$ alkyl benzenes | 0.25 | 0 | 0.066 | 1.7 |
| Dichlorobenzenes | 0.23 | 0 | 0.060 | 1.6 |
| Trichlorobenzenes | 0.099 | 0 | 0.062 | 1.6 |
| Naphthalene | 0.24 | 0 | 0.062 | 1.6 |
| Methyl-naphthalenes | 0.54 | 0 | 0.14 | 3.7 |
| $C_3$ and above naphthalenes | 0.0023 | 0 | 0.00062 | 0.016 |
| Butyl benzoate | 1.5 | 0 | 0.40 | 10.7 |
| Biphenyl | 0.94 | 0 | 0.25 | 6.5 |
| Dimethyl phthalate | 0.21 | 0 | 0.054 | 1.4 |
| Diethyl phthalate | 0.00035 | 100 | 0.00009 | 0.0024 |
| Di-$C_8$ alkyl-phthalate | 0.0030 | 93 | 0.00080 | 0.021 |
| Bromochlorobenzene | 0.018 | 0 | 0.0048 | 0.13 |
| Bromodinitrobenzene | 0.93 | 0 | 0.24 | 6.4 |
| Anthraquinone | 2.8 | 0 | 0.74 | 19.0 |
| Aminoanthraquinone | 0.36 | 0 | 0.093 | 2.5 |
| Methyl myristate | 0.014 | 0 | 0.0036 | 0.094 |
| Methyl palmitate | 1.1 | 0.07 | 0.30 | 7.8 |
| Methyl stearate | 2.5 | 0.02 | 0.66 | 17.5 |
| Aliphatics | 6.5 | 2 | 1.7 | 44.8 |

TABLE 48. NONMETHANE TOTAL HYDROCARBON EMISSION DATA - PLANT B (McCurley, 1980)

| Equipment | Operation sampled | Average total hydrocarbon concentration ppm as $CH_4$ [a] | Average methane concentration ppm as $CH_4$ [a] | Nonmethane total hydrocarbon concentration $mg/m^3$ as $CH_4$ | Nonmethane total hydrocarbon emission rate kg/day | Nonmethane total hydrocarbon emission factor g/kg of fabric |
|---|---|---|---|---|---|---|
| Thermosol dye range | Dyeing | 602 | 461 | 101 | 26 | 1.3 |

[a] The conversion factor for ppm ($mL/m^3$) as $CH_4$ to $mg/m^3$ as $CH_4$ is (16 g/mole) (mole/22,400 mL) (1,000 mg/g).

TABLE 49. CHARACTERISTICS OF THE EFFLUENT GAS STREAMS - PLANT C (McCurley, 1980)

| Effluent parameter | Units | 2nd zone of thermosol oven No. 11 |
|---|---|---|
| Moisture ($H_2O$) content | Volume % | 2.54 |
| Molecular weight of stack gas | g/mole | 28.818[a] |
| Stack gas temperature (average) | °C | 154 |
| Stack gas temperature (range) | °C | 152 to 158 |
| Average stack gas velocity | m/s | 6.89 |
| Stack gas flow rate (actual) | $m^3/s$ | 3.39 |
| Stack gas flow rate (standard conditions) | $m^3/s$ | 2.26 |

[a]Based on an assumed dry molecular weight of 29.10 (estimated from previous measurements of similar effluent streams).

TABLE 50. ORGANIC EMISSION DATA, DYEING ON A THERMOSOL DYE RANGE, 2ND ZONE OF THERMOSOL OVEN - PLAND C (McCurley, 1980)

| Organic species | Concentration in the effluent gas stream mg/actual $m^3$ | Percentage found in the particulate phase weight % | Emission rate[a] kg/day | Emission factor mg/kg of fabric |
|---|---|---|---|---|
| 2-Ethylhexanol | 0.088 | 00 | 0.026 | 0.78 |
| $C_3/C_4/C_5$-alkyl benzenes | 0.16 | 0 | 0.046 | 1.4 |
| Ethyl sytrene | 0.023 | 0 | 0.0067 | 0.20 |
| Naphthalene | 0.19 | 0 | 0.0056 | 0.17 |
| Methyl-naphthalenes | 0.0030 | 0 | 0.00087 | 0.026 |
| Dimethyl-naphthalenes | 0.0041 | 0 | 0.0012 | 0.036 |
| Biphenyl | 0.0038 | 0 | 0.13 | 0.034 |
| Dimethyl phthalate | 0.099 | 0 | 0.0011 | 0.88 |
| Diethyl phthalate | 0.00028 | 0 | 0.029 | 0.0025 |
| Dipropyl phthalate | 0.0049 | 30 | 0.000083 | 0.043 |
| Dibutyl phthalate | 0.033 | 13 | 0.0014 | 0.29 |
| Di-$C_8$ alkyl phthalate | 0.093 | 1 | 0.0096 | 0.82 |
| Bromodinitrobenzene | 0.015 | 0 | 0.027 | 0.14 |
| Anthraquinone | 0.028 | 0 | 0.0045 | 0.25 |
| Methyl myristate | 0.020 | 0 | 0.0081 | 0.18 |
| Methyl palmitate | 0.54 | 0.1 | 0.0058 | 4.8 |
| Methyl stearate | 0.70 | 0.2 | 0.16 | 6.2 |
| Palmitic acid | 7.7 | 0 | 0.21 | 68.6 |
| Diphenyl ethane | 0.013 | 0 | 2.3 | 0.11 |
| Ethyl-phenyl-phenyl-ethane | 0.020 | 0 | 0.0037 | 0.18 |
| Aliphatics | 0.46 | 42 | 0.0058 | 4.1 |

TABLE 51. CHARACTERISTICS OF EFFLUENT GAS STREAMS ANALYZED BY GAS CHROMATOGRAPHY - PLANT C (McCurley, 1980)

| Stack identification | Moisture content volume % | Stack gas temperature °C | Stack gas velocity m/s | Stack gas flow rate $m^3/s$ (actual) |
|---|---|---|---|---|
| Atmospheric beck no. 12 | 28.79 | 68 | 1.44 | 0.63 |
| Wash box no. 2 - vent A | 3.80 | 34 | 11.33 | 7.03 |
| Wash box no. 2 - vent B | 5.10 | 36 | 11.08 | 6.88 |
| Thermosol dye range - stack A (zone 1) | ≅5 | 70 | 12.87 | 3.59 |
| Thermosol dye range - stack B (zone 2) | ≅5 | 68 | 1.71 | 0.48 |

TABLE 52. NONMETHANE TOTAL HYDROCARBON EMISSION DATA - PLANT C (McCurley, 1980)

| Equipment sampled by GC | Operation sampled | Average hydrocarbon concentration ppm as $CH_4$[a] | Average methane concentration ppm as $CH_4$[a] | Nonmethane total hydrocarbon concentration $mg/m^3$ as $CH_4$[a] | Nonmethane total hydrocarbon emission rate[b] kg/day[c] | Nonmethane total hydrocarbon emission factor g/kg of fabric |
|---|---|---|---|---|---|---|
| Atmospheric beck no. 12 | Dyeing | 1,506 | 28 | 1,056 | 57 | -[d] |
| Wash box no. 2 - vent A | Dyeing | 13 | 13 | 0 | 0 | 0 |
| Wash box no. 2 - vent B | Dyeing | 28 | 6 | 16 | 9.5 | 440 |
| Thermosol dye range - 1st zone | Dyeing | 318 | 281 | 26 | 8.1 | 280 |
| Thermosol dye range - 2nd zone | Dyeing | 315 | 152 | 116 | 4.8 | 170 |

[a]Conversion factor for ppm ($mL/m^3$) to $mg/m^3$ is (16 g/mole) (mole/22,400 mL) (1,000 mg/g).

[b]Based on continuous operation for a 24-hour period.

[c]Emission rate = ($mg/m^3$) ($m^3$/min) (1,440 min/day) (kg/$10^6$ mg).

[d]Emission factors cannot be calculated, the data needed is not applicable to these processes.

TABLE 53. $C_1$-$C_6$ HYDROCARBON EMISSION DATA - PLANT C (McCurley, 1980)

| Equipment sampled by GC | Operation sampled | Number of $C_6$-$C_8$ compounds detected | Average concentration ppm as $CH_4$ |
|---|---|---|---|
| Atmospheric beck no. 12 | Dyeing | 2 | 8 |
| | | | 663 |
| Wash box no. 2 - vent A | Dyeing | 1 | 19 |
| Wash box no. 2 - vent B | Dyeing | 2 | 27 |
| | | | 20 |
| Thermosol dye range - 1st zone | Dyeing | 0 | |
| Thermosol dye range - 2nd zone | Dyeing | 1 | 3 |

Note: Blanks indicate that no $C_1$-$C_6$ compounds were detected.

[a]Other than $CH_4$.

EPA's Background Information for Proposed Standards Draft Document presents the small amount of information collected on air emissions from the Fabric Printing Industry. Table 54 lists those emissions for their relative industry category.

TABLE 54. ORGANIC SOLVENT EMISSIONS FROM FABRIC PRINTING OPERATIONS (EPA, April 1981)

| Category | Organic content of print paste (%) | Emissions[a] |
|---|---|---|
| Roller printers | 26 | 0.142 kg VOC/kg fabric |
| Rotary screen | 3 | 0.023 kg VOC/kg fabric |
| Flat screen printers | 23 | 0.181 kg VOC/dozen terry towels |

[a]These emission factors were based on an American Textile Manufacturers Institute survey of organic solvent use in the industry and data received from two fabric printing industries.

# References

1. Aldrich Chemical Co., Inc. 1978. 1979-1980 Aldrich Catalog Handbook of Fine Chemicals. Catalog 19. Aldrich Chemical Co., Inc. Milwaukee, Wisconsin.

2. Althouse. a. Althouse Direct Dyes. Althouse Chemical Co., Division of Crompton and Knowles.

3. Althouse. b. Althouse Neutral Acid Dyestuffs. Althouse Chemical Co., Division of Crompton and Knowles.

4. American Association of Textile Chemists and Colorists (AATCC). 1981. Dyeing Primer: A Series of Short Papers on the Fundamentals of Dyeing. Reprinted from the Textile Chemist and Colorist. North Carolina.

5. American Association of Textile Chemists and Colorists. 1982. Textile Chemist and Colorist (Buyer's Guide). Volume 13.

6. American Textile Manufacturers Institute, Inc. (ATMI). 1980. 1979 Survey of Textile Printing Machines in the United States (Revised). Washington, D.C.

7. Apparel Institute, Inc. 1963. So You Want to Know About Nonwovens. Apparel Institute, Inc. New York.

8. BASF. 1969. Celliton Dyes and Palanil Dyes on Triacetate. Badische Anilin and Soda Fabrik AG. West Germany.

9. Bates Textile Machine Co. LTD. 1982. Bates Textile Machinery. Sales Brochure Package. Leicester, United Kingdom.

10. Belcher, J. 1982. Dyeing Textured Woven Polyester. Presented at Conference "Workhorse Apparel Fabrics" at Clemson University on February 3, 1982.

11. Bomberger, D. C. and R. L. Boughton. 1981. Solid Wastes from Manufacture of Dyes and Pigments (Benzidine and Its Congeners Subsector). Draft EPA report prepared by SRI International.

12. Bruckner Machinery Ltd. 1979. Bruckner: Supraflex. Brochure #HP11/79. Spartanburg, South Carolina.

13. Bruckner Machinery Ltd. 1979a. Bruckner: Wet Batching Machine for Dyeing Beams. Brochure #HP979WA. Spartanburg, South Carolina.

14. Bruckner Machinery Ltd. 1979b. Comparison of the Efficiency - Bruckner Short Ratio Dyeing Machines Haspelflow/Spiralflow in Comparison to Conventional Dyeing Winches. Information TI22/79.

15. Bruckner Machiner Ltd. 1980. Haspelflow - A New Generation of Perfected Short Liquor Ratio Dyeing Machines. Information TI31/80. Spartanburg, South Carolina.

16. Clarke, W. 1977. An Introduction to Textile Printing. Fourth Edition. Boston: Newnes-Butterworths.

17. Coulston, F. (ed.) 1975. Fluorescent Whitening Agents. Environmental Quality and Safety, Supplement Volume IV. Academy Press. New York. Georg Thieme Publishers. Stuttgart, Germany.

18. Coulston, F. and F. Koree (ed.) 1975. Fluorescent Whitening Agents. Environmental Quality and Safety, Supplement Vol. IV. New York/London. Georg Thieme Verlag, Stuttger and Academic Press.

19. Davies, R. R. 1972. Developments in Reactive Dyes. Review of Progress in Coloration and Related Topics. Volume 3. The Society of Dyes and Colourists.

20. Dawson, J. F. 1972. Developments in Disperse Dyes. Review of Progress in Coloration (June 1967 - September 1971). Volume 3.

21. Day-Glo Color Corporation. 1981a. Fluorescent Pigments. Technical Bulletin 2001.

22. Day-Glo Color Corporation. 1981b. Fluorescent Yellow Dyestuffs. Technical Bulletin 1232.

23. DuPont. 1981. DuPont Technical Information: Fibers. Technical Information Section. Wilmington, Delaware.

24. EDANA. 1974. Nonwovens, the Fabric of a New Society. Gothenberg Convention, 6-7 June, 1974. European Disposables and Nonwoven Association. Belgium.

25. Federal Register. 1980. Rules and Regulations. Appendix VIII. Volume 45, No. 98. Monday, May 19, 1980.

26. Francolors. 1982. Excerpts from technical information documents supplied by Henry Hollingsworth, Customer Service Manager.

27. Gaffney, P. E. 1977. Chlorobiphenyls and PCB's: Formation During Chlorination. Journal of Water Pollution Control Federation, Issue 3, Volume 49, Part 1, March 1977.

28. Gessner Company. 1980. Gessner Transcolorizer. Brochure #SL-1080-3M. Worcester, Massachusetts.

29. Greene, R. D. 1958. Calco Dyes for Printing. American Cynamid Company, Dyes Division. Boundbrook, New Jersey.

30. Haigh, D. 1972. Dyeing Machinery Survey. Leicester, England, Hoisery Trade Journal.

31. Hall, A. J. 1926. Textile Bleachings, Dyeing, Printing, and Finishing Machinery. New York. Van Nostrand Co.

32. Hawks, Ronald. 1977. Hydrocarbon Carrier Emissions From Atmospheric Dye-Becks. AQSS-78-002. N.C. Department of Natural Resources and Community Development. Raleigh, North Carolina.

33. Horning, R. H. 1978. Textiles Dyeing Wastewaters: Characterization and Treatment. EPA-600/2-78-098. U.S. Environmental Protection Agency.

34. Hudak. 1976. The Textile Industry: A Study of Capital Investment, Technology, and Other Factors Affecting Prescribed Capital Recovery Allowances of Textile Machinery. Office of Industrial Economics, Department of Treasury, U.S. Government, Printing Office Stock #048-600-00288-9.

35. Imperial Chemical Industry Limited (ICI). Dyestuffs Division. 1965a. Technical Information Dyehouse No. 795; Manchester, England.

36. Imperial Chemical Industry Limited (ICI). Dyestuffs Division. 1965b. Technical Information Dyehouse No. 860; Manchester, England.

37. Imperial Chemical Industry Limited (ICI). Dyestuffs Division. 1971. Technical Information D1211; Manchester, England.

38. International Non-woven and Disperse Association (INDA). 1978. Guide to Nonwoven Fabrics. International Nonwoven and Disposables Association. Washington, D.C.

39. International Trade Commission (ITC). 1980. Synthetic Organic Chemicals: U.S. Production and Sales. Report 1183. Washington, D.C.: U.S. Government Printing Office.

40. Jordan, E. C. Company. "General Plant Information in Textile Plants: BAT-NSPS-Pretreatment Data Sheets; January 1983.

41. Kent, J. A. 1974. Riegel's Handbook of Industrial Chemistry. Seventh Edition. Von Nostrad Reinhold Co. New York.

42. Kenyon, G. H. 1982. Fiber Reactive Dyes. Presented at Conference "Workhorse Apparel Fabrics" at Clemson University on February 3, 1982.

43. Kirk-Othmer. 1978. Kirk-Othmer Encyclopedia of Chemical Technology. Third Edition. New York. John Wiley and Sons, Inc.

44. Klingsberg, E. 1980. How to do Organic Chemistry with Vat Dyes: Well-behaved Polycyclic Quinones. Presented before the Division of Petroleum Chemistry, Inc. ACS Symposium on the Chemistry of Polynuclear Aromatics. San Francisco Meeting, August 24-29, 1980.

45. Laptev, N. G. 1973. Dye Chemistry. Second Edition. NTIS Publication No. AD-764-371.

46. Lewis, J. L. and R. L. Tatken. 1979. Registry of Toxic Effects of Chemical Substances. NIOSH No. 80-111. National Institute for Occupational Safety and Health. Rockville, Maryland.

47. Lowry, J. F. et al. 1977. Energy Conservation in the Textile Industry, Phase I Technical Report. Department of Energy Project, E(40-1)-5099. Engineering Experiment Station. Georgia Institute of Technology. Atlanta, Georgia.

48. Lubs, H. A. (ed.) 1955. The Chemistry of Synthetic Dyes and Pigments. New York. Reinhold Publishing Company.

49. McCurley, W. D. and G. D. Rawlings, Source Assessment: Cotton and Woven Synthetic Fabric Finishing. EPA-600/2-80-042a. U.S. Environmental Protection Agency, Research Triangle Park, North Carolina. January 1980.

50. Martin Marietta Chemicals. 1982. The Use of Sulfur Liquid and Sulfurized Vat Dyes in Workhorse Apparel Fabrics. Presented at Conference "Workhorse Apparel Fabrics" at Clemson University on February 3, 1982.

51. Mayer, V. and S. Ernst. 1974. Basic Dyes for Synthetic-polymer Fibers. Review of Progress in Coloration and Related Topics. Volume 5. The Society of Dyes and Colourists.

52. Morgans, W. M. Pigments for Paints and Inks: Physical and Chemical Properties. Selection and Industrial Training Administration Limited.

53. Morrison Machine Co. 1982. The Transmorr 960. Patterson, New Jersey.

54. National Institute for Occupational Safety and Health (NIOSH). 1978a. (Report A) Industrial Hygiene of Benzidine Azo Dyes at Clyde Fabrics, Inc. Cincinnati, Ohio. U.S. Department of Health and Human Services.

55. National Institute for Occupational Safety and Health (NIOSH). 1978b. (Report B) Industrial Hygiene Study of Hanes Dye and Finishing Co. in Winston Salem, North Carolina. Cincinnati, Ohio. U.S. Department of Health and Human Services.

56. National Institute for Occupational Safety and Health (NIOSH). 1978c. (Report C) Industrial Hygiene Study of Benzidine-Derived Dyes at Peninsula Paper Co. Cincinnati, Ohio. U.S. Department of Health and Human Services.

57. National Institute for Occupational Safety and Health (NIOSH). 1978d. (Report D) Industrial Hygiene Study of Benzidine-Azo Dyes at Leathers, Inc. in Santa Cruz, California. Cincinnati, Ohio. U.S. Department of Health and Human Services.

58. Neal B. 1982. Achieving Success in Exhaust Dyeing of Disperse Dyestuffs on Polyester Fibers. Presented at The AATCC Workshop, May 27, 1982. Charlotte, North Carolina. American Hoechst.

59. NIOSH. 1979. Registry of Toxic Effects of Chemical Substances. DHHS (NIOSH) Publication #80-111. Cincinnati.

60. Noller, C. R. Chemistry of Organic Compounds. Chapter 33: Color, Dyes and Dyeing. Organic Pigments. Thi North Carolina State University (NSCU), School of Textiles. Fundamentals of Dyeing and Finishing. Short Course held June 28-30, 1982.

61. North Carolina State University (NCSU), School of Textiles. Fundamentals of Dyeing and Finishing. Short Course held June 28-30, 1982.

62. Occupational Safety and Health Adminstration (OSHA). 1980. Accident Inspection Report of Malan Dyeing and Finishing Co., Inc. in Patterson, New Jersey.

63. Patterson, D. 1972. The Importance of Physical Form of Colouring Matters. Review of Progress in Coloration and Related Topics. Volume 3. The Society of Dyers and Colourists.

64. Patton, T. C. (ed.) 1973. Pigment Handbook. New York. John Wiley and Sons, Inc.

65. Porter, J. J. 1973. A Study of the Photodegradation of Commercial Dyes. EPA-R2-73-058. U.S. Environmental Protection Agency, Washington, D.C.

66. Reichman, C. 1976. Transfer Printing Manual. New York: National Knitted Outerwear Association.

67. Research Traingle Institute. 1981. Fabric Printing Industry: Background Information for Proposed Standards (Draft). EPA Contract No. 68-02-3052. Research Triangle Park, North Carolina.

68. Sax, I. 1968. Dangerous Properties of Industrial Materials. Reinhold Book Corporation. New York.

69. Shenai, V. A. 1973. Chemistry of Dyes and Principles of Dyeing. Bombay, India. Skuak Publications.

70. Society of Dyers and Colorists (SDC). 1971. Colour Index (CI). Third Edition. Yorkshire, England.

71. Society of Dyers and Colourists (SDC). 1973. Dye at Clyde Fabrics, Inc. Cincinnati, Ohio. U.S. Department of Health and Human Services.

72. Society of Dyers and Colourists (SDC). 1974. Vat Dyes and Their Application. Review of Progress in Coloration and Related Topics. Volume 5.

73. Sollenberger, W. S. 1982. Vat Dyes. Presented at Conference "Workhorse Apparel Fabrics" at Clemson University on February 3, 1982.

74. Stead, C. V. 1975. Direct Dyes and Acid Dyes. Review of Progress in Coloration and Related Topics. 6:1.

75. Steadman, T. R., E. W. Helper, et al. 1977. Industrial Process Profiles for Environmental Use: Chapter 7 - Organic Dyes and Pigments Industry. EPA-600/2-77-023g. U.S. Environmental Protection Agency, Washington, D.C.

76. Steenland, W. H. 1980. Letter to D. Crumpler on Results of the ATMI Study. Washington: American Textile Manufacturing Institute, Inc.

77. Sullivan, G. A. 1982. Challenges and Opportunities Face American Dye Manufacturers. Textile Chemist and Colorist. 14:36-38.

78. Textile Month - International Textile Journal. Yearly Bound Volumes. IPC-Industrial Press Limited. Manchester, England.

79. Thomas, T. J. 1982. Quality Parameters Affecting Disperse Dyestuffs. Presented at Conference "Workhorse Apparel Fabrics" at Clemson University on February 3, 1982.

80. Trotman, E. R. 1970. Dyeing and Chemical Technology of Textile Fibers. Fifth Edition. London, England. Charles Griffin & Co.

81. United States Environmental Protection Agency (EPA). 1974. Development Document for Effluent Limitations Guidelines and New Source Performance Standards for the Textile Mills Point Source Category. EPA-440/1-74-022.

82. United States Environmental Protection Agency (EPA). 1977. Recommended List of Priority Pollutants. (Draft)

83. United States Environmental Protection Agency (EPA). 1978. Assessment of Potential Toxic Releases from Leather Industry Dyeing Operations. EPA-600/2-78-215.

84. United States Environmental Protection Agency (EPA). 1979. Development Document for Effluent Limitations Guidelines and New Source Performance Standards for the Textile Mills Point Source Category. EPA-440/1-79-022b.

85. United States Environmental Protection Agency (EPA). Treatability Manual (EPA-600/8-80-042). Office of Research and Development, Washington, D.C., July 1980.

86. Uyeta, M., S. Taue, et al. 1976. Polychlorinated Biphenyls in the Phthalocyanine Pigments. Bulletin of Environmental Contamination and Toxicology. Series 16, Issue 4.

87. Vald. Henriksen A/S. 1982. Gru: Dyeing and Bleaching Type Gru. Brochure #706E. Copenhagen, Denmark.

88. Vald. Henriksen A/S. 1982. Henriksen: Gru-Intermix. Brochure #601E. Copenhagen, Denmark.

89. Vald. Henriksen A/S. 1982. Henriksen: VH-Jet SLA. Brochure #205 TEFS. Copenhagen, Denmark.

90. Vald. Henriksen A/S. 1982. Henriksen VH-Jet 80. Brochure #210 TE. Copenhagen, Denmark.

91. Vald. Henriksen A/S. 1982. Henriksen: VH-Super. Sales Brohcure #106E. Copenhagen, Denmark.

92. Venkataraman, K. (ed.) 1971. The Chemistry of Synthetic Dyes. Volume IV. "Basic Dyes". Academic Press. New York.

93. VPI. 1981. Dyeing Manual for the Shift Dyer. Albemarle, North Carolina.

94. Wood, W. E. 1976. Sulfur Dyes - 1966-1976. Review of Progress in Coloration and Related Topics. Volume 7. The Society of Dyers and Colourists.

# Appendix A: Glossary

acid dyes: Anionic dyes for wool, silk, acrylics, nylon; produced from benzidine or congeners; bind to free amine groups for example; these dyes are sodium salts of sulfonic acid and are applied from an acidified bath. Has COOH, $NH_3$+ groups. Examples: sulphuric, hydrochloric, formic, acetic, citric, lactic, tartaric, tannic acids.

add-on: $$\% \text{ add-on} = \frac{\% \text{ wet pickup} \times \% \text{ bath concentration}}{100}$$

$$= \text{wet pickup} \times \text{bath concentration}$$

Ref: NCSU, 1982

alkalies: Examples: caustic soda, soda ash, sodium bicarbonate, ammonia

autoclave: An apparatus using superheated steam under pressure.

azo dyes: [azo______ (-N=N-)]; most commercially important class in U.S.; prepared by diazoitization and coupling reactions; account for about 2/3 of the volume of dyes produced.

azoic dyes: Used to produce water insoluble azo dyes *in situ* onto the fiber itself frequently in an ice water bath; produces in relatively small amounts; produces colors directly onto fiber; usually for cotton.

barre pattern: Marked by or divided off by bars.

basic dyes: Hydrochlorides or zinc chloride complexes of dyes having basic groups; frequently they are prepared as salt forms to make them water soluble; applied from a neutral bath usually to a tannic acid treated fiber; have $NH_2$, NHR, $NR_2$ groups.

calenders: A system of rollers or plates between which cloth is pressed for smoothing and glazing.

carrier: Any substance which when added to a dyebath causes a marked increase in the color value obtained in the final dyeing. Also, they generally increase dyeing rates. Examples: alkyl carbonates, benzyl alcohol, carbon tetrachloride, chlorinated hydrocarbons, dichlorobenzene, emulsifying agents, leveling agents, phenols, solvent assisted dyeing, surfactants, swelling agents, toluene, trichlorobenzene, wetting agents.

chemical add-on: $\% \text{ chemical add-on} = \frac{\text{weight of chemical}}{\text{weight of fabric}} \times 100$

Ref: NCSU, 1982.

chromogen: A compound not itself a dye but containing a chromophore and so capable of being one.

chromophore: The part of the dye molecule which absorbs light in the visible region and so imparts color to the dyestuff.

continuous filament fiber: The yarn form that synthetic fibers leave the last manufacture operation.

coupling: Conversion of a diazonium salt (diazo component) to an azo component by reaction with an aromatic compound (coupling component); coupling reactions are competitive with decomposition to form terminated by-products.

covalent bonding: Chemical bonding by a more or less equal sharing of electrons. A much stronger bonding scheme than the electrostatic attraction of cations and anions or hydrogen bonds.

detergents: A cleansing agent. Examples: amphoteric surfactants, anionic surfactants, antiredeposition agents, bleaching agents, builders, cationic surfactants, emulsifying agents, leveling agents, nonionic surfactants, soaps, soap soda scouring, surfactants, wetting agents.

developed dyes: Adsorbed on fiber, then transformed to a less soluble dye chemically by diazo coupling.

diazotization: Conversion of an aromatic amine to the corresponding diazonium chloride using nitrous acid; diazonium salts are unstable and many are explosive in the dry state; (see coupling).

direct dyes (or substantive dyes): anionic dyes for cellulose; designed to have long coplanor aromatic groups as opposed to acid dyes which are more compact; applied to fiber or cloth from a hot aqueous solution; have molecular weights high enough to give colloidal solutions. Salt solutions are used to promote adsorption onto fibers.

dischargeability: The ability to intentionally render portions or all of a dyed fabric colorless for special dyeing or printing effects, or to correct a faulty dyeing.

disperse dyes: Colloidal aqueous suspensions of azo or anthraquinone dyes used to dye cellulose acetate, polyester and other synthetics; subject to fading.

dispersing agents: Substances for promoting the formation and stabilization of a dispersion of one substance in another. Examples: colloids, emulsifying agents, foams, lignin sulfonates, naphthalene formaldehyde sulfonates, plasticizers, surfactants, suspending agents, wetting agents.

dyeing: Permanently coloring fabric by transferring dye molecules into fiber.

ending: Dyeing defect when there is a variation in shade depth or hue from one end of the fabric to the other.

ends (jig dyeing): Each pass of a roll is an "end" and the number of ends run for dyeing is always even.

exhaustion: The degree of exhaustion (expressed a as percentage) is a measure of the total dyestuff that resides on the fiber as opposed to the dyestuff in solution in the dye liquor. Exhausting agents, such as salt for some dyes, help to "drive" the dye molecules onto the fiber.

$$\text{exhaustion (\%)} = \frac{(\text{gm/L Dye})\ \text{initial} - (\text{gm/L Dye})\ \text{final}}{(\text{gm/L Dye})\ \text{initial}}$$

exhaustion agents: Increase the overall dye uptake.

exhaustion rate: The speed with which the dye is taken up by the fiber(s).

fixing agents: An agent capable of reacting with a dye on a fiber to improve fastness to a water or washing. It is usually applied as an after-treatment to dyes which already possess some affinity for the textile substrate and are so distinquished from mordants.

lakes: Dye plus a base (usually alumina hydrate).

level dyeing: The transfer or migration of dye from a dyed fiber to the dyebath and then to another fiber, until both fibers contain the same amount of dye.

leveling agents or retarding agents: Substances that facilitate even distribution of dyes. Examples: anionic surfactants, carriers, cationic surfactants, detergents, emulsifying agents, foams, glaubers salt, lignin, nonionic surfactants, vinyl pyrrolidone, soaps, sodium chloride, sodium sulfate, surfactants, wetting agents.

liquor ratio: The ratio by total weight of the dyebath liquor to the weight of the goods to be dyed (ex. 20:1 means the weight of the dyeing liquor is twenty times the weight of the fabric). Also called liquor-to-goods ratio (AATU, 1981).

listing: Dyeing defect when there is a variation in shade from side-to-side on the fabric.

mercerizing: Treating cotton material under tension with a strong solution of caustic soda (≅24%) and washing off the caustic after 1-3 minutes while still holding the material under tension. The cotton shrinks longitudinally (and swells laterally) considerably when impregnated with this solution. The shrinkage is prevented by the tension applied. As a result, mercerization takes place and the material acquires the desired properties of lustre, increased strength, increased dye uptake, and increased absorbancy towards moisture.

metal salts (such as chromium after treatments): Examples: sodium dichromate, chromate, chromium chloride

mordant dyes (or adjective dyes) and chrome dyes: A mordant is any material that can be fixed to a fiber and later dyed. Mordant and chrome dyes form complexes with metal ions and bind to fibers by metal complexation. Examples: tannic acid, sulphurised phenolic compounds.

nip: The point in a pad batch dyeing machine where the excess dye is squeezed out.

oxidizing agents: sodium hydrochlorite, bleaching powder, hydrogen peroxide, nitrous acid, potassium chlorate, sodium chlorite, sodium perborate, peracetic acid.

pigments: Can be prepared by combining by combining dyes with a dye precipitant and are characterized by low solubility in $H_2O$ and organic solvents. Pigments are defined as any opaque insoluble powder that is used to color another material and are classified as either a lake or a toner.

retarding (leveling) agents: Chemicals used to decrease the dyeing rate. If the dyes are taken up by the fiber being dyed too fast from the dyebath, uneven (unlevel) dyeing may occur.

reducing agents: Sodium hydrosulphite, sodium sulphoxylate formaldehyde (sulfoxylates), sodium sulphide, sodium thiosulphate, stannous chloride, glucose, dextrin, acetaldehyde sulfoxylates, aldehydes, bisulfites, boron hydrides, disulfides, dithionites, hydroxylaminc, oxidizing agents, pyrosulfites; redox catalysis, sodium bisulfite, sodium borohydride, sodium dithionite, thiourea dioxide, zinc formaldehyde sulfoxylate.

salts: Examples: common salt, Glauber's salt ($Na_2SO_4 \cdot 10H_2O$), diammonium hydrogen phosphate, magnesium chloride hexahydrate, zinc chloride, zinc nitrate, zinc acetate, zinc fluoborate.

selvedges: The edge on either side of a woven or flat-knitted fabric so finished as to prevent raveling.

sequestering agents: Chemical agents applied to hard water in textile process to soften the water. Examples: ethylene diamine tetracetic acid (EDTA), nitrilotriacetic acid (NTA), sodium hexametaphosphate, detergents, calgon (TN), citric acid, pyrophosphates, tetrapotassium phosphate.

shade dyeing: The percentage of weight of dye to weight of fabric. Note that since exhaustion is never complete, this does not directly equal the dye uptake of the fabric.

staple: Short lengths of extended fibers.

substantivity: The affinity that a dye has for the particular fiber references. High substantivity means that the dye prefers to interact with the textile as oppossed to staying in the dyebath liquor.

sulfur dyes: Applied to cotton from the solution in aqueous sodium sulfide. The reduced dye form adhers to cotton and then is oxidized.

tenter frame: A machine which is used primarily to dry, straighten, and remove wrinkles from fabrics which have been treated with various chemical finishes.

textile printing: The production through a combination of various mechanical and chemical means of colored designs or patterns on textile substrates.

toner: Full strength organic or organometallic dye.

tops: Fiber form when a sliver is wound into a ball of a foot or more in diameter.

tow: Long strand of extended fibers.

tow bundles: 1,000 to 1,000,000 individual filaments yarns gathered in a bundle after the final manufacturing step of synthetic fibers. Generally crimping is used to hold the bundle together.

vat dyes: Water insoluble but can be made soluble by reduction in alkaline solution. Cotton adsorbs the reduced form and then oxidation is allowed to occur (to fix to fabric). As a class these dyes show best light and washing fastness. Indigo is a vat dye.

wet out: Coat a surface with a substance that prevents the surface from repelling the wetting liquid.

wet pickup: $\% \text{ wet pick-up} = \frac{\text{weight of solution}}{\text{weight of fabric}}$

wet pickup for padding is 60-150% and for low water techniques 5-40% (NCSU, 1982). Varies will roller pressure and fabric type.

wetting agents or penetrants: alkylnaphthalene sulfonate, amphoteric surfactants, anionic surfactants, antifoam agents, carriers, catonic surfactants, detergents, dispersing agents, emulsifying agents, foams, leveling agents, nanionic surfactants, soaps, tetrahyoronaphthalene sulfonates.

yarn dyeing: Dyeing of yarns before they are reformed into fabrics.

# Appendix B: Dyeing Procedures

The dyeing procedure for a beck machine using direct dyes with a 30:1 liquor ratio on rayon is as follows (Horning 1978):

Set bath at 30°C (100°F) with 1.0 gram/liter Levegal KN (leveling agent).

1. Circulate for 10 minutes and add 4.0% C.I. Direct Black 38.
2. Raise temperature to 49°C (120°F) and circulate for 10 minutes.
3. Raise temperature to 93°C (200°F) over 30 minutes and add 20.0% sodium sulfate.
4. Add salt over a 30 minute period, run at 93°C (200°F) for 60 minutes, cool to 71°C (160°F).
5. Drop bath.
6. Give two cold rinses (original volume).
7. Drop bath.

A graphical representation of the dyeing procedure is presented in Figure 35.

Copper aftertreated direct dyes were produced for the dyeing of cotton and polyester/cotton blends. These dyes could improve light fastness without lowering wash fastness.

An example dyeing procedure for a beck machine using after-copperable direct dyes with a 30:1 liquor ratio on bleached mercerized cotton follows (Horning 1978).

Add to bath 0.5 gram/liter soda ash (pH 8.5), 0.5% Barisol BRM (anionic surfactant), 0.5% Calgon (sequestrant):

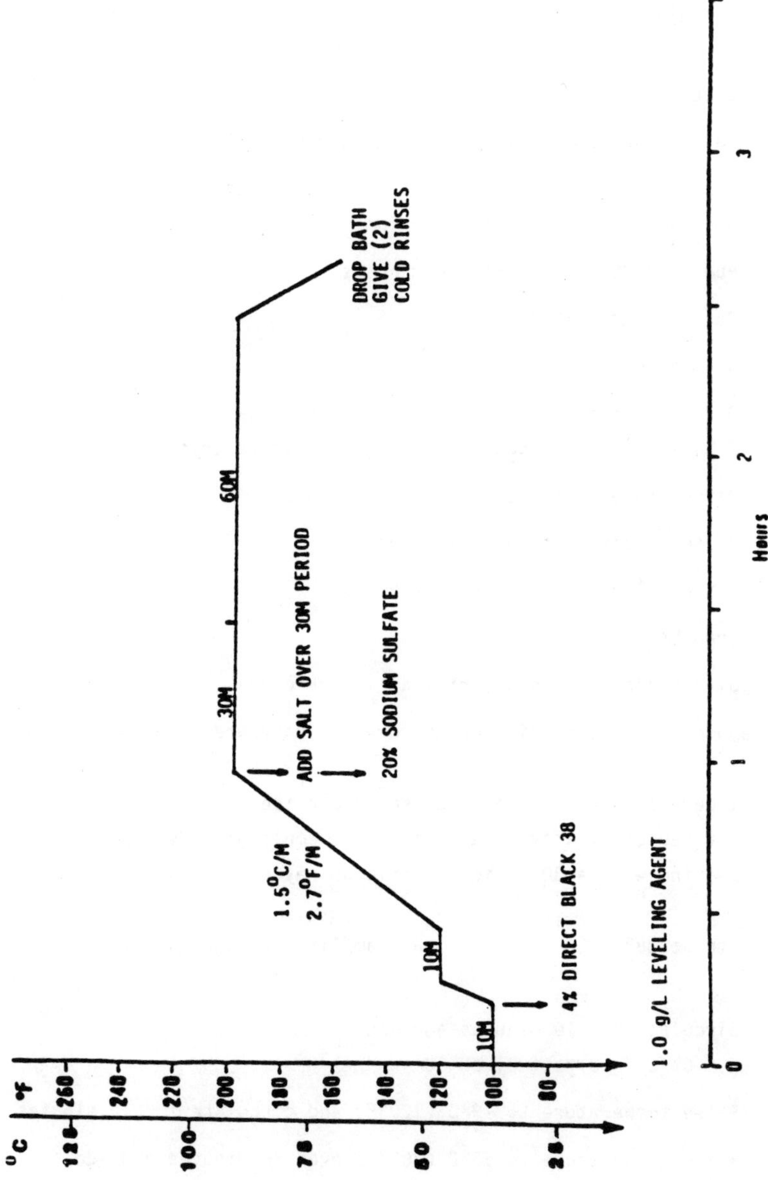


Figure 35. Dyeing rayon with direct dyes: exhaust dyeing with sample beck @ 30:1 liquor ratio.

1. Circulate for 10 minutes at 49°C (120°F) and add dye 4.0% C. I. Direct Blue 160.
2. Circulate 10 minutes.
3. Raise temperature in 30 minutes to 93°C (200°F).
4. Run 15 minutes at 93°C (200°F) then add 3.0% salt - (calcium and magnesium free) in 4 portions over 15 minutes.
5. Run at 93°C (20u°F) for 45 minutes.
6. Cool to 71°C (160°F).
7. Drop bath.
8. Give cold rinse (original volume) aftertreatment bath with 2.0% acetic acid (56%); 2.0% copper sulfate crystals.
9. Circulate at 38°C (100°F). for 5 minutes.
10. Raise temperature to 71°C (160°F).
11. Run at 71°C (160°F) for 20 minutes.
12. Drop bath.
13. Give two cold rinses (original volume each).

A graphical representation of the dyeing procedure is presented in Figure 36.

Direct developed dyes were produced to provide good wet fastness but require a series of aftertreatment. An example of a dye procedure on a beck machine with a 30:1 liquor ratio on rayon is as follows (Horning 1978):

Set bath at 38°C (100°F) with 1.0 gram/liter Levegal KN (leveling agent).

- Circulate for 10 minutes and add:
  - 4.0% C.I. Direct Black 38
- Raise temperature to 49°C (120°F) and circulate for 10 minutes
- Raise temperature to 93°C (200°F) over 30 minutes and add:
  - 20.0% sodium sulfate

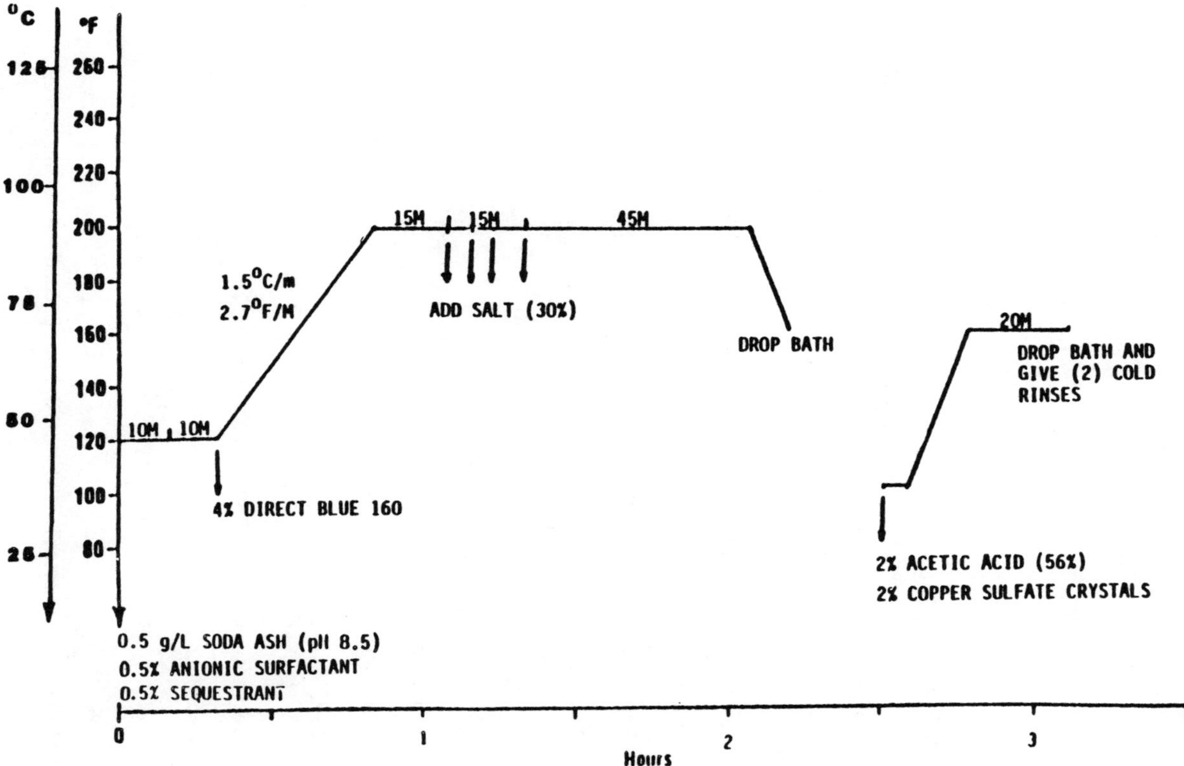


Figure 36. Dyeing bleached mercerized cotton with after-copperable direct dyes: exhaust dyeing with sample beck @ 30:1 liquor ratio.

- Add over a 30 minute period
- Run at 93°C (200°F) for 60 minutes
- Cool to 71°C (160°F)
- Drop bath
- Give two cold rinses (original volume)

Diazotizing Bath

- Set bath at 27°C (80°F) and add:
  - 3.0% sodium nitrite
- Circulate for 5 minutes, then add:
  - 7.5 hydrochloric acid 20° B$^{e}$
- Run 20 minutes at 27°C (80°F)
- Drop bath
- Give three cold rinses

Develop Bath

- Set bath at 27°C (80°F) and add:
  - 1.5% Developer Z
- Run for 20 minutes at 38°C (100°F)
- Drop bath
- Give three cold rinses

Scouring Bath

- Set bath at 38°C (100°F) and add: - 0.5% Barisol BRM (surfactant)
- Heat bath to 54°C (130°F) and run for 10 minutes
- Drop bath
- Give two warm rinses at 49°C (120°F)
- Drop bath

A graphical representation of the dyeing procedure is presented in Figure 37.

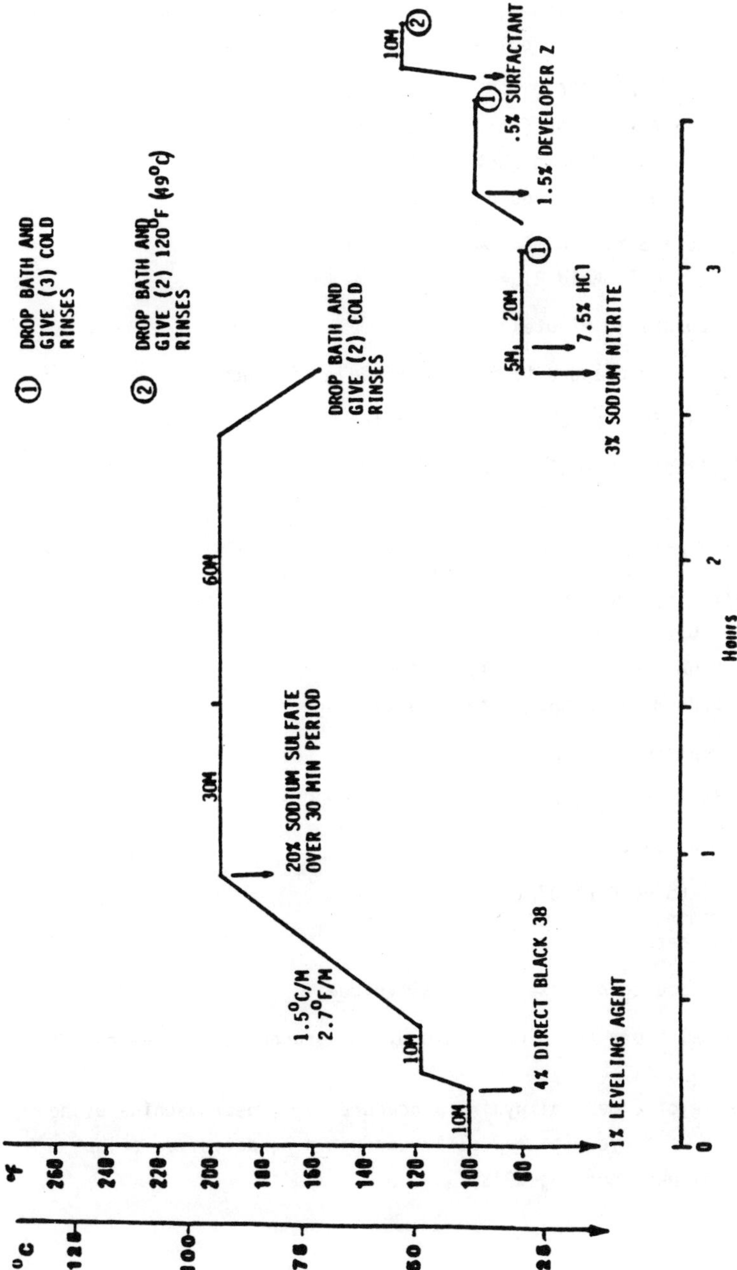


Figure 37. Dyeing rayon with direct-develop dyes: exhaust dyeing with sample beck @ 30:1 liquor ratio.

A general dyeing procedure for a beck machine using true acid dyes with a 30:1 liquor ratio on polyamide is as follows (Horning 1978):

- Set bath at 38°C (100°F) with:
  - 1.5% Alkanol ND (anionic surfactant)
  - 20.% acetic acid (56%) pH 5-5.5
  - 5.0% anhydrous sodium sulfate
- Circulate for 10 minutes, then add:
  - 3.0% C.I. Acid Blue 40
- Circulate 10 minutes
- Raise temperature to 98°C (208°F) in 45 minutes
- Run at 98°C (208°F) for 60 minutes
- Cool to 60°C (140°F)
- Drop bath
- Give cold rinse (original volume); drop bath

<u>Aftertreatment Bath</u>

- Set bath at 38°C (100°F) with:
  - 2.0% acetic acid (56%) pH 4-4.5
  - 5.0% Mesitol NBS (after-treating agent)
- Circulate for 5 minutes
- Raise temperature rapidly to 93°C (200°F)
- Run at 93°C (200°F) for 20 minutes
- Cool to 60°C (140°F)
- Drop bath
- Give one cold rinse (original volume)

A graphical representation of the dyeing procedure is presented in Figure 38.

An example of a general dyeing procedure for a beck machine using pre-metallized acid dye with a 30:1 liquor ratio on polyamide tricot fiber is as follows (Horning 1978):

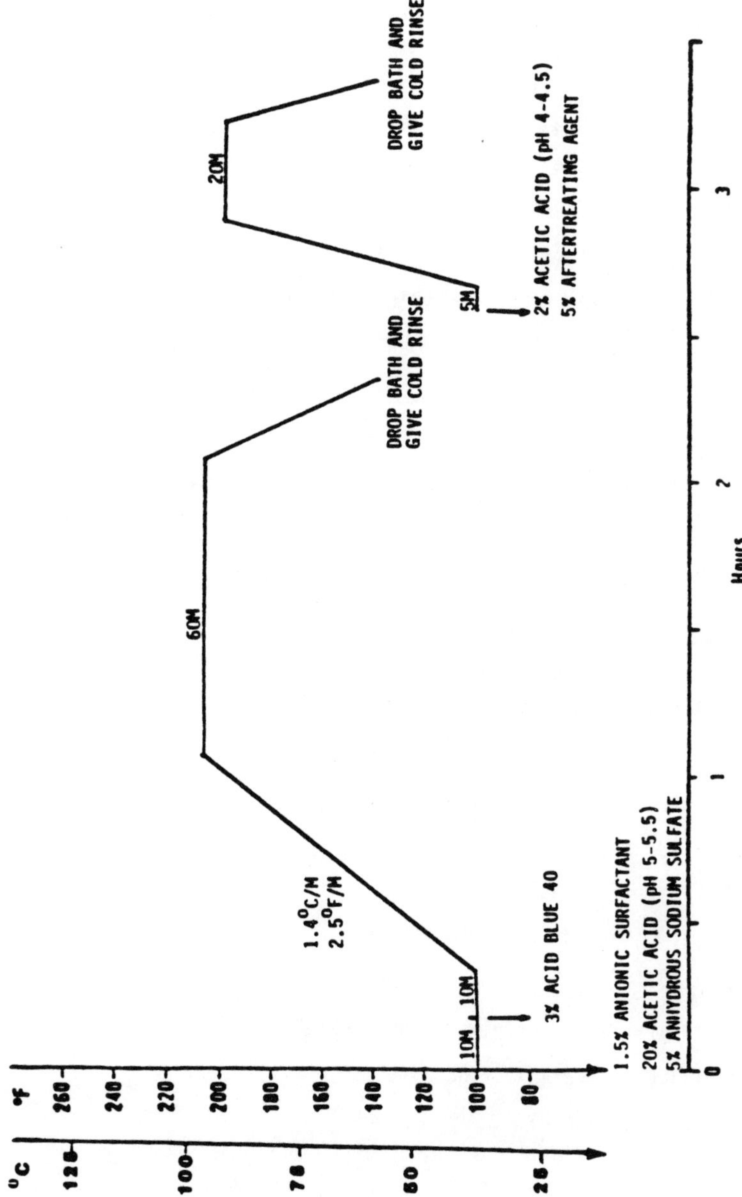


Figure 38. Dyeing polyamide filament with acid dyes: atmospheric exhaust dyeing with sample beck @ 30:1 liquor ratio.

- Set bath at 38°C (100°F) with the following:
  - 1.0% Capracyl leveling salt (nonionic surfactant)
  - 4.0% ammonium acetate
  - 5.0% sodium sulfate
  - 20.% C.I. Acid Black 52
  - Bath pH 6.5
- Circulate fabric for 10 minutes at 38°C (100°F)
- Raise temperature in 45 minutes to 96°C (205°F)
- Run at 96°C (205°F) for 60 minutes
- Cool to 60°C (140°F)
- Give one cold rinse (original volume)

An example of a typical dyeing procedure for a beck machine utilizing acid dyestuff at a 30:1 liquor ratio on wool fabric is as follows (Horning 1978):

- Set bath at 38°C (100°F) and add:
  - 2.0% Acetic acid (56%)
  - 5.0 anhydrous sodium sulfate
  - 5.0% C.I. Mordant Black 11
- Circulate for 10 minutes at 49°C (120°F)
- Raise temperature in 30 minutes to 100°C (212°F)
- Run at 100°C (212°F) for 30 minutes, then add 2.0% formic acid (pH 3.5-4)
- Run for 30 minutes at 100°C (212°F)
- Cool to 77°C (170°F); add 3.0% sodium bichromate
- Raise temperature rapidly to 100°C (212°F)
- Run at 100°C (212°F) for 30 minutes
- Cool to 60°C (140°F)
- Drop bath
- Give two warm rinses 49°C (120°F) (original volume)
- Drop bath

A graphical representation of the dyeing procedure is presented in Figure 39.

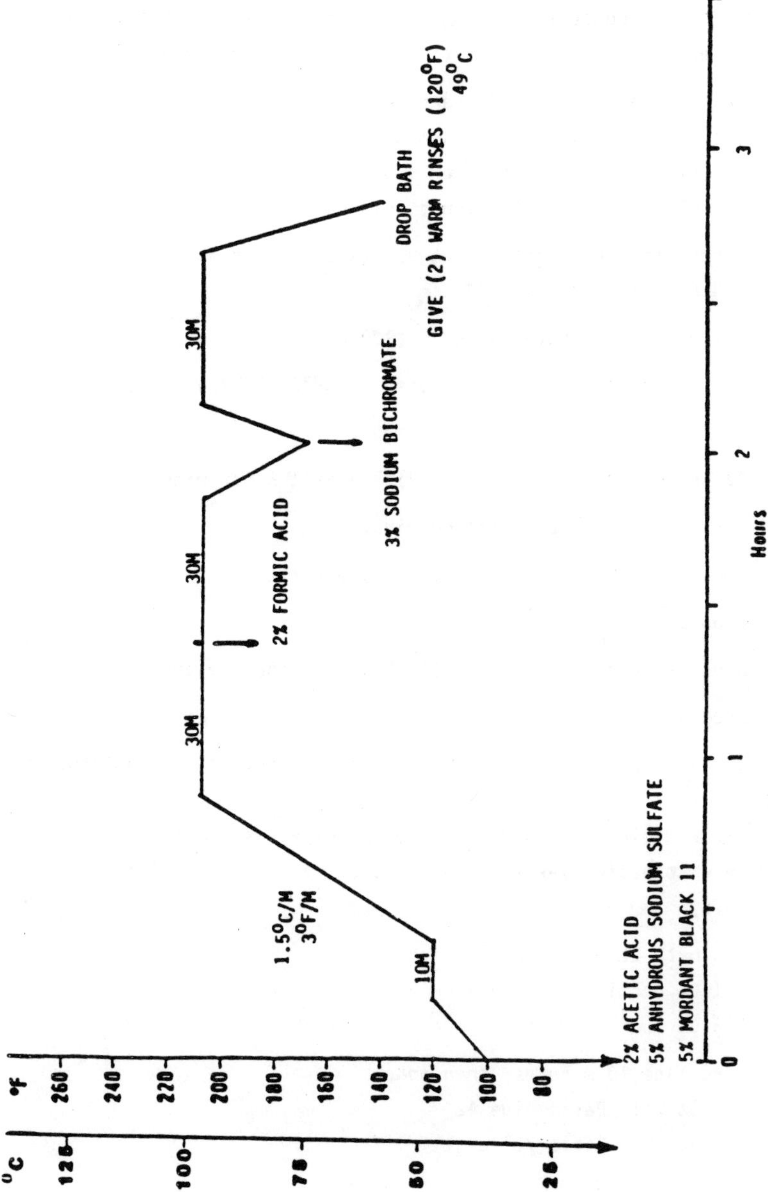


Figure 39. Dyeing wool fabric with acid dyes: exhaust dyeing with 20" sample beck @ 30:1 liquor ratio.

The dyeing procedure for dyeing acrylic fiber on a beck machine with basic dyes at a 30:1 liquor ratio is as follows (Horning 1978):

- Set bath at 38°C (100°F) and add:
  - 10.0% anhydrous sodium sulfate
  - 2.0% acetic acid (56%) pH 4.5
  - 2.0% Retarder HP (cationic retarder)
- Circulate for 10 minutes at 99C (120°F) then add:
  - 3.0% C.I. Basic Red 23
- Circulate 10 minutes at 49°C (120°F)
- Raise temperature in 45 minutes to 88°C (190°F)
- Hold at 88°C (190°F) for 15 minutes
- Raise temperature to 100°C (212°F) at 1°F per minute
- Run at 100°C (212°F) for 60 minutes
- Cool to 60°C (140°F) at 2°C (4°F) per minute
- Drop bath
- Give two warm rinses 43°C (110°F) (original volume)
- Drop bath

A graphical representation of this dyeing procedure is presented in Figure 40.

An example dyeing procedure for dyeing polyester (Dacron T-92) on a beck machine with basic dyes at a 30:1 liquor ratio is as follows (Horning, 1978):

- Set bath at 49°C (120°F) with:
  - 1.0% acetic acid (56%) pH 5
  - 5.0% sodium sulfate
- Circulate 10 minutes, then add:
  - 1.5% C.I. Basic Blue 42
  - 1.5% C.I. Basic Yellow 11

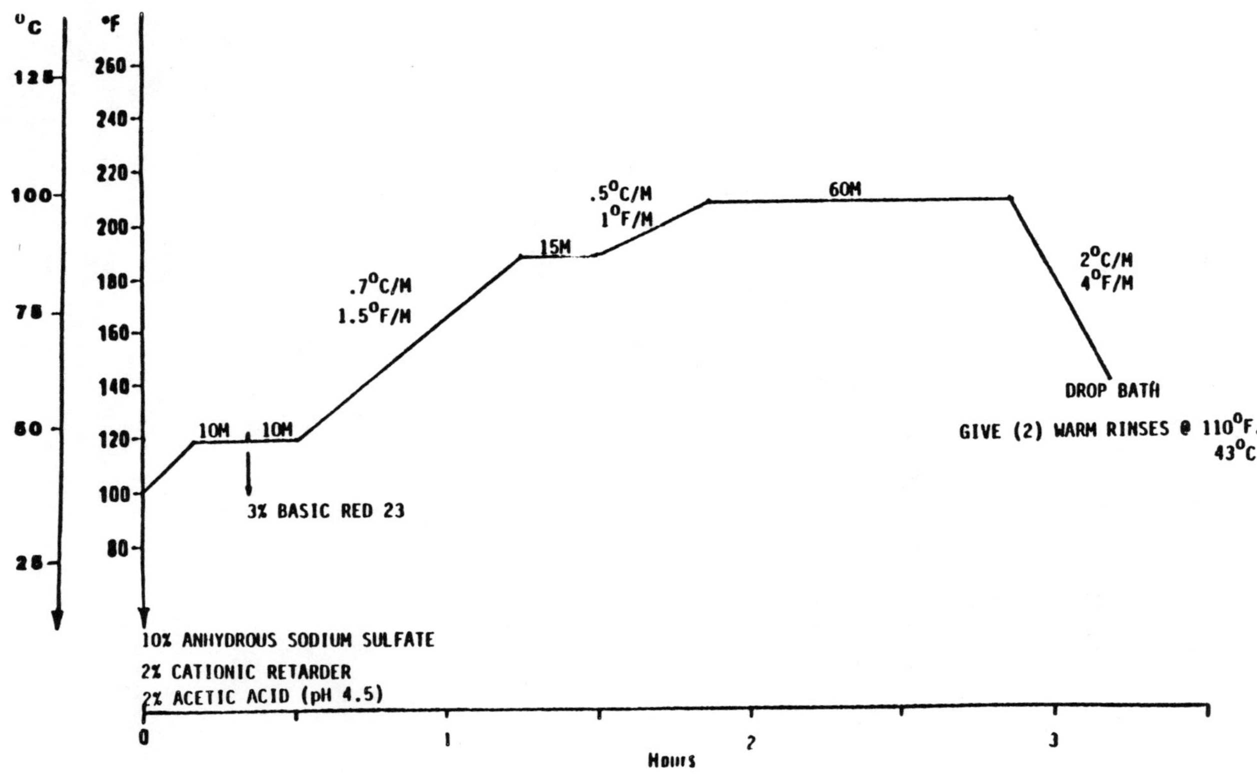


Figure 40. Dyeing acrylic fabric with basic dyes: exhaust dyeing with sample beck @ 30:1 liquor ratio.

- Heat bath to 71°C (160°F) at 1°C (2°F) per minute, then add:
  - 5.0 g/l Chemocarrier KD5W (carrier)
- Circulate 10 minutes
- Raise temperature in 25 minutes to 100°C (212°F)
- Run at 100°C (212°F) for 60 minutes
- Cool slowly to 71°C (160°F)
- Drop bath
- Give two rinses at 49°C (120°F)
- 5 minutes each rinse (original volume)

A graphical representation of this procedure is presented in Figure 41.

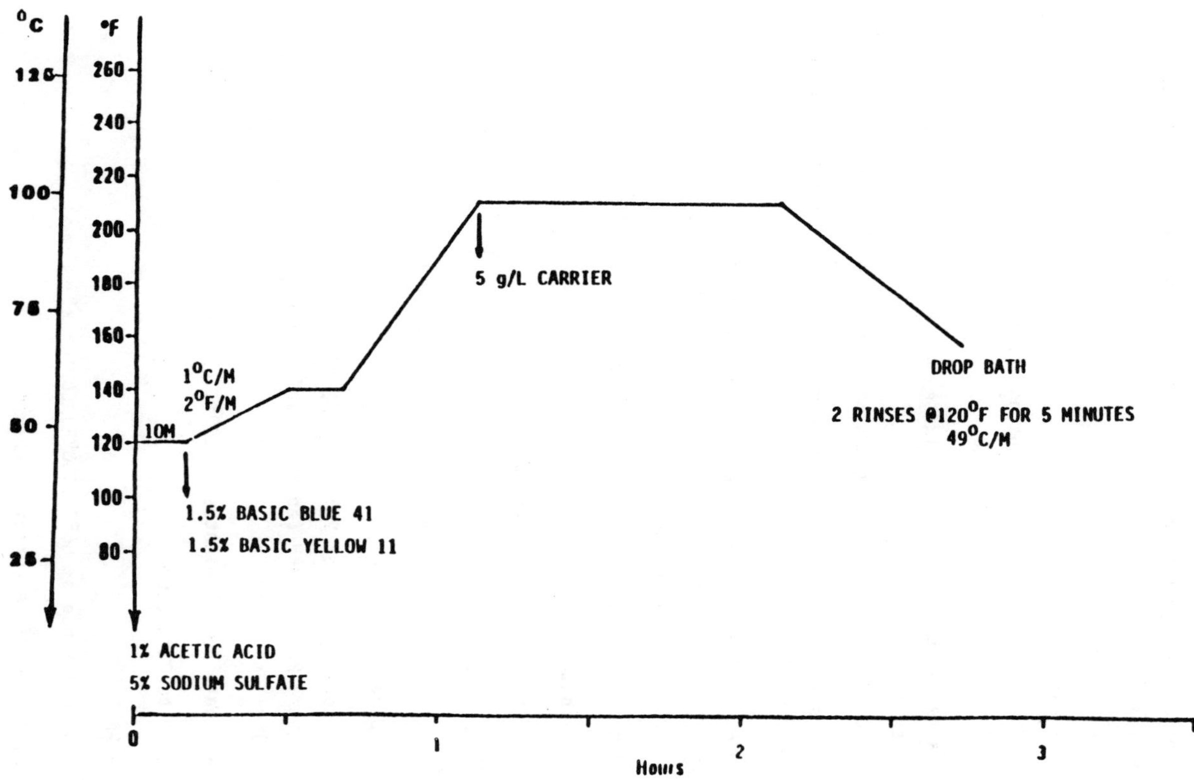


Figure 41. Dyeing polyester "Dacron" T-92 with basic dyes: atmospheric exhaust dyeing with 20" sample beck @ 30:1 liquor ratio.

An example dyeing procedure for bleached, mercerized cotton using reactive dyes in a beck machine at a 20:1 liquor ratio is as follows (Horning 1978):

- Set bath at room temperature with:
  - 2.0 g/o Ludigol (anti-reducing agent)
  - 3.0% C.I. Reactive Red 120
- Raise temperature to 49°C (120°F) and hold for 10 minutes, then add:
  - 100.0 g/l salt (calcium and magnesium free)
- Add salt in 4 portions over 40 minutes while raising temperature to 79°C (175°F)
- Dye at 79°C (175°F) for 20 minutes, then add:
  - 20 g/l soda ash
  - 1.2 g/l caustic soda
- Run at 79°C (175°F) for 50 minutes
- Drop bath
- Cold rinse (original volume)
- Drop bath
- Hot rinse at 66°C (150°F) (original volume)
- Drop bath
- Set soaping bath at 38°C (100°F) with:
  - 1 g/l Barisol BRM (anionic surfactant);
  - 1 g/l soda ash
- Run bath for 15 minutes at 100°C (212°F)
- Cool to 71°C (160°F)
- Drop bath
- Give hot rinse at 66°C (150°F) (original volume)
- Give cold rinse (original volume)

A graphical representation of this dyeing procedure is presented in Figure 42.

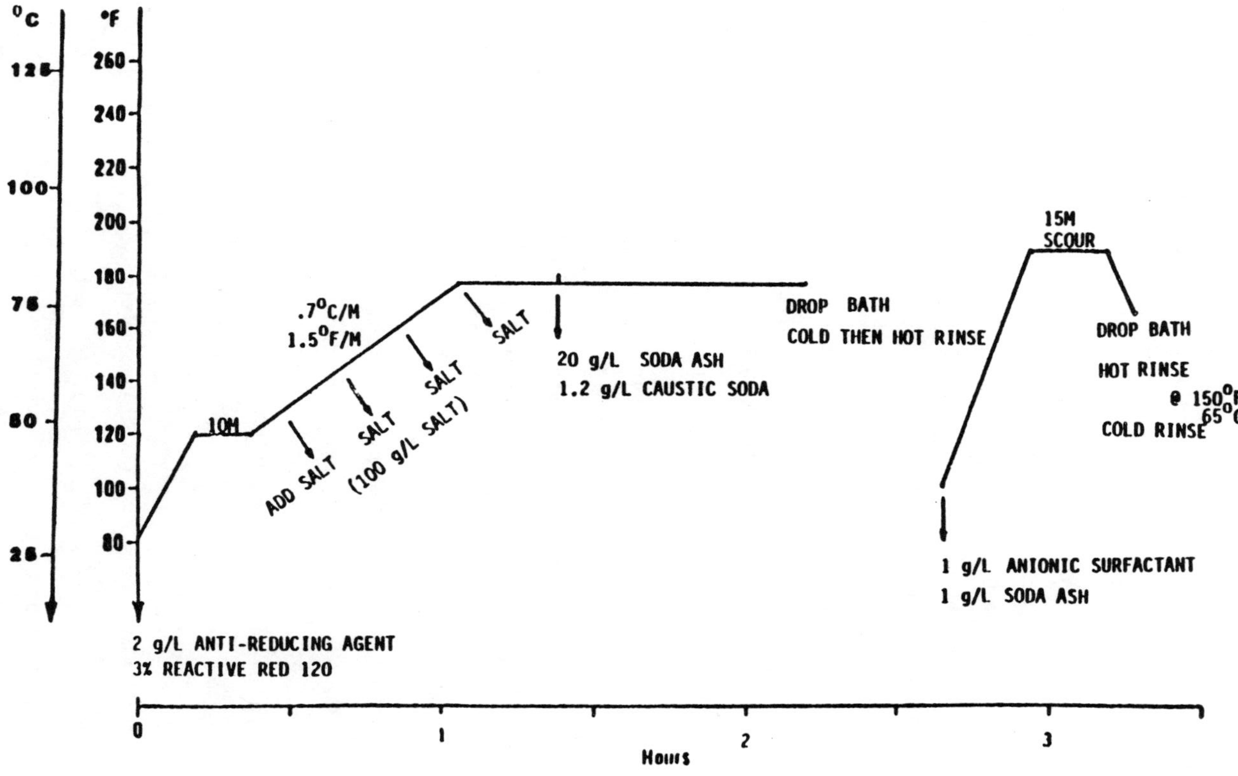


Figure 42. Dyeing bleached mercerized cotton with reactive dyes: exhaust dyeing with sample beck @ 20:1 liquor ratio.

An example of a one-bath procedure for beck dyeing with Remazol (reactive) and Samaron (disperse) dyeing on cotton/polyester fabric was prepared by American Hoechst and follows (Neal 1982):

1. Set bath @ 29°C (85°F) with:
   1.0 g/l LEOMIN® HNF/REMOL® ELA
   4.0 - 8.0 g/l HOSTATEX® LO
   .25 g/l Quadrofos
   Run 5 minutes.

2. Add: X g/l Salt
   Run 10 minutes.

3. Add over 10 minutes Y g/l TSP crystalline (see chemical chart);
   Run 20 minutes.

4. Add: Z g/l REMAZOL® dye (dissolved in boiling water and cooled to 140°F) over 10 minutes;
   Run 20 minutes
   Raise temperature @ 1°C (2F°) per minute to 60°C (140F°) and run 20 minutes.

5. Add acetic acid to adjust dyebath to pH 5.0-5.5.

6. Add disperse dye; raise temperature @ 1-1.5°C (2-3°F) per minute to 99°C (210°F); hold 45-60 minutes.

7. Cool to 77°C (170°F) and patch.

8. Overflow rinse for 10 minutes.

9. For maximum fastness on medium to dark shades add:
   2.0 g/l EGANAL® PS
   0.5 g/l LEOMIN® HNF/REMOL® ELA

10. Raise at maximum rate of rise to 93°C (200°F) and run 15 minutes
    Cool back to 77°C (170°F); drop out.

11. Rinse 10 minutes @ 77°C (170°F), drop out.

12. Rinse 10 minutes @ 66°C (150°F), drop out.

13. Apply fixation or softener, run 10-20 minutes @ 60°C (140°F); unload.

RECOMMENDED AMOUNTS OF CHEMICALS FOR REMAZOL® DYEBATH

| % dyestuff | Salt | TSP crystalline |
|---|---|---|
| up to 1.00% | 50 g/l | 3.5 g/l |
| 1.01-3.00 g/l | 75 g/l | 5.0 g/l |
| above 3.00 g/l | 100 g/l | 7.5 g/l |

A graphical representation of this procedure is presented in Table 43.

An example dyebath procedure of disperse dyeing with a beck at a 30:1 liquor ratio on tufted carpet is as follows (Horning 1978):

- Set bath at 43°C (110F°) with:
  - 0.25% Irgaformal S 2 E (antifoam agent)
  - 1.0% Calgon
  - 1.0% monosodium phosphate
  - 0.5% acetic acid (56%) pH 4.5-5.0
- Circulate 10 minutes, then add over a 10 minute period the following:
  - 1.5% C.I. Disperse Yellow 42
  - 1.5% C.I. Disperse Blue 87
  - 0.5% Compound 8-S (surfactant)
- Raise temperature to 71°C (160°F) at 1.5°C (3°F) per minute, then add over 15 minute period:
  - 10.0% Carolid 3F (biphenyl carrier)
- Run 10 minutes at 71°C (160°F)
- Raise temperature to 100°C (212°F) at 1.5°C (3°F) per minute, then add over 15 minute period:
  - 10.0% Carolid 3F (biphenyl carrier)
- Run 10 minutes at 71°C (160°F)
- Raise temperature to 100°C (212°F) at 1.5°C (3°F) per minute
- Run at 100°C (212°F) for 90 minutes

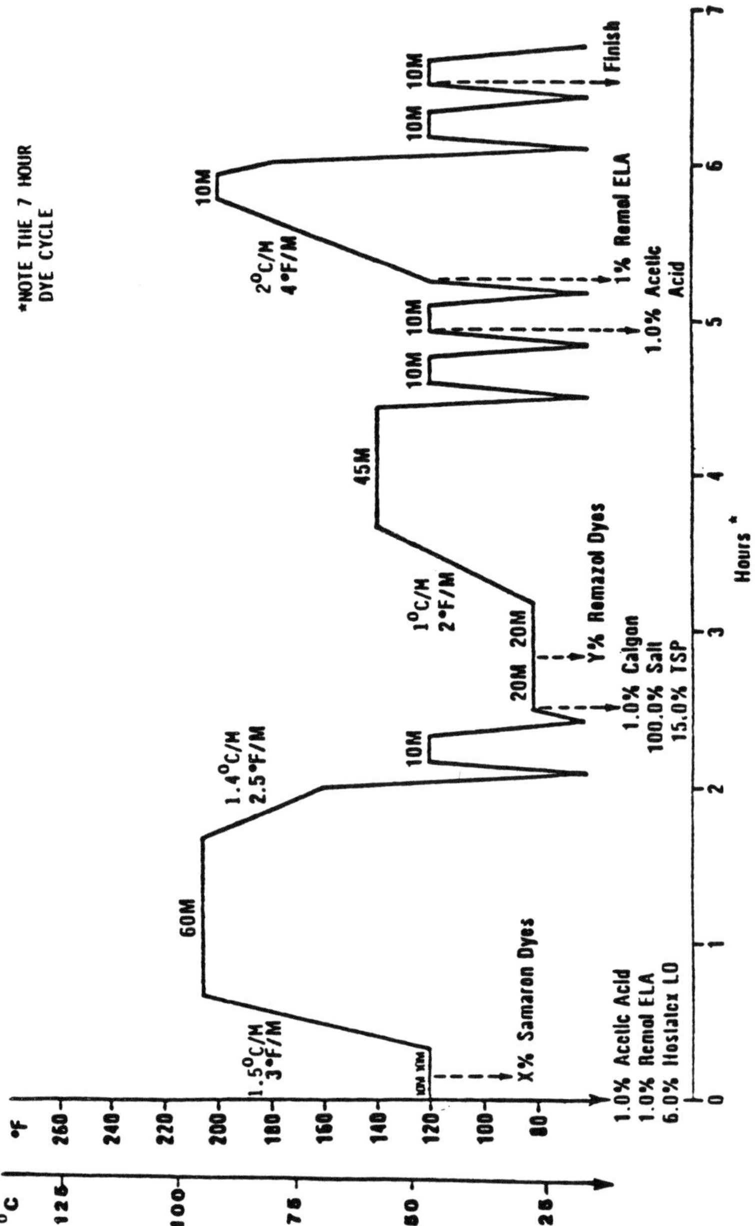


Figure 43. Dyeing polyester/cotton blend with disperse/reactive dyes: exhaust dyeing with a beck machine.

- Cool to 71°C (160°F)
- Drop bath
- Give hot rinse 71°C (160°F) for 10 minutes (original volume)
- Drop bath

Post Scour Treatment

- Set bath at 38°C (100°F) and add:
  - 1.0% Merpol DA (nonionic surfactant)
  - 1.0 & trisodium phosphate
  - 1.0% sodium hydrosulfite
- Raise temperature to 71°C (160°F) and run for 15 minutes
- Drop bath
- Give two warm rinses 49°C (120°F) (original volume)
- Drop bath

The graphical representation of this procedure is presented in Figure 44.

An example of dyebath procedure of disperse dyeing with a beck at a 20:1 liquid ratio on polyamide (nylon) tufted carpet is as follows (Horning 1978):

- Set bath at 38°C (100°F) with:
  - 0.5% Avitone T (anionic surfactant)
  - 1.0% Merpol DA (nonionic surfactant)
  - 0.5% Versene 100 (sequestrant)
- Circulate 5 minutes and add dyes:
  - 0.22% C.I. Disperse Yellow 3
  - 0.075% C.I. Disperse Red 55
  - 0.006% C.I. Disperse Violet 28
- Add trisodium phosphate (pH 9.0-0.5)
- Raise temperature to 88-93°C (190-200°F) over 45 minutes

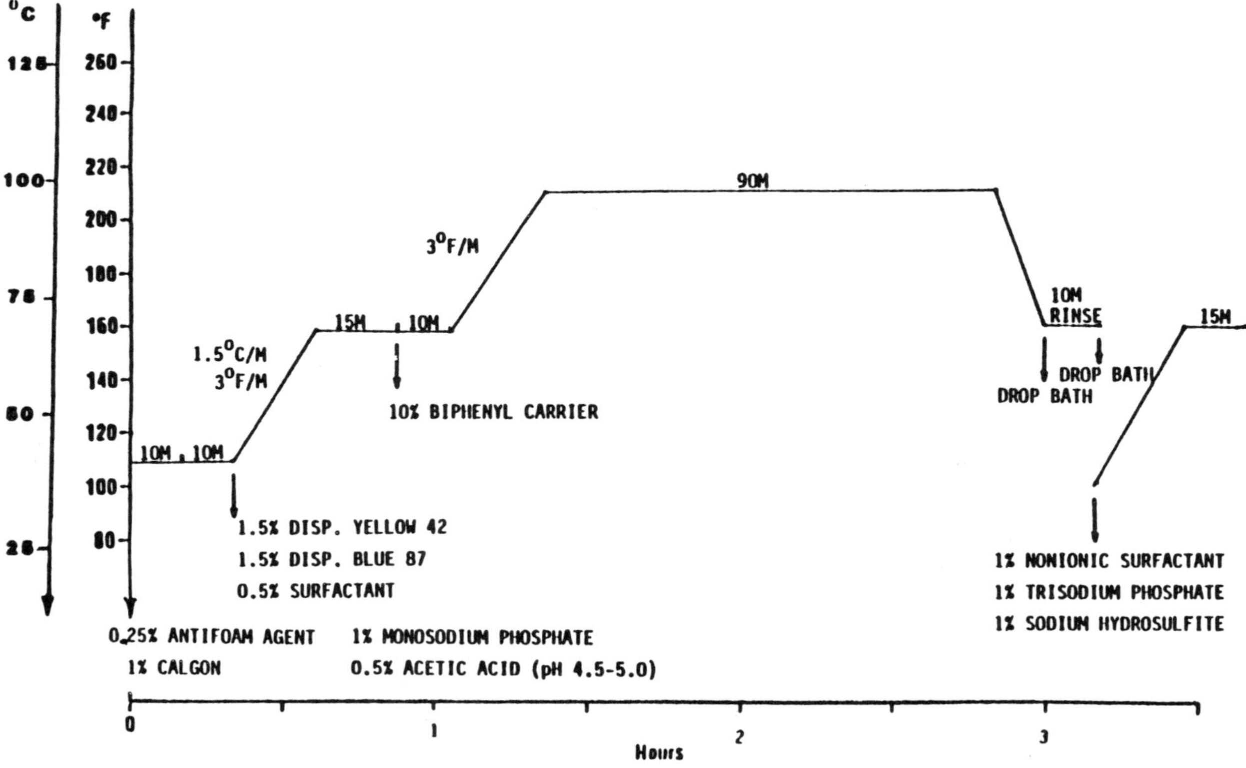


Figure 44. Dyeing tufted carpet with disperse dyes: atmospheric exhaust with sample beck @ 30:1 liquor ratio.

- Dye one hour
- Cool bath to 71°C (160°F) and drop
- Give one rinse at 43°C (110°F) (original volume)

A graphical representation of this procedure is presented in Figure 45.

An example dyebath procedure of disperse dyeing with a beck at 30:1 liquid ratio on polyester texturized double knit is as follows (Horning 1978):

- Set bath at 49°C (120°F) with:
  - 1.0 g/l Compound 8-S (surfactant)
  - 5.0 g/l Carolid FLM (ortho-phenyl-phenol carrier)
  - 1.0% acetic acid (56%) to pH of 5.4
  - 3.0% C.I. Disperse Blue 87
  - 1.0% C.I. Disperse Yellow 42
  - 1.0 g/l Compound 8-S (surfactant)
- Raise temperature of bath to 100°C (212°F) in 40 minutes
- Dye at 100°C (212°F) for 90 minutes
- Cool to 71°C (160°F)
- Drop bath
- Give one rinse (original volume)
- Scour at 71°C (160°F) for 10 minutes with:
  - 1.0 g/l Merpol HCS (surfactant)
  - 1.0 g/l soda ash
  - 1.0 g/l sodium hydrosulfite
- Drop bath
- Rinse at 71°C (160°F) (original volume)
- Rinse at 49°C (120°F) (original volume)

A graphical representation of this procedure is presented in Figure 46.

Another example of a dyebath procedure uses basic, disperse, and acid dyes on a beck at a 30:1 liquor ratio on carpet of nylon styling yarn. The procedure is as follows:

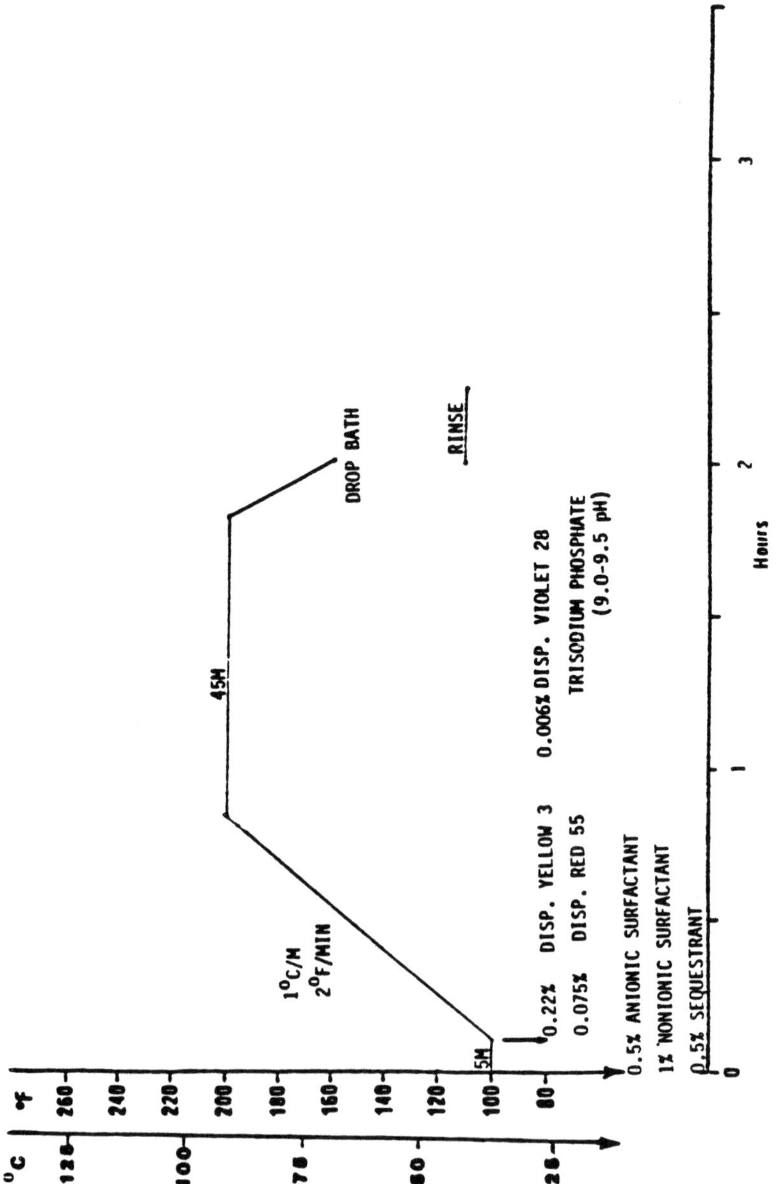


Figure 45. Dyeing polyamide carpet with disperse dyes: exhaust dyeing with sample beck @ 20:1 liquor ratio.

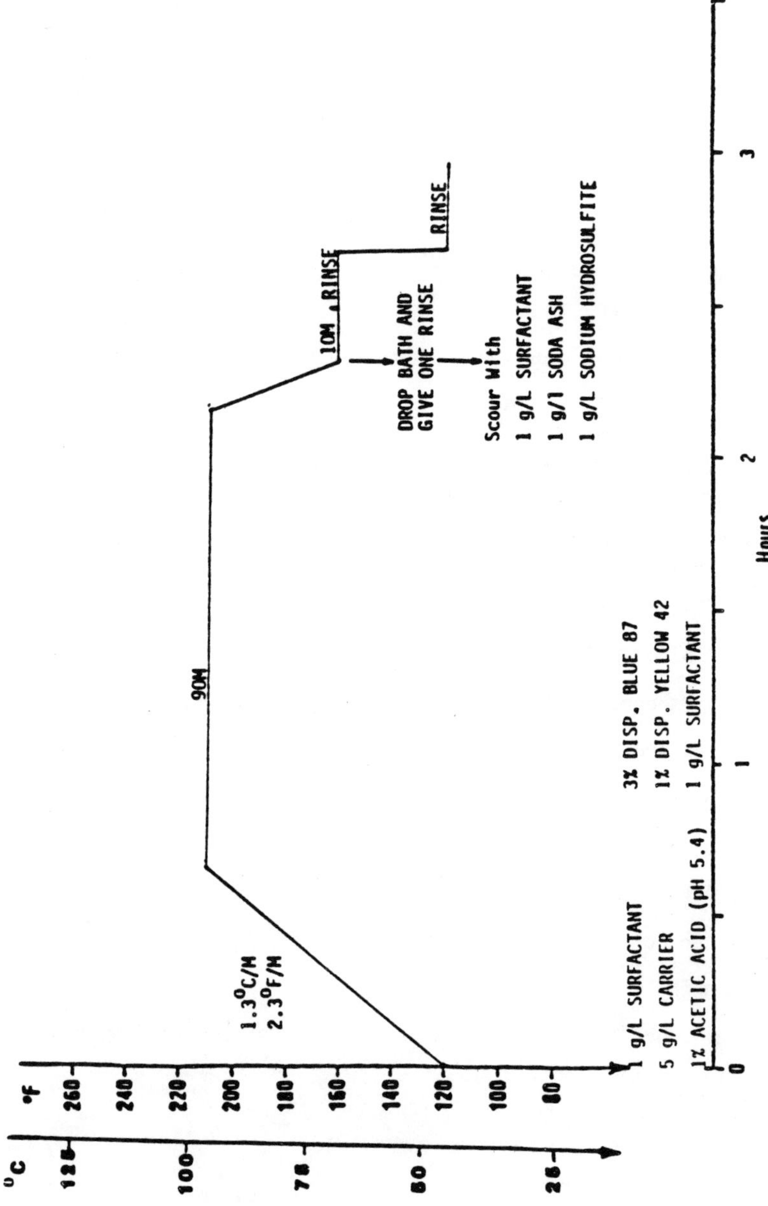


Figure 46. Dyeing polyester with disperse dyes: atmospheric exhaust with sample beck @ 30:1 liquor ratio.

- Set bath at 27°C (80°F) with:
  - 0.25% Alkanol A-CN (surfactant)
  - 0.25% trisodium phosphate
  - 1.0% monosodium phosphate (pH 6.0-6.2)
  - 0.25% Sequestrene ST (sequestrant agent)
- Circulate bath for 10 minutes, then add the below dyes over a ten-minute period:
  - 0.5% C.I. Basic Red 73
  - 0.1% C.I. Basic Blue 92
- Run for 5 minutes, then add the following dyes over a five-minute period:
  - 0.3% C.I. Disperse Yellow 3
  - 0.1% C.I. Disperse Red 55
  - 0.02% C.I. Disperse Blue 7
  - 0.5% C.I. Acid Red 145
  - 1.20% C.I. Acid Blue 122
  - 0.10% C.I. Acid Yellow 198
- Run 10 minutes
- Raise temperature to 96°C (205°F) at 1°C (2°F) per minute
- Check pH and adjust to 6.0-6.2
- Dye for 60 minutes at 96°C (205°F)
- Cool bath to 60°C (140°F)
- Drop bath
- Give two cold rinses 21-27°C (70-80°F).
- Drop bath

A graphical representation of this procedure is presented in Figure 47.

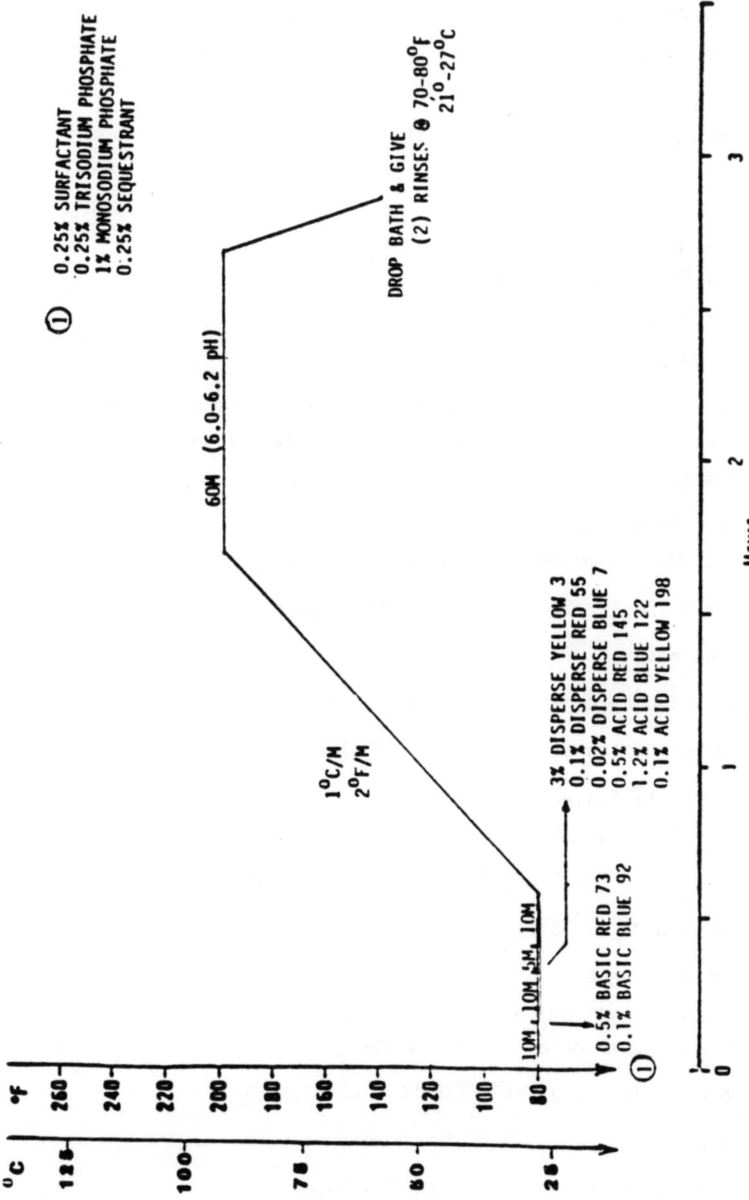


Figure 47. Dyeing carpet of nylon with basic, disperse, and acid dyes: atmospheric dyeing with sample beck @ 30:1 liquor ratio.

An example dyeing procedure for 15 one-pound packages of mercerized cotton yarn using vat dyes in a 35 pound package dyeing machine at a 15:1 liquor ratio is as follows (Horning, 1978):

- Set bath at 38°C (100°F) with:
  - 2.0% compound 8-S
  - 10.0% Caustic soda
  - 5.0% C.I. Vat Blue 18
  - 3.5% C.I. Vat Black 13
  - 1.0% C.I. Vat Orange 2
- Circulate five minutes
- Raise temperature -16.1°C (3°F) per minute to 82°C (180°F). Continue to circulate bath for 20 minutes (cycle machine 4 minutes inside-out; 4 minutes outside-in)
- Cool bath to 60°C (140°F) and add:
  - 10.0% sodium hydrosulfite (½ inside-out; ½ outside-in)
- Circulate for 30 minutes reversing cycle each 4 minutes
- Drop bath
- Give two cold rinses - (original volume)
- Set oxidizing bath at 43°C (110°F) with 1.0% acetic acid (56%)
- Circulate 5 minutes, add:
  - 2.0% sodium perborate
- Raise bath to 60°C (140°F) and run 10 minutes
- Raise bath to 88°C (190°F)
- Set soaping bath with:
  - 1.0% Avitex AD (surfactant)
  - 0.5% tetrasodium pyrophosphate
- Run 10 minutes at 88°C (190°F)
- Drop bath
- Give two cold rinses (original volume)

Hydroextraction and oven drying is required to complete dyeing. A graphical representation of this dyeing procedure is presented in Figure 48.

Also, the application of disperse dyes can be achieved with package machines. The central application principal and uses of the disperse dyestuffs is presented in Section 5.2.1.6. An example dyeing procedure for 15 one-pound packages of polyester yarn using disperse dyes in a 35 pound package dye machine at a 8:1 liquor ratio is as follows (Horning, 1978):

- Set bath at 49°C (120°F) with:
  - 1.0 g/l Compound
  - 8-S (Anionic surfactant)
  - 4.0% Tanalon Jet (carrier)
  - 1.0% acetic acid (56%) pH = 5-6
- Circulate 10 minutes, and add:
  - 4.0% C.I. Disperse Blue 56; dye was pasted up with equal amount of the above surfactant
- Raise temperature to 121°C (250°F) in 45 minutes
- Dye at 121°C (250°F) for 60 minutes
- Cool to 71°C (160°F)
- Give one rinse at 38°C (100°F) for 5 minutes
- Drop bath
- Set scour bath at 38°C (100°F) and add:
  - 1.0 g/l caustic soda
  - 1.0 g/l sodium hydrosulfite
  - 1.0 g/l Product BCO (surfactant)
- Run at 71°C (160°F) for 10 minutes
- Drop bath
- Give one rinse at 71°C (160°F) for 5 minutes
- Give one rinse at 49°C (120°F) for 5 minutes

Oven drying is required to complete dyeing. A graphical representation of this dyeing procedure is presented in Figure 49.

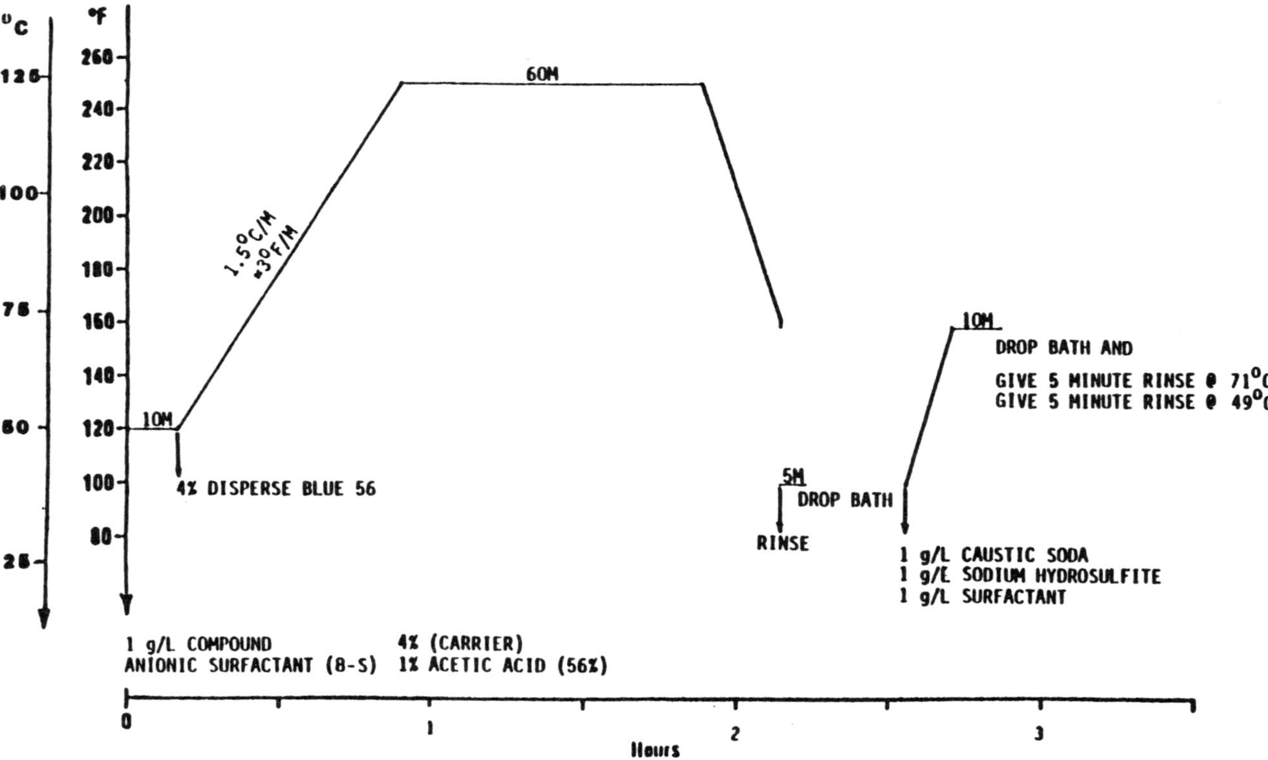


Figure 48. Dyeing mercerized cotton with vat dyes: exhaust dyeing with a 35 pound package machine at 15:1 liquor ratio.

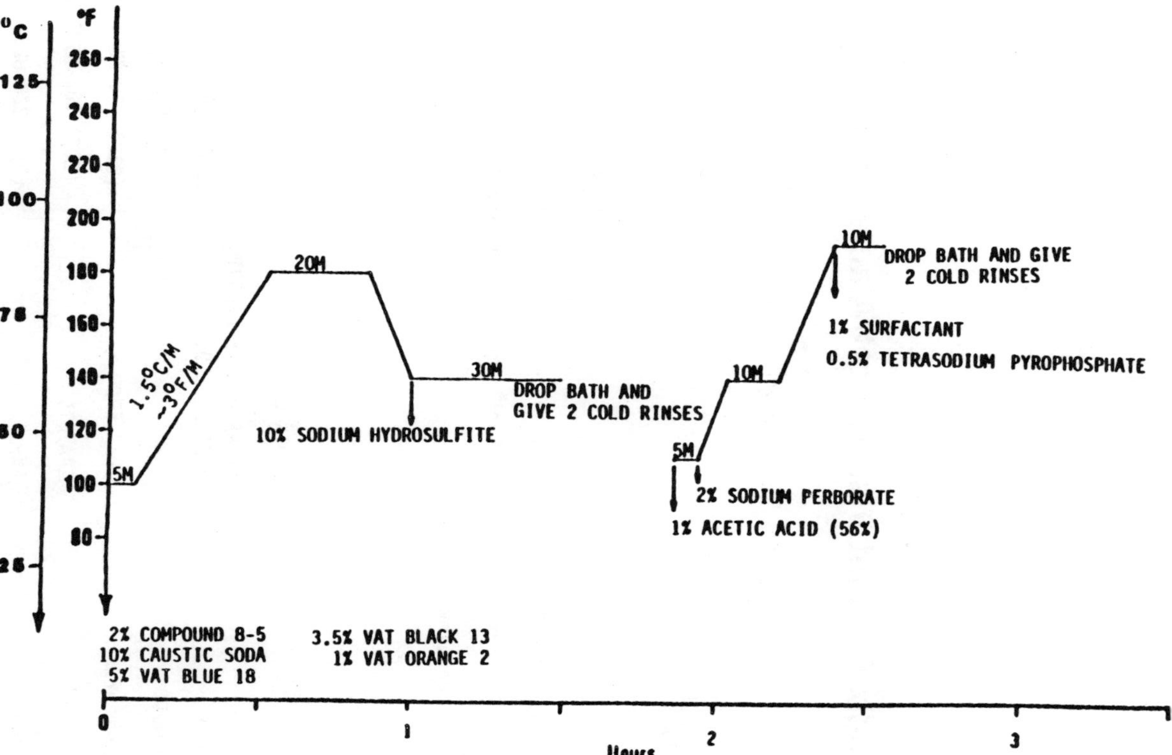


Figure 49. Dyeing polyester yarn with disperse dyes: exhaust dyeing with a 35 pound package machine @ 8:1 liquor ratio.

# Appendix C: Plant Visit Report/Alamance Knit

TEXTILE DYESTUFFS EMISSION/RELEASE STUDY

Plant Name: Alamance Knit Fabrics, Inc.

Plant Location: Interstate 85 North; Burlington, North Carolina

Date of Visit: January 12, 1983

APPENDIX G

REPORT ON QUALITY ASSURANCE EFFORT

| Persons Present | Representing | Telephone |
|---|---|---|
| Charles Blackwell | TRW | (919) 541-9100 |
| John S. Ruppersberger | EPA/IERL | (919) 541-2734 |
| Jerry Vorbach | EPA/OTS | (202) 382-3695 |
| Edwin Armstrong | AKF | (919) 228-0261 |
| Sam Kiser | AKF | (919) 228-0261 |

PLANT VISIT QUESTIONNAIRE
TEXTILE DYESTUFFS EMISSION/RELEASE STUDY

I. GENERAL PLANT INFORMATION

A. Corporate Information

1. Name of corporation Alamance Knit Fabrics, Inc.

2. Address of corporation headquarters

Street I-85 North

City Burlington State NC Zip 27215

B. Plant Information

1. Name of plant Same as Above

2. Address of plant

Street Same

City ______ State ______ Zip ______

3. Mailing address of plant (if different from above)

P.O. Box 2320

4. Name(s) of personnel to be contacted for additional information pertaining to this questionnaire.

| Name | Title | Telephone |
|---|---|---|
| Edwin B. Armstrong | President | 919/228-0261 |
| Lloyd V. Edmonds | Executive Vice-Pres. | 919/228-0261 |
| James E. Faircloth | Adm. Vice-President | 919/228-0261 |

C. Type of Plant Operations

1. Indicate the type(s) and percentage of dyeing/printing operations conducted at this facility.

| | Batch(%) | Semi-Continuous(%) | Continuous(%) |
|---|---|---|---|
| Stock Dyeing | 0 | 0 | 0 |
| Yarn Dyeing | 0 | 0 | 0 |
| Piece Dyeing | 97 | 0 | 3 |
| Printing | 0 | 0 | 100 |

2. Indicate any operations other than dyeing/printing operations conducted at this facility.

| | Yes | No |
|---|---|---|
| Wool scouring | | X |
| Slashing | | X |
| Weaving | | X |
| Desizing | | X |
| Scouring | X | |
| Bleaching | X | |
| Mercerizing | | X |
| Carbonizing | | X |
| Other | | X |

3. Indicate the number of dyeing/printing machines at your plant. Also, list the type and estimated amount of fabric processed by each machine type. (Example - Beck (4) Polyester & 50 Polyester/50 Cotton; 500 lb/day.)

Beck (4) Polyester, Poly/cotton, Nylon, Acrylic; 5,000 #/day

Beam (5) Polyester, Nylon and Blends; 10,000 #/day

Jig ______

Package ______

VAT ______

Pad-Batch ______

Transfer Printer (2) Polyester; 15,000 yds./day

Roller Printer ______

Rotary Screen ______

Other (3) Jet Dyeing, Polyester and Blends; 6,000 #/day

4. Estimate the dye substance usage for the following dye classes and the amount of fabric dyed. (Example - Disperse 100 lb/day at 4,250 lb wools/day.)

Acid 20 #/day - 1,500 #/day

Direct 1 #/day - 100 #/day

Azoic ______

Disperse 133 #/day - 12,000 #/day

Sulfur ______

Reactive ______

Drug Room

- 1½ dye weighers/8 hr. day.
- Dye is mixed, pumped to machines; tank is washed down and dye lines are flushed.
- Dye mixed in 50 gallon containers or tanks approximately 3/4 full (i.e., 37½ gal.); containers are steam heated.
- Clean-up of containers requires 50 gallons of water.
- Three shifts used - but no chemicals received on second or third shift.
- Black colors require 75-80 lbs. of dye/1000 lbs. cloth.

Beam

- Estimate 20 dye containers/shift of basic dye for 7 hours of dyeing.
- Dye cycle is approximately 2½ hours/shift. Goal is 3 cycles per machine per shift.
- Each cycle (i.e. batch) uses approximately 900 to 1,2500 gallons of water.
- Cloth is washed once with the 900-1,250 gallon and the dye is added.
- Approximately 300 gallons of dye bath discharged to sewer every dye cycle.
- Usually 500-600 lbs. of cloth dyed per cycle.
- Exhaustion rate is 90-95% for dark shades. Degree of exhaustion is greater than 95% for medium to light shades.
- There is a 3-5% rejection rate for dyed goods. These are either redyed or sold as off-spec. goods.

Wastewater Treatment

- Wastewater from AKF goes to an on-site pretreatment facility with a design capacity of 0.8 MGD. Surface aeration is provided. Facility has a 24 hour detention time. Effluent from this facility is discharged to the city's wastewater treatment plant which has a design capacity of 20-30 MGD.
- Alamance Knit Fabrics, Inc. contributes approximately 0.5 MGD to the pretreatment facility. The hosiery operation next door contributes the rest.

5. For each dye class, estimate the amount of dye purchased in a typical purchase order. (Example - Sulfur 10 lbs/3 months.)

   Acid 10-50 lbs. Average about 50 lbs.

   Direct ____

   Azoic ____

   Disperse Average approximately 200 lbs.

   Sulfur ____

   Reactive ____

6. For batch operations, provide an estimate of the amount of fabric dyed per batch for the following machines.

   | | | | |
   |---|---|---|---|
   | Beam | ____ | VAT | ____ |
   | Beck | ____ | Jet | ____ |
   | Jig | ____ | Package | ____ |

7. Estimated number of machines that are used concurrently in a dyeing campaign.

   | | | | |
   |---|---|---|---|
   | Beam | ____ | VAT | ____ |
   | Beck | ____ | Package | ____ |
   | Jig | ____ | Pad-Batch | ____ |
   | Transfer Printer | 4,000-12,000 yds/shift | Roller Printer | ____ |
   | Rotary Screen | ____ | Other | ____ |

## II. WORKER EXPOSURE

### A. Drug Room Operations

1. Provide flow diagram for the different operations used at your facility for preparing the dyes. Also, list the number of workers involved and time of each operational step. (Example -

   Weighing (1 - 45 minutes) ⟶ Mixing (2 - 60 minutes) ⟶

   ⟶ Transport of Dye Solution to Dye Room (2 - 15 minutes)

- A dye campaign will range from 10,000 to 15,000 lbs. of cloth per campaign. This will usually be multiple shades.
- Typical dye purchase orders range from 5 lbs. to 1,000 lbs., depending upon frequency of use and size of dye campaigns, either planned or currently in-house.
- Typically, 3% of the total weight of light shade cloth is dye. For dark shade dyes, this will be about 5% of the total weight.

Fabric Weights

- 1,000 lb. - 1,600 yds. for 12 oz. fabric. (range 8-12 oz.)
- 1,000 lb. - 5,000 yds. for 2½ oz. sheer fabric.

Amount of Dye Substance Added to Drug Room Dye Pot (per 1,000 lbs. of goods):

- Acid - 2-5 lbs.
- Direct - 5-15 lbs.
- Disperse - 1-75 lbs.
- Basic - 5-35 lbs.
- Reactive - approximately 2 lbs.

(Note: The more dye added, the darker the shade.)

2. Are the above procedures followed for all dye machines? ___________

3. List other additives to the dye solution present in the drug room.

   1,000 grams - Acetic Acid
   1 lb. - Burzene (sequestering agent for iron removal)
   3 lbs. - Lormard (a dispersing agent)

   3 (for light) to 10 (for dark) lbs. carriers, e.g. AK, NFCB, Abican from AB Chemical of Greensboro, NC

4. Identify controls used to reduce worker exposure.

   Dust mask, gloves, and apron
   Face shield
   1 wash-up per shift (use approximately 50 gallons of water)

5. Identify industrial hygiene practices used to reduce worker exposure.

B. Dye Room Operations

1. Provide one-line flow diagram for the operational steps of the different dyeing/printing equipment used at your facility. Also, list the number of workers and time of each operational step. (Example - See previous drug room flow diagram.)

   1 supervisor and 1 floor man

   5 beams: 2 operators/shift (10 min. to load)
   1 drugroom man
   1 batch operator

   4 Jet: 2 operators

   3 Atm. Becks: 1 operator
   1 operator for pull-down. Load and unload time - 30 min. ea.

2. List other inputs to the dyeing/printing process present in the dye room. (Example - steam, chemical additives, etc.)

3. Identify controls and/or industrial hygiene practices used to reduce worker exposure.

   Gloves when handling fabrics
   Rubber gloves at dye machines
   Washed air system

III. PROCESS DESCRIPTION

A. Provide process flow diagrams for the different "workhorse" dye/equipment/fabric combinations used at this facility. Provide the following information in the flow diagram.

1. The workhorse dye and other chemicals required in the dyeing process on a weight volume per pound of fabric, temperature, pressure, concentration of dye and other agents, pH, volume of dyebath (batch size), and bath time.

   pH of acid dyes 4-4.5

2. The dyebath process conditions including temperature, pressure, concentration of dye and other agents, pH, volume of dyebath (batch size), and bath time.

   Atm. beck batch volume: 1,000-1,500 gal.

B. **Provide standard operating procedures for the pieces of equipment in the flow diagrams. Include the following:**

1. **Amount of water used in each step.** Dye batch water mixed with existing water and pre-scour water.
2. **Estimate of exhaustion rate.**
3. **Estimate of the frequency of recycling of dye liquor, including the percent of dye liquor recycled and the number of times the dye liquor can be recycled before being discharged.** Jet and beck water reused after wash; but beam cycle is dumped to sewer.

**IV. OPERATIONAL PROCEDURES**

A. **Do you monitor energy conservation on a piece of equipment or a complete dyeing/printing process? Provide the following information if available.**

1. **Number of batches per machine per shift.**

   10,000-15,000 lbs. fabric/campaign/machine for 20 hrs.
   Light shade: 3 batch/machine/shift; dark shade: 2 batch/machine/shift

2. **Number of dyeing machines used per shift.**

3. **Number of shifts per day.**

   Atm. beck does not run all the time; rest: 24 hr/day, 5 day/week.
   Plant shuts down one week each year for Christmas and for July 4.

B. **Provide dyestuff information such as the following.**

1. **Dye capacity per machine batch.**

2. **Estimate of the range in the quantity of fabric in a dyeing campaign using one particular dye.**

3. **Provide an estimate of the consumption per plant per year, frequency of use, and prices of an example dye for major color in the following dye classes or your workhorse colors: acid, direct, disperse, and fiber-reactive.**

| | | | |
|---|---|---|---|
| Disperse: | Orange 2RA | $ 4.00/lb. | |
| | Red F3Bs | $18.87/lb. | - $30.00/lb. |
| Direct: | Diagonal Black BG | $ 4.00/lb. | (range $2.50-$10.00/lb.) |
| Fiber Reactive: | | $ 5.00-$10.00/lb. | |
| Acid: | | $ 2.00-$31.00/lb. | |

V. CURRENT WASTE DISPOSAL METHODS

A. Describe your process wastewater. Include the following information.

1. Segregation and/or integration of different dye bath water streams.

2. Efficiencies of dye and dye agent capture related to workhorse dye classes (dye content and % in water after dyeing process).

3. Effectiveness of various in-plant techniques.

4. Estimate of the wastewater volume discharged per machine batch.

B. Describe your wastewater treatment system from dyeing and/or printing processes.

C. Provide wastewater characterization data including the following.

1. Final release concentrations and magnitude of release to POTWs and/or receiving waters.

2. List effluent concentrations (as available).

Volume ____________

BOD ____________

COD ____________

TSS ____________

pH ____________

Turbidity ____________

Total Color ____________

# Appendix D: Plant Visit Report/Carlisle Finishing

TEXTILE DYESTUFFS EMISSION/RELEASE STUDY

Plant Name: Carlisle Finishing Plant (Cone Mills Corp.)

Plant Location: Highway No. 72; Carlisle, South Carolina

Date of Visit: January 13, 1983

| Persons Present | Representing | Telephone |
|---|---|---|
| Charles Blackwell | TRW | (919) 541-9100 |
| John S. Ruppersberger | EPA/IERL | (919) 541-2734 |
| Jerry Vorbach | EPA/OTS | (202) 382-3695 |
| J. Patrick Danahy | Cone Mills Corp. | (803) 427-6221 |
| M.R. "Chip" Witcher, Jr. | Cone Mills Corp. | (919) 379-6965 |

PLANT VISIT QUESTIONNAIRE
TEXTILE DYESTUFFS EMISSION/RELEASE STUDY
EPA CONTRACT NO. 68-02-3174, Work Assignment 86

I. GENERAL PLANT INFORMATION

A. Corporate Information

1. Name of corporation Cone Mills Corporation

2. Address of corporation headquarters

Street 1201 Maple Street

City Greensboro State NC Zip 27405

B. Plant Information

1. Name of plant Carlisle Finishing Plant

2. Address of plant

Street Highway #72

City Carlisle State SC Zip 29031

3. Mailing address of plant (if different from above)

________________

4. Name(s) of personnel to be contacted for additional information pertaining to this questionnaire.

| Name | Title | Telephone |
|---|---|---|
| J. Patrick Danahy | V.P. & General Mgr. | 803/427-6221 |
| | | |
| | | |

C. Type of Plant Operations

1. Indicate the type(s) and percentage of dyeing/printing operations conducted at this facility.

| | Batch(%) | Semi-Continuous(%) | Continuous(%) |
|---|---|---|---|
| Stock Dyeing | | | |
| Yarn Dyeing | | | |
| Piece Dyeing | | 20 | 80 |
| Printing | | | |

2. Indicate any operations other than dyeing/printing operations conducted at this facility.

| | Yes | No |
|---|---|---|
| Wool scouring | ___ | ___ |
| Slashing | ___ | ___ |
| Weaving | ___ | ___ |
| Desizing | ___ | ___ |
| Scouring | ___ | ___ |
| Bleaching | ___ | ___ |
| Mercerizing | ___ | ___ |
| Carbonizing | ___ | ___ |
| Other | ___ | ___ |

3. Indicate the number of dyeing/printing machines at your plant. Also, list the type and estimated amount of fabric processed by each machine type. (Example - Beck (4) Polyester & 50 Polyester/50 Cotton; 500 lb/day.)

*Beck (1)- Est. capacity 2 yd. wt. (24 hrs.) 12,000 lbs. (cottons - poly/cottons)

*~~Beam~~ (1) Jet - Est. capacity 2 (24 hrs.) 5,333 lbs. (polyesters/ poly/cottons

Jig (8) Cottons - 8600 lbs. day

Package N/A

VAT (2) Dye ranges - cotton-poly/cottons/rayons - 17,000 lbs. day

*Not Active at Present

Pad-Batch (1) Pad range (1) pad batch (Cottons - pad range 11,200 lb/day) (Cottons - pad batch 3,000 lb/day)

Transfer Printer N/A

Roller Printer (12) 83,500 lbs/day-cotton/poly-cottons/poly-rayon/ polyester

Rotary Screen (7) 59,500 lbs/day - cottons/poly/cottons/nylons

Other (1) Pigment dye range 8,400 lbs/day - cottons/poly-cotton/ poly/rayon

4. Estimate the dye substance usage for the following dye classes and the amount of fabric dyed. (Example - Disperse 100 lb/day at 4,250 lb wools/day.)

Basis: 3 shifts

Acid 112 lbs/day @ 4241 lbs. cloth

Direct 1¼ lbs/day @ 87 lbs. cloth

Azoic 673 lbs/day @ 16,185 lbs. cloth

Disperse 27 lbs/day @ 991 lbs. cloth

Sulfur 117 lbs/day @ 10,022 lbs. cloth

Reactive 302 lbs/day @ 19,087 lbs. cloth

5. For each dye class, estimate the amount of dye purchased in a typical purchase order. (Example - Sulfur 10 lbs/3 months.)

Acid 110 lbs. per color per mo. (no. of colors vary)

Direct 100 lbs. per color per mo. (no. of colors vary)

Azoic 6750 lbs. - 3 colors per mo. (no. of colors vary)

Disperse 500 lbs. - 2 colors per mo. (no. of colors vary)

Sulfur 2000 lbs. - 4 colors per mo. (no. of colors vary)

Reactive 2750 lbs. - 10 colors per mo. (no. of colors vary)

6. For batch operations, provide an estimate of the amount of fabric dyed per batch for the following machines.

Beam ______ VAT ______

Beck ______ Jet ______

Jig ______ Package ______

7. Estimated number of machines that are used concurrently in a dyeing campaign.

Beam ______ VAT ______

Beck ______ Package ______

Jig 2 Pad-Batch 1

Transfer Printer N/A Roller Printer 1

Rotary Screen 1 Other ______

## II. WORKER EXPOSURE

### A. Drug Room Operations

1. Provide flow diagram for the different operations used at your facility for preparing the dyes. Also, list the number of workers involved and time of each operational step. (Example -

   Weighing (1 - 45 minutes) ⟶ Mixing (2 - 60 minutes) ⟶

   ⟶ Transport of Dye Solution to Dye Room (2 - 15 minutes)

2. Are the above procedures followed for all dye machines? ___________

3. List other additives to the dye solution present in the drug room.

4. Identify controls used to reduce worker exposure.

5. Identify industrial hygiene practices used to reduce worker exposure.

Dye Room Operations

1. Provide one-line flow diagram for the operational steps of the different dyeing/printing equipment used at your facility. Also, list the number of workers and time of each operational step. (Example - See previous drug room flow diagram.)

2. List other inputs to the dyeing/printing process present in the dye room. (Example - steam, chemical additives, etc.)

3. Identify controls and/or industrial hygiene practices used to reduce worker exposure.

## III. PROCESS DESCRIPTION

A. Provide process flow diagrams for the different "workhorse" dye/equipment/fabric combinations used at this facility. Provide the following information in the flow diagram.

1. The workhorse dye and other chemicals required in the dyeing process on a weight volume per pound of fabric, temperature, pressure, concentration of dye and other agents, pH, volume of dyebath (batch size), and bath time.

2. The dyebath process conditions including temperature, pressure, concentration of dye and other agents, pH, volume of dyebath (batch size), and bath time.

B. Provide standard operating procedures for the pieces of equipment in the flow diagrams. Include the following:

1. Amount of water used in each step.

2. Estimate of exhaustion rate.

3. Estimate of the frequency of recycling of dye liquor, including the percent of dye liquor recycled and the number of times the dye liquor can be recycled before being discharged.

IV. OPERATIONAL PROCEDURES

A. Do you monitor energy conservation on a piece of equipment or a complete dyeing/printing process? Provide the following information if available.

1. Number of batches per machine per shift.

2. Number of dyeing machines used per shift.

3. Number of shifts per day.

B. Provide dyestuff information such as the following.

1. Dye capacity per machine batch.

2. Estimate of the range in the quantity of fabric in a dyeing campaign using one particular dye.

3. Provide an estimate of the consumption per plant per year, frequency of use, and prices of an example dye for major color in the following dye classes or your workhorse colors: acid, direct, disperse, and fiber-reactive.

V. CURRENT WASTE DISPOSAL METHODS

A. Describe your process wastewater. Include the following information.

1. Segregation and/or integration of different dye bath water streams.

   All dye bath water merges into one single stream.

2. Efficiencies of dye and dye agent capture related to workhorse dye classes (dye content and % in water after dyeing process).

   Vat. 85% - on cloth; 15% in water

   Pig. 90% - on cloth; 10% in water

3. Effectiveness of various in-plant techniques.

   70%

4. Estimate of the wastewater volume discharged per machine batch.

   150 gallons per minute per machine

B. Describe your wastewater treatment system from dyeing and/or printing processes.

   Bar screen, stationary screens .030", extended aeration (17 days), sludge recirculation and polishing impoundment

C. Provide wastewater characterization data including the following.

1. Final release concentrations and magnitude of release to POTWs and/or receiving waters.

   Discharge to Broad River
   Flow rate averages approximately 4,000 cfs

2. List effluent concentrations (as available).

| Volume | 2,000,000 gal/day | Influent (ppm) |
|---|---|---|
| BOD | 40 | 800 |
| COD | 300 | ≈900-1,000 |
| TSS | 75 | 450 |
| pH | 8.5 | |
| Turbidity | Not measured | |
| Total Color | Not required | |

# TRANSCRIPT OF HANDWRITTEN NOTES TAKEN DURING CARLISLE FINISHING PLANT VISIT JANUARY 13, 1983

## I. PLANT OVERVIEW

The plant is divided into three (3) departments:

1. Rotary Screen Printing
2. Roller Printing
3. Dyeing

Each department has its own drug room, which is dedicated to that department.

Ten (10) percent of the plant's work is for other Cone Mill operations; the remaining ninety (90) percent is for outside customers. Approximately sixty (60) percent of the plant's work originates from outside the United States, with the remaining forty (40) percent coming from within the U.S. Roughly fifteen (15) percent of the plant's completed work is exported.

Normal plant operations are three (3) shifts per day and five (5) to six (6) days per week, depending upon work load.

## II. ROTARY SCREEN PRINTING DEPARTMENT

### A. Drug Room

This operation recovers and reuses all of their unexhausted dye: 100-55 gallon drums per week, average.

Composition of a typical dye solution batch:

4.5 gallons of varsol
450 gallons of water
220 pounds of locust bean gum
0.1 percent preservative (dimethoxyone)

Dye substances by volume (including carriers) shown below as appropriate:

| | |
|---|---|
| Vat | - 10% maximum |
| Fiber Reactive | - 5% maximum |
| Acid Dye | - 5-7% maximum |
| Disperse Dye | - 5-7% maximum |

Assuming 100 percent fabric coverage, 60-70 percent of the dye (including carriers) will be printed on the fabric. This solution has approximately 6-7 percent dye solids. Thus, using vat dyes as an example, the total dye solids in the batch would be:

$$\left(\frac{450 \text{ gal. of } H_2O}{\text{batch}}\right) (0.1 \text{ dye component}) (0.06 \text{ dye solids in dye})$$

$$= \frac{2.7 \text{ gal. solids}}{\text{batch}}$$

Also, the estimated amount of dye solids which will remain on the fabric would be, based on a 60 percent fabric retention:

$$\left(\frac{2.7 \text{ gal. dye solids}}{\text{batch}}\right) (0.6 \text{ fabric retention of dye solution})$$

$$= 1.62 \text{ gal./batch retained on fabric}$$

and,

$$\frac{2.7 \text{ gal. dye solids}}{\text{batch}} - 1.62 \text{ gal. retained on fabric/batch}$$

$$= \frac{1.08 \text{ gal}}{\text{batch}}. \text{ of dye solids recycled for reuse.}$$

Approximately 4,000 gallons of gum is used per eight (8) hour shift.

For a fully coated fabric, the above dye batch will print about 1,000 yards of fabric per 250 liters of dye batch solution.

## III. ROLLER PRINTING DEPARTMENT

### A. Drug Room

Composition of a typical pigment batch:

5 gallons of pigment per 500 gallons of resin melimine
80 gallons of solvent
25 gallons of fixer
12 gallons of concentrate

Approximately 1,000 gallons used per 8 hour shift.

The drippings from the dye mixing are discharged to an undergrate sump and then to the wastewater treatment plant.

One dye weigher per shift is used.

Twelve (12) pigment mixing stations where pigments are mixed together in 50 gallon containers, after being pumped from the formulation room.

B. Printing Operations

100% of the dye remains on the fabric, except for discharge colors. 20-25 gallons of dye will cover 1,000 yards of fabric.

Dyes prepared in 300 gallon tanks, approximately 2-3 gallons of pigment is used for dark colors, and one (1) pint used for light colors.

A continuous machine will run 75,000-80,000 yards of fabric per shift.

Dyes are ordered once per month. Mainly pigments and vats are ordered.

IV. DYEING DEPARTMENT

A. Drug Room

For the jigs, vat dyes are used about 40% of the time, fiber reactive dyes about 30% of the time.

Typical formulation using a rust color shade as an example; using a two-stage mixing procedure:

160 gallon mix:

3 gal. of cellusolve
1.82 pounds of naphthol dye
16.98 pounds of ASITR dye
2.2 pounds of AS Buline dye
3 gallons of caustic

The above chemicals are mixed and then the following are added and mixed.

63.44 pounds of fast scrub
0.5 gallons of stabilizer
3 gallons of acetic acid

Approximately 2½ batches will dye 10,000 yards of fabric.

Powder dyes are used.

B. Dyeing Operations

Pad-batch:

Roll of fabric will range between 900-5,000 yards and weigh approximately 7,000 pounds.

The pad-batch is rinsed for 4 hours with a 7-10 gpm flow. This rinse water is discharged to the sewer. Exhaustion will range from 60-95%, based on dye card recommendations, which are fairly accurate.

Production rage of pad-batch machine is approximately 75 yards/ minute for a 400 yard machine.

Jig:

Dyes used are: sulfur, fiber reactive (obsolete), and direct. No disperse dyes are used.

Full dyeing cycle lasts 4-6 hours. Approximately 85 percent of the dye applied is retained on the fabric. Water is dumped after each batch.

Amount of dye used per batch ranges from 0 to 150 pounds per 160 gallon total batch. Typically, 15-30 pounds of dye is used in 100 gallons of water. Cloth has about a 30 percent liquid retention, or holds approximately 30 gallons.

Estimated amount of dye per batch discharged to sewer is: 100%-85% exhaustion = 15% dye nonexhausted and 100 gal.-30 gal. = 70 gal.; or 15 percent of the original dye substance dispersed in 70 gallons of water.

# Appendix E: Results of NIOSH Monitoring Studies

E-1. SUMMARY OF MONITORING RESULTS FROM A DYE AND FINISHING PLANT

E-2. SUMMARY OF MONITORING RESULTS FROM A TEXTILE PLANT

E-3. SUMMARY OF MONITORING RESULTS FROM A PAPER PLANT

(Abstracted from Industrial Hygiene Study Survey Reports prepared for Industrial Hygiene Section, Division of Surveillance, Hazard Evaluations, and Field Studies. National Institute for Occupational Safety and Health Cincinnati, Ohio 45202)

## APPENDIX E-1

## SUMMARY OF MONITORING RESULTS FROM A DYE AND FINISHING PLANT

TABLE 55. SUMMARY OF MONITORING RESULTS FROM A DYE AND FINISHING PLANT

| Job description | Environmental concentration[a] | Urinary excretion | Notes |
|---|---|---|---|
| Dye Weigher I | 1) 1.39 $mg/m^3$ | 3.2 ppb aromatic amines expressed as BZD.<br>4.4 ppb expressed as Bzd; Bzd not confirmed by EC-GC. | Wore no respirator. General ventilation only. |
| Dye Weigher II | 2) 1.06 $mg/m^3$ | 8 ppb expressed as Bzd; Bzd confirmed by TLC.<br>5.8 ppb expressed as Bzd; 39 ppb confirmed as Bzd by EG-GC; 5 ppb MAB. | Wore no respirator. General ventilation only. Boiled up dye by hand. |
| Dye Weigher III | 3) 2.09 $mg/m^3$<br>4) 1.15 $mg/m^3$<br>1.62 TWA | 7 ppb MAB - <1 ppb as Bzd.<br>5 ppb expressed as Bzd. | No respirator worn. Beginning of shift dustiest. |
| Dye Weigher IV | 5) 3.93 $mg/m^3$<br>6) 1.20 $mg/m^3$ | <1 ppb detected by EC-GC.<br>5 ppb expressed as Bzd. | No respirator worn. Beginning of of shift dustiest. |
| Pad Dye Operator I | 7 1.07 $mg/m^3$ | 4.5 ppb expressed as Bzd; <1.4 ppb found as Bzd by EC-GC.<br><1 ppb expressed as Bzd. | Carried dye solution to dye baths and diluted to desired concentration. Spent 80% of time in nonexposure area loading grey goods into pad dyeing machine. |
| Pad Dye Operator II | 8) 1.12 $mg/m^3$ | 9 ppb expressed as Bzd; confirmed by TLC.<br>13 ppb expressed as Bzd; 16 ppb confirmed by EC-GC; 38 ppb MAB | Wore no respirator. No contact with dry dye. |

(continued)

TABLE 55. SUMMARY OF MONITORING RESULTS FROM A DYE AND FINISHING PLANT (continued)

| Job description | Environmental concentration[a] | Urinary excretion | Notes |
|---|---|---|---|
| Jigg Dyer | 9) 2.56 | 3.4 ppb expressed as Bzd | Wore no respirator. Spend much |
| | 10) 1.40 | 3.0 ppb expressed as Bzd | time near steamy jigg baths |
| | 1.98 TWA | 4.0 ppb expressed as Bzd | making adjustments on cloth rolls. |
| | | 3.2 ppb expressed as Bzd | No contact with dry dyes. |

[a]Concentrations expressed as airborne particulates per cubic meter of air sampled.

[b]Neither aromatic amines or metabolites expressed as benzidines (Bzd or MAB) were detected by EC-GC.

TABLE 56. ENVIRONMENTAL DATA FOR TABLE 55

| Field No. | mg/filter total weight | Air volume (liters) | $mg/m^3$ | λ max[a] (nm) | mg/filter azo dyes | Percent azo dyes |
|---|---|---|---|---|---|---|
| 1 | 0.61 | 437.5 | 1.39 | N | <0.010 | 0 |
| 2 | 0.46 | 432 | 1.06 | N | <0.010 | 0 |
| 3 | 0.69 | 231 | 2.98 | 577 | 0.148 | 21.4 |
| 4 | 0.57 | 495 | 1.15 | N | <0.010 | 0 |
| 5 | 0.93 | 236 | 3.94 | 577 | 0.270 | 29.0 |
| 6 | 0.60 | 499 | 1.20 | 577 | 0.133 | 22.2 |
| 7 | 0.46 | 430.5 | 1.07 | N | <0.010 | 0 |
| 8 | 0.82 | 735.0 | 1.12 | N | <0.010 | 0 |
| 9 | 0.53 | 136.5 | 3.88 | N | <0.010 | 0 |
| 10 | 0.65 | 463 | 1.40 | N | <0.010 | 0 |
| 11 | 0.27 | 126 | 2.14 | N | <0.010 | 0 |
| 12 | 0.55 | 136 | 3.89 | N | <0.010 | 0 |
| 13 | 0.57 | 355 | 1.70 | N | <0.010 | 0 |

| [a]λ max | Trade name |
|---|---|
| 577 | Black JXA |
| 577 | Blue 2B |

# APPENDIX E-2

## SUMMARY OF MONITORING RESULTS FROM A TEXTILE PLANT

TABLE 57. SUMMARY OF MONITORING RESULTS FROM A TEXTILE PLANT

| Job description | Environmental concentration[a] | Urinary concentrations | Notes |
|---|---|---|---|
| Dye Weigher I | 1) 1.54 mg/m³<br>2) 1.31 mg/m³<br>1.45 mg/m³ TWA | 4 ppb aromatic amines.[b]<br>4.8 ppb aromatic amines; <1.4 ppb Bzd; 4 ppb MAB.<br>3.6 ppb aromatic amines; <1.4 ppb Bzd; <4 ppb MAB. | Weighed dyes in Drug Room before dissolving in boil-up tubs. Worker sometimes wore a half-face pad type respirator and gloves when weighing dyes. General ventilation from roof exhaust fans only. |
| Dye Weigher II | 3) 1.15 mg/m³<br>4) 1.11 mg/m³<br>1.13 mg/m³ TWA<br>Area sample over scales<br>5) 0.55 mg/m³ | <1 ppb aromatic amines.<br><1 ppb aromatic amines.<br>1.3 ppb aromatic amines; <1.4 ppb Bzd; <4 ppb MAB. | Same as above. |
| Dye Tub Operator I | 6) 5.31 mg/m³ (void) | <1 ppb aromatic amines.<br><1 ppb aromatic amines. | Worker loads and unloads cloth from rolls to and from dye tubs. Tubs were ventilated by top hood exhaust and had front hood moveable doors No respirators worn. Rubber globes worn sometimes. Worker is splashed by dye liquor during work. |
| Dye Tub Operator II | 7) 0.90 mg/m³ | <1 ppb aromatic amines. | Same as above. |

(continued)

TABLE 57. SUMMARY OF MONITORING RESULTS FROM A TEXTILE PLANT (continued)

| Job description | | Environmental concentration[a] | Urinary concentrations | Notes |
|---|---|---|---|---|
| Dye Tub Operator III | 8) | 1.58 mg/m$^3$ | 3.2 ppb aromatic amines. | Same as above. |
| Dye Tub Operator IV | 9) | 0.67 mg/m$^3$ | <1 ppb aromatic amines. | Same as above. |
| Dye Tub Operator V | 10) | 0.63 mg/m$^3$ | 3.2 ppb aromatic amines. | Same as above. |
| Dye Tub Operator VI | 11) | 0.20 mg/m$^3$ | <1 ppb aromatic amines.<br><1 ppb aromatic amines.<br><1 ppb aromatic amines. | Same as above. |
| Dye Tub Operator VII | 12) | 0.60 mg/m$^3$ | <1 ppb aromatic amines. | Same as above. |
| Roll-Up Machine Operator | 13) | 0.48 mg/m$^3$ | <1 ppb aromatic amines. | Worker operates steam-press roll-up machine. Considerable heat and resultant steam evolved. No respirator worn. |

[a]Environmental concentrations expressed as total airborne particulates per cubic meter of sampled air.

[b]Aromatic amines and the metabolites are expressed as benzidines (Bzd and MAB).

TABLE 58. ENVIRONMENTAL DATA TO TABLE 57

| Sample no. | Air volume sampled (liters) | Total dust per filter | Total dust in mg/m$^3$ | λ max[a] | Azo dye per filter | Percent azo dye per filter |
|---|---|---|---|---|---|---|
| 1 | 455 | 0.85 | 1.54 | 450 | 0.076 | 9 |
| 2 | 320.2 | 0.57 | 1.31 | 450 | 0.060 | 10.5 |
| 3 | 207.8 | 0.62 | 1.15 | 495 | 0.065 | 10.5 |
| 4 | 488.3 | 0.69 | 1.11 | 495 | 0.160 | 23.2 |
| 5 | 728.0 | 0.55 | 0.55 | N | - | - |
| 6 | 740.2 | 4.08 | 5.31 | N | - | - |
| 7 | 735.0 | 0.81 | 0.90 | N | - | - |
| 8 | 728.0 | 1.30 | 1.58 | N | - | - |
| 9 | 731.5 | 0.64 | 0.67 | N | - | - |
| 10 | 666.8 | 0.57 | 0.63 | N | - | - |
| 11 | 750.8 | 0.30 | 0.20 | N | - | - |
| 12 | 749.0 | 0.60 | 0.60 | N | - | - |
| 13 | 745.5 | 0.51 | 0.48 | N | - | - |

| [a]λ max | Trade name |
|---|---|
| 450 | Brown 3GN |
| 495 | Black GX and Seal Brown C.F. |

TABLE 59. RESIDUAL BENZIDINE ANALYSIS RESULTS

| Dye name | Benzidine concentration (in ppm) w/w |
|---|---|
| Direct Brown 3GN (C.I. Direct Brown 95) | <1 |
| Direct Scarlet 3B (C.I. Direct Orange 8?) | <1 |
| Direct Orange WS (C.I. Direct Orange 8?) | 7 |
| Direct Black GX (C.I. Direct Black 38) | 20 |
| Seal Brown CF (C.I. Direct Brown and Direct Black 38) | 4 |
| Direct Blue 2GF (C.I. Direct Blue 2) | <1 |
| Direct Black OB (C.I.?) | <1 |
| Directo Black BH (C.I.?) | <1 |

## APPENDIX E-3

## SUMMARY OF MONITORING RESULTS FROM A PAPER PLANT

TABLE 60. SUMMARY OF MONITORING RESULTS FROM A PAPER PLANT

| Day | Shift | Sample Location | Env. Conc. ($mg/m^3$) | Urine Conc. (Parts/billion) Aromatic Amines | Benzidine | Notes |
|---|---|---|---|---|---|---|
| 1 | 1 | Dye Weigher I | | ND | | Dye Weigher weighed all dyes and delivers to dye tub. Worker wore respirator during weighing. |
| | | Operator I | | | ND | Operator delivered pulp by forklift and maintained dye tub operation. |
| 1 | 2 | Dye Weigher II | | 1 | ND | |
| 2 | 1 | Dye Weigher I | | | ND<br>ND | Worker wore respirator when weighing dyes. |
| | | | | ND | ND | |
| | | Operator I | | | ND | |
| 2 | 2 | Dye Weigher II | | | ND | Worker wore respirator when weighing dyes. |
| | | | | 2 | ND | |
| | | Operator II | | | ND | |
| | | | | ND | ND | |
| 2 | 3 | Dye Weigher III | | 1 | ND | Began using Direct Black 38 towards end of this shift. |
| | | | | ND | ND | |
| | | Operator III | | 1.3 | ND | |
| | | Lg. Weigh Scale | 1) 0.65 $mg/m^3$ | | ND | |
| | | Sm. Weigh Scale | 2) 0.36 $mg/m^3$ | | | |
| 3 | 1 | Dye Weigher I | 3) 3.30 $mg/m^3$ | 1.4 | ND | First shift using Direct Black 38 |
| | | Operator I | 4) 2.31 $mg/m^3$ | | ND | First shift using Direct Black 38 |
| | | Lg. Weigh Scale | 5) 0.36 $mg/m^3$ | | | |
| | | Sm. Weigh Scale | 6) 0.70 $mg/m^3$ | | | |

TABLE 60. SUMMARY OF MONITORING RESULTS FROM A PAPER PLANT (continued)

| Day | Shift | Sample Location | Env. Conc. 1 ($mg/m^3$) | Urine Conc. (Parts/billion) 2 Aromatic Amines | Urine Conc. (Parts/billion) 2 Benzidine | Notes |
|---|---|---|---|---|---|---|
| 3 | 2 | Dye Weigher II | 7) 1.61 $mg/m^3$ | 2.2 | ND | Using Direct Black 38 |
| | | Operator II<br>Lg. Weigh Scale | 8) 3.70 $mg/m^3$<br>9) 0.17 $mg/m^3$<br>10) 0.17 $mg/m^3$ | 1.3 | ND | |
| 3 | 3 | Dye Weigher III | 11) 2.85 $mg/m^3$ | ND<br>ND<br>1.3 | ND<br>ND<br>ND | Using Direct Black 38. Worker wore respirator when weighing dyes. |
| | | Operator III<br>Lg. Weigh Scale<br>Sm. Weigh Scale | 12) 2.64 $mg/m^3$<br>13) 0.53 $mg/m^3$<br>14) 0.50 $mg/m^3$ | | | |
| 4 | 1 | Dye Weigher | 15) 3.43 $mg/m^3$ | ND<br>ND<br>1 | ND<br>3MAB | Using Direct Black 38. |
| | | Operator I<br>Area at Pulper 2<br>Lg. Weigh Scale<br>Sm. Weigh Scale | 16) 5.10 $mg/m^3$<br>17) 1.41 $mg/m^3$<br>18) 0.58 $mg/m^3$<br>19) 0.91 $mg/m^3$ | | ND<br>ND | |
| 4 | 2 | Dye Weigher II | 20) 2.51 $mg/m^3$ | | ND<br>ND<br>ND<br>ND | |
| | | Operator II<br>Area at Beater 2<br>Lg. Weigh Scale | 21) 0.56 $mg/m^3$<br>22) 1.43 $mg/m^3$ | | | |

TABLE 60. SUMMARY OF MONITORING RESULTS FROM A PAPER PLANT (continued)

| Day | Shift | Sample Location | Env. Conc.* ($mg/m^3$) | Urine Conc. (Parts/billion)2 Aromatic Amines** | Urine Conc. (Parts/billion)2 Benzidine+ | Notes |
|---|---|---|---|---|---|---|
| 4 | 3 | Dye Weigher III | 23) 2.26 $mg/m^3$ | | ND<br>ND<br>ND | Using Direct Black 38 |
| | | Operator III | Void | | 2MAB | |
| 4 | 3 | Operator IIIA | | | 3MAB<br>3DAAB | |
| 5 | 1 | Dye Weigher I | | 4.9 | 3MAB<br>1Bzd<br>32DAAB | Stopped using Direct Black 38 towards end of this shift |
| | | Operator I | | 2.9 | 1Bzd<br>5DAAB | |
| 5 | 2 | Dye Weigher II | | 2.6 | ND<br>ND | |
| | | Operator II | | ND | ND | |
| | | Area at Pulper I | 24) 2.93 $mg/m^3$ | | | Using Carbon Black |
| 5 | 3 | Dye Weigher III | | | 2DAAB | Washed down equipment for next color run |
| | | Operator III | | | ND<br>2MAB | |
| | | Operator IV A | | | 2MAB | |
| 6 | 1 | Dye Weigher I | | | 8MAB<br>2DAAB | |
| | | Operator I | | | ND | |

*Concentrations expressed as milligrams of total airborne particulates per cubic meter air
**Concentration of non-specific colorimetric procedure with the limit of detection at 1 ppb
+Concentration of specific aromatic amines in ppb with the following detection limits: benzidine 1.0 ppb, MAB, 1.8 ppb; DAAB, 0.8ppb, diacetylbenzidine, 0.2ppb.

TABLE 60. SUMMARY OF MONITORING RESULTS FROM A PAPER PLANT (continued)

| | Day 1 | | Day 2 | | Day 3 | | Day 4 | | Day 5 | | Day 6 | |
|---|---|---|---|---|---|---|---|---|---|---|---|---|
| | Env. Conc.* ($mg/m^3$) | Urine (ppb) | Env. Conc. ($mg/m^3$) | Urine (ppb) | Env. Conc. ($mg/m^3$) | Urine (ppb) | Env. Conc. ($mg/m^3$) | Urine (ppb) | Env. Conc. ($mg/m^3$) | Urine (ppb) | Env. Conc. ($mg/m^3$) | Urine (ppb) |
| Worker I | - | N.D+ (N.D)++ | - | N.D (N.D) | 3.3 | N.D (1.4) | 3.4 | 3 MAB (1) | Void | 3 MAB 1 Bzd 32 DAAB (4.9) | - | 8 MAB 2 DAAB |
| Worker II | - | N.D | - | N.D (N.D) | 2.3 | N.D - | 5.1 | N.D - | - | 1 Bzd 5 DAAB (2.9) | | N.D |
| Worker III | - | N.D (1.0) | - | N.D (2.0) | 1.6 | N.D 2.2 | 2.5 | N.D - | - | N.D (2.6) | | |
| Worker IV | - | | - | N.D (N.D) | 3.7 | N.D (1.3) | Void | N.D | - | (N.D) (N.D) | | |
| Worker V | | | | N.D (1.0) | 2.9 | N.D (N.D) | 2.3 | N.D - | - | 2 DAAB (N.D) | | |
| Worker VI | | | - | N.D (1.3) | 2.6 | N.D (1.3) | Void | 2 MAB - | - | 2 MAB | | |
| Worker | | | | | | | | 3 MAB 3 DAAB | | 2 MAB | | |

* environmental concentrations expressed as milligrams total airborne particulates per cubic meter of air.
\+ concentration of specific aromatic amines in ppb with the following detection limits: benzidine, 1.0 ppb; monoacetylbenzidine, 1.8 ppb; 2,4-diaminoazobenzene, 0.8 ppb; diacetylbenzidine, 0.2 ppb.
++ concentration of non-specific colorimetric precedure with the limit of detection at 1 ppb.

NOTE: Area within heavy black line signifies period of Direct Black 38 useage.

TABLE 61. SUPPLEMENTAL DATA TO TABLE 60

| Field No. | mg/filter Total Wt. | Air Volume (liters) | Calculated mg/m$^3$ | λ max* (nm) | mg/filter Azo Dyes | Percent Azo Dyes |
|---|---|---|---|---|---|---|
| 1 | 0.49 | 749 | 0.65 | N | <0.01 | -- |
| 2 | 0.24 | 744 | 0.35 | 400 | 0.19 | 79 |
| 3 | 2.42 | 734 | 3.30 | 410 | 0.19 | 7 |
| 4 | 1.84 | 796 | 2.31 | N | <0.01 | -- |
| 5 | 0.29 | 807 | 0.36 | 550 | U | U |
| 6 | 0.56 | 796 | 0.70 | 400 | 0.10 | 18 |
| 7 | 1.28 | 793 | 1.61 | 410 | 0.42 | 33 |
| 8 | 2.93 | 791 | 3.70 | 485 | 0.04 | 1 |
| 9 | 0.13 | 773 | 0.17 | N | <0.01 | -- |
| 10 | 0.13 | 768 | 0.17 | 405 | 0.17 | 100 |
| 11 | 2.20 | 773 | 2.85 | 490 | 0.08 | 4 |
| 12 | 2.06 | 779 | 2.64 | N | <0.01 | -- |
| 13 | 0.42 | 793 | 0.53 | N | <0.01 | -- |
| 14 | 0.40 | 791 | 0.50 | N | <0.01 | -- |
| 15 | 2.52 | 735 | 3.43 | 490 | 0.12 | 5 |
| 16 | 2.90 | 569 | 5.10 | N | <0.01 | -- |
| 17 | 1.12 | 796 | 1.41 | 485 | 0.12 | 11 |
| 18 | 0.46 | 796 | 0.58 | 485 | 0.09 | 20 |
| 19 | 0.32 | 350 | 0.91 | N | <0.01 | -- |
| 20 | 1.93 | 786 | 2.51 | 485 | 0.25 | 13 |
| 21 | 0.22 | 394 | 0.56 | N | <0.01 | -- |
| 22 | 1.09 | 760 | 1.43 | 485 | 0.40 | 37 |
| 23 | 1.69 | 749 | 2.26 | 485 | 0.32 | 19 |
| 24 | 1.94 | 663 | 2.93 | N | <0.01 | -- |

Key to Abbreviations:

- N None
- U Unknown dye
- λ Absorbance wavelength maximum

*Absorbance Maxima

| λ | Dye Name | λ | Dye Name |
|---|---|---|---|
| 400 | Paper Direct Brown NPC | 490 | Orange RO |
| 405 | Paper Direct Brown NPC | 510-535 | Direct Black 38E |
| 410 | Paper Direct Brown NPC | 595 | Phenamine Black E 200 |
| 485 | Orange 5R | 500 | Phenamine Blue BB |

TABLE 62. COMPARISON OF RESPIRABLE TO TOTAL AIR PARTICULATE SAMPLES AT A LARGE DYE WEIGHING SCALE

| | | |
|---|---|---|
| Respirable<br>Total | 0.35[a]<br>0.53 | 1:1.2 |
| Respirable<br>Total | 0.11<br>0.58 | 1:5.2 |
| Respirable<br>Total | 0.00<br>0.36 | - |
| Respirable<br>Total | 0.26<br>0.17 | 1:0.7 |

[a]Given in mg/m$^3$.